# The Aging Client
# and Long-Term Care

**CCH**
a Wolters Kluwer business

*2nd Edition*

Published by CCH Canadian Limited

**Library and Archives Canada Cataloguing in Publication**

Figas, Jacqueline E., 1952-
    The aging client and long term care / Jacqueline E. Figas. — 2nd ed.

First ed. published under title: Evaluating long-term care insurance.
ISBN 9781553678663

1. Insurance, Long term care — Canada  I. Title.

HG9390.F53 2008        368.38′2        C2008-905529-2

Typeset by CCH Canadian Limited.
Printed in The United States of America.

# PREFACE

According to the Financial Planning Association, comprehensive financial planning encompasses a number of key areas including retirement planning, estate planning, insurance, tax planning, investment management, cash management and budgeting. Depending on client needs, it may also include education funding, charitable and planned giving, trust management and planning for long-term care. As our population continues to age and baby boomers prepare for retirement, this latter area of planning is gaining increased focus.

Financial Planning tools often place finances at the centre. The "person-centered" approach looks at the whole person as an individual that interacts with their environment mentally, socially, physically, and financially. Each aspect impacts the other and is dynamic not stagnant. The more you understand about the inter-connectedness of all of these aspects the better you will understand your clients. Helping clients to plan for life transitions involves a lot of introspection, values clarification, education and prioritization. The goal should be to place life at the centre. This holistic big picture approach is based on the premise that the whole is greater than merely the sum of the parts.

## Know Your Client as a Whole Person

We have all heard of the saying, "know your client", but do you really know who your client is as a whole person, as well as what assets they have? Do you understand what they value? Do you explore life issues as they relate to finances? The whole person approach involves demonstrating to your client your interest in the individual as a whole. It also involves moving beyond thinking transactionally, and seeing your role as a transition planner, educator, and resource. By helping your clients to anticipate life events you can help them to make financial preparations for these transitions.

As an educator your role is to create awareness and stimulate intellectual curiosity and growth related to issues that can impact their lives. Some planners shun being seen as a resource outside the financial arena. But being a resource and advocate for seniors issues does not mean becoming an expert in non-financial fields. Learn about the issues and form partnerships with others to whom you can refer your clients for expert advice on non-financial issues. By communicating your interest to your client as a whole person you forge stronger relationships and become a better planner.

## Walk a Mile in My Shoes

We have all heard the saying, "walk a mile in my shoes". A senior who was asked to comment on what this meant to him, replied, "You should suspend judgment of other people until you have similar life experiences". Perhaps for planners, this means that the journey to better understanding senior clients should begin by gaining insight to the events and influencers that have shaped individuals to being who they are today. Armed with this insight, we may be in a better position to understand and appreciate their values, and to not only know them, but also better understand them.

Consequently, we will examine the aging consumer from the perspective of who they were as well as who they are today, relevant societal issues, physical changes and cognitive changes. The goal will be to better understand how seniors interact with their environment mentally, socially and physically, their needs as consumers of health services, and thereby understand their financial issues as a whole person.

## The Future Isn't What It Used To Be

We all grow old. Aging is a biological process beginning at birth and ending at death. Being "senior" on the other hand, is a social construct traditionally associated with reaching age 65 — a milestone which used to trigger a life transition to retirement and the right of passage to "old age". Today people retire based on lifestyle, values, circumstance and personal priorities. Society is redefining what it means to be a senior.

How long we can expect to live has statistically been changing over the past century. A person born in 1960 can expect to live 20 years longer than their ancestors who were born in 1900. Baby boomers have many modern conveniences their parents never had such as microwaves, personal computers, cell phones, and more cars per family. Yet one thing that parents of boomers could say is that although they struggled through the Great Depression, throughout their lives they could always see improvement. They experienced the introduction of Medicare, the Canada Pension Plan, and Old Age Security. As our population continues to age, will boomers be able to say the same thing as their parents? Or will this new generation of seniors experience a much different reality.

Using past experience as a model for future planning has less relevance today because many things have changed that render the past as an unlikely predictor of future experience. Consider for instance, the changes in family structure, our aging population and our ailing health care system. Planning for long term care is an essential part of preparing for the future and insurers are stepping up to the plate with new solutions for those who choose to take control of their own destiny. Consequently we will examine financial solutions such as long term care insurance, and the options seniors have available for services through home care and residential care.

## Acknowledgements

The author wishes to acknowledge and thank Donna Ritch, RN, EPC, of Change of Season for generously sharing her time and wisdom with me regarding chronic conditions and health issues in the elderly.

# TABLE OF CONTENTS

# The Aging Consumer

Futurist Paul Saffo once said "The goal of forecasting is not to predict the future but to tell you what you need to know to take meaningful action in the present." In this regard, we begin with a look at "the big picture" not with the goal of becoming experts in demographic issues, but to gain a general appreciation for the complex and uncertain issues facing today's decision makers. These issues are the driving forces behind changes made in policies and programs that affect our clients and their plans for the future.

## POPULATION GROWTH

The growth in population is both a recent and a worldwide phenomenon. A demographer and population expert, Dr. Carl Haub of the Population Reference Bureau once calculated an estimate of the total number of people that have ever lived. He used the year 50,000 BC as his starting point of modern man with a population of two. This was selected as the starting point based on the United Nations' Determinants and Consequences of Population Trends, which stated modern homo sapiens may have appeared about 50,000 B.C. (Some people argue his figures should be adjusted to use a starting point of 4,000 BC as the origin of modern man). Haub's calculations for global population expansion ultimately determined that by 2002 the total number of people who had ever lived on Earth was 106.5 billion. That same year, the current world population was about 6.2 billion.

Table 1.0

| World Population Milestones | | |
|---|---|---|
| **World Population Reached:** | | |
| Milestone | **Year** | **Elapsed Time** |
| 1 billion | 1804 | Beginning of time |
| 2 billion | 1927 | 123 years |
| 3 billion | 1960 | 33 years |
| 4 billion | 1974 | 14 years |
| 5 billion | 1987 | 13 years |
| 6 billion | 1999 | 12 years |
| **World Population May Reach:** | | |
| 7 billion | 2013 | 14 years |
| 8 billion | 2028 | 15 years |
| 9 billion | 2054 | 26 years |
| 10 billion | 2183 | 129 years |

Source: United Nations Population Division.

Consequently, we can estimate that about 5.8% of the total population that ever lived, is alive today. It wasn't until the early 1800s the population crossed the first billion. By 1900 it was roughly 1.7 billion, an increase of 1.6 times over the century. In 2008 the population is now roughly 6.7 billion. Today's population is nearly four times what it was in 1900. The world population is predicted to surpass seven billion by 2013. Assuming a continued reduction in the global rate of fertility, world population is projected to hit 9.2 billion in 2050.[1] Even more astounding is the comparative elapsed time between milestones as reflected in Table 1.0. It took from the inception of time to 1804 to hit the first billion, then 123 years to grow from one

[1] POPULATION Newsletter, United Nations Secretariat (June 2007)

billion to two billion, but a mere 12 years to grow from five billion to six billion. The 20th century witnessed unprecedented growth. This is a trend that is now reversing as predictions show continued slowing growth in population.

## Factors That Influence the Rate of Population Growth

Why are there changes in the population growth rates? Causes of changing trends in population patterns are quite complex. Changes in fertility and mortality rates have been impacted by many different factors including:

- Biological conditions

- Cultural developments

- Religious beliefs

- Economic conditions

- Geographic and climatic conditions

- Political issues

- Social factors

For instance, the age at which women marry, have children, and the size of their families is influenced by cultural and religious beliefs, economic conditions and education. Mortality rates are affected by biological conditions and climatic conditions amongst other things. In early centuries, life expectancy was very short. Infant mortality was thought to be as high as 500 deaths per 1,000 births. Famines and plagues caused many deaths. Life expectancy in early 12th century England was as low as 24.3 years, but by the 1800s it had risen to 40.8 years.

The largest population growth occurred in the 20th century as we all know, because of the mid-century baby boom.

Immigration also plays a role in population growth and changes in age structure. Immigration will continue to be an important component in Canada's strategies for growth throughout the 21st century, but by itself is unlikely to prevent the reduction of the labour force or to reverse the aging trend because the number of migrants required to achieve this would be too high.

## Where Growth Is Occurring

According to the United Nations Population Information Network, six countries accounted for half of the world's annual growth in population in 2000 as follows:

- India contributed 21%

- China — 12%

- Pakistan    5%

- Nigeria — 4%

- Bangladesh — 4%

- Indonesia — 3%

The population of more developed regions over the next 50 years is expected to change little due to fertility levels falling below replacement levels. By 2050, 39 countries are projected to have populations smaller than today. Some of these countries include Japan, Germany, Italy, Hungary, the Russian Federation, Georgia and Ukraine.

In less developed regions, the population is expected to continue to increase. The most rapid growth, however, will take place in a group of 48 countries classified as least developed, where it is projected that the population will triple between 2000 and 2050.

## Demographic Transition

The rate of growth in global population peaked in the 1960s, and has been slowly descending as birth rates have dropped in many regions. Demographic experts believe social modernization is responsible for the shift from low birth rates and from low to high life expectancy. This involves a number of changes including improvement in health care, access to family planning, achievement of higher levels of education and egalitarian gender roles, economic growth, rising income levels, urbanization and increasing employment. Therefore, whether we achieve population stabilization globally will largely be influenced by how rapidly developing countries evolve in these areas. Some of the obstacles that could impede this transition include lack of economic growth, continuing poverty, and cultural influences such as religion that may continue to advocate large families. Demographers believe these obstacles could cause world population to keep rising for another 100 years.

Countries around the world are at different stages of the demographic transition. Changes in fertility rates are a universal phenomenon in which every country can be placed on a continuum of progress in transition.[2] It is influenced by social, economic and cultural change.

There have been many different theories and models to explain demographic transition. A recent United Nations newsletter referred to three stages that characterized transition:

---

[2] Kirk, Dudley, 1996, *Demographic Transitions Theory*, Population Studies

**First Stage**

In the first stage, mortality rates fall and the proportion of children increases.

**Second Stage**

In the second stage, both fertility and mortality rates fall and the proportion of adults (working age) increases.

**Third Stage**

In the third stage, fertility and mortality rates reach low levels and the proportion of older adults increases.

While not all theories describe the various stages in the same manner, they agree the tendency towards having smaller families is largely related to cultural values, economic and social advantages and that education plays a significant role whereby women with more education are more likely to control their fertility.

## World Vital Events Per Time Unit: 2006

Table 2.0 that follows is a look at the rate of births, deaths and net increase globally.

**Table 2.0**

| World Vital Events Per Time Unit: 2006 | | | |
|---|---|---|---|
| **Time Unit** | **Births** | **Deaths** | **Increase** |
| Year | 129,886,900.00 | 56,595,880.00 | 73,291,020.00 |
| Month | 10,823,908.33 | 4,716,323.33 | 6,107,585.00 |
| Week | 2,497,825.00 | 1,088,382.31 | 1,409,442.69 |
| Day | 355,854.52 | 155,057.21 | 200,797.31 |
| Hour | 14,827.27 | 6,460.72 | 8,366.55 |
| Minute | 247.12 | 107.67 | 139.45 |
| Source: Population Connection (2006) | | | |

## Life Expectancy

World life expectancy at birth (2005) is 64.33 years, representing nearly a 20-year increase since 1950. But this number varies significantly through different regions, ranging from a high of 83.51 years in Andorra to a low of 33.87 years in Botswana. Canada is amongst the highest of nations at 80.01 years (2005 figure). Table 3.0 illustrates the range in life expectancy for various countries.

Table 3.0

| 2005 Life Expectancy Comparison Table (Partial List of Countries) | | |
|---|---|---|
| **Country** | **Gender-Combined Life Expectancy** | **Ranking** |
| World | 64.33 | |
| Andorra | 83.51 | 1 |
| Japan | 81.15 | 6 |
| Sweden | 80.15 | 7 |
| Australia | 80.39 | 8 |
| Canada | 80.01 | 12 |
| Italy | 79.68 | 14 |
| United Kingdom | 78.38 | 38 |
| United States | 77.71 | 45 |
| Mexico | 75.19 | 75 |
| Poland | 74.41 | 84 |
| China | 72.27 | 104 |
| Vietnam | 70.61 | 125 |
| Russia | 67.1 | 147 |
| The Bahamas | 65.54 | 153 |
| India | 64.35 | 162 |
| Pakistan | 63.0 | 166 |
| Uganda | 51.59 | 191 |
| Nigeria | 46.74 | 205 |
| Mozambique | 40.32 | 217 |
| Angola | 36.61 | 221 |
| Botswana | 33.87 | 224 |

Source: World Fact Book, Central Intelligence Agency (2005) Washington, D.C.

## Aging of the Population

Population aging is a slow process but its cumulative impact can be considerable and far-reaching, affecting public institutions, family, and work. According to the United Nations,[3] as a result of declining fertility and increasing longevity, the global population is getting older. Slow population growth due to reduced fertility rates leads to populations where the percentage of older people increases while the percentage of younger people decreases. This is of concern because of the broad economic and social

[3] *The World at Six Billion*, Population Division, Department of Economic and Social Affairs United Nations Secretariat (12 October 1999)

consequences. In 2005 there were 673 million persons age 60 or over and this represented just over 10% of the world's population. Projections are that by 2050 there will be three times this, with two billion people over age 60 representing 22% of the world population. In the more developed regions, 20% of the population is already comprised of people who are age 60+ and this number will grow to 33% by 2050. The increase in the number of "oldest old" (those over age 80) is going to be even more remarkable, as this segment of the population will increase from 88 million (2005) to 402 million (2050), which represents more than a five-fold increase.[4] In some developed countries the older population has already surpassed the younger population. By 2050 there will be two older adults for every child (0–14) in the developed regions. The impact will be felt in many areas such as economic growth, savings and investments, labour supply and employment, pension schemes, health, and long-term care.

## Looking Back: The 20th century Issues

Many significant events occurred during the 1900's that have impacted the lives of clients we deal with today. The impact is often both economic and social. Events of the 20th century have shaped individuals' value systems and for this reason it is important to look at some of the major events that took place.

The 20th century was marked by:[5]

- Two devastating world wars

- The Great Depression of the 1930s

- The end of vast colonial empires

- Rapid advances in science and technology

- Explosion in world population from 1 billion in 1820 to 6 billion in 2000

- The Cold War between the Western Alliance and the Warsaw Pact nations

- A sharp rise in living standards in North America, Europe, and Japan

- Increased concerns about the environment

- The break-up of the Soviet Empire and the end of the Cold War

- The effective end to Communism

- The emergence of the U.S. as the only world super power

- The onset of the AIDS epidemic

- Globalization

---

[4] United Nations Population Information Network (POPIN)

[5] *The World Fact Book*, Central Intelligence Agency

## How Does Canada Compare?

Table 4.0 shows important statistics for Canada as compared with global trends. These figures are based on 2007 year-end estimates as at July 2007.

Table 4.0

| Statistics Projected to Year-end As at July 2007 | | |
|---|---|---|
| **World** | **Category** | **Canada** |
| 6,602,224,175 | **Population** | 33,390,141 |
| | **Age Structure** | |
| 27.4 percent | **0 - 14** | 17.3 percent |
| 65.1 percent | **15 – 64** | 69.2 percent |
| 7.5 percent | **65 plus** | 13.5 percent |
| | **Median Age** | |
| 28.0 years | **Total** | 39.1 years |
| 27.4 years | **Male** | 38.1 years |
| 28.7 years | **Female** | 40.2 years |
| 1.167 percent | **Population Growth Rate** | 0.869 percent |
| 20.09 per 1,000 | **Birth Rate** | 10.75 per 1,000 |
| 8.37 per 1,000 | **Death Rate** | 7.86 per 1,000 |
| | **Infant Mortality** | |
| 43.52 deaths Per 1,000 live births | **Total** | 4.63 deaths Per 1,000 live births |
| 46.32 deaths Per 1,000 live births | **Male** | 5.08 deaths Per 1,000 live births |
| 40.52 deaths Per 1,000 live births | **Female** | 4.17 deaths Per 1,000 live births |
| | **Life Expectancy at Birth** | |
| 65.82 years | **Total** | 80.34 years |
| 63.89 years | **Male** | 76.98 years |
| 67.84 years | **Female** | 83.86 years |
| 2.59 children born Per woman | **Total Fertility Rate** | 1.61 children born Per woman |

Source: <u>World Fact Book</u>, Central Intelligence Agency (2007) Washington, D.C.

The Canadian census for 2001 revealed that the median population was 37.6 years. This represented an increase of 2.3 years since 1996 and marked the biggest census-to-census increase in a century. One quarter of the Canadian population was aged 45 to 64. By 2011 this group will comprise one-third of the population. Almost one-third of all Canadian women are now over the age of 50, and 13% of the total population is over 65. It is predicted that by 2015, the number of senior citizens will outnumber children for the first time in Canada's history. Statistics indicate that by 2031, 25% of the population will be over 65. By 2056, one out of every 10 Canadians will be over 80. This is a significant increase from current numbers which indicate one in every 30 Canadians to be over 80.

Canada has had below replacement fertility rates since the early 1970s, measuring 1.8 since 1976. Despite this, the population is still growing because of fewer deaths than births. However, when a population has a fertility rate that is below 2.0, eventually there will be more deaths than births. This is likely to happen for Canada some time after 2025 (Statistics Canada, 2001). Immigration may help postpone this somewhat, but will not reverse this trend.

After 2011, Canada will experience "aging at the top" which will mean fewer people in the work force and eventually significant numbers of frail elderly. It is anticipated that this will put high pressure on health care systems especially in the last months of life where health care costs are statistically high.

As people are living longer, the older population is growing substantially. Longevity is a double edged sword. Thanks to technological advancements and improvements in medicine, we are living longer lives, but with chronic conditions that were once the leading causes of death. Many seniors live with chronic diseases, impairments, physical limitations — often with no one to help them. Statistics show that an increasing number of seniors, especially women, are living alone.

## Life Expectancy in Canada

Life expectancy from birth is continuing to improve, and stands at 80.4 years, based on the 2005 census. Gender-specific rates indicate a narrowing in the gap between male and female life expectancy. Female life expectancy is 82.7, while male life expectancy is 78. There are regional differences, and when broken down by province, life expectancy ranges from 78.2 years in Newfoundland and Labrador to 80.7 in Ontario. Table 5.0 shows a breakdown by province.

Table 5.0

| Life Expectancy by Province for 2005 Births | | | |
|---|---|---|---|
| Ontario | 80.7 | Saskatchewan | 79.3 |
| Quebec | 80.4 | Nova Scotia | 79.3 |
| Alberta | 80.3 | Manitoba | 79.0 |
| New Brunswick | 79.8 | Newfoundland and Labrador | 78.2 |
| P.E.I. | 79.8 | | |
| Source: Statistics Canada as reported by CBC News January 14, 2008 | | | |

# CHANGING NORMS IN FAMILY LIFE CYCLES

## Canadian Families

Without question, family behaviours have evolved because of changes in economics and culture. For instance, a female who matured in the 1950s or early 1960s most often married almost immediately after leaving high school around age 20 or 21. She lived at home until she married. She may have worked at a clerical or retail job until she started her family just a few short years after setting up a household with her husband. He earned enough for her to stay home and raise the family, which was her principal role in the family unit.

Compare this to 50 years later. The woman maturing in the 1980s and 1990s is most likely to have a university degree, an established successful career, and postpones marriage until she is at least 25. She will have lived on her own or with her partner before marrying, if she marries at all. She may return once or twice to live with her parents before settling down with a long-term partner. If she has children, it will most often be after age 30 and she will continue her career while simultaneously rearing a child. Unlike the woman of the 1950s the order is not necessarily marriage first and children second. She and her partner will have established a lifestyle built on dual incomes, and they will mutually see their roles as equal partners. She is far more likely to divorce and remarry, if she marries at all. These contemporary couples also have less distinctive gender roles.

It is no longer possible to trace their life course through the vision of a traditional nuclear family. Before the 1980s demographers could conduct meaningful studies of various family life stages. By the late1980s their methods no longer yielded credible results because of the increased number of variables in life stages. The traditional family life cycle as described by demographer Paul Glick[6] consisted of Formation, Extension, Completed Extension, Contraction, Completed Contraction, and Dissolution.

"Formation" refers to the first marriage, "Extension" refers to the birth of the first child or the start of parenthood, "Completed Extension" refers to the birth of the last child, "Contraction" refers to the first child leaving home, "Completed Contraction" refers to the last child leaving home or empty-nesting, and "Dissolution" refers to termination of the union. These stages were predictable in sequence and timing and their trajectories could be anticipated and studied. But the family life cycle has changed so significantly that there is no longer one prevalent model. The concept of family cycle has been replaced with a different way of studying human lives called the "life course perspective".

## Life Course Perspective

The life course perspective focuses on the duration, timing and ordering of major life events and their consequences for later social

---

[6] Glick, P.C., 1945, *The Family Life Cycle*, American Sociological Review 12(2): 164-74.

development. Trajectories, transitions and adaptation are studied not just by academics but in policy circles as well to see how people age in the context of changing societies. They study the interaction between historical events, personal opportunities and decisions, and their subsequent outcomes. Trajectories are pathways in life seen as a sequence of linked states studied as a long-term pattern (career, parenthood, retirement, etc.). Transitions refer to specific short-term life events within a trajectory (graduation, divorce, etc.). Trajectories and transitions are intertwined and generate changes and turning points throughout life. Adaptations to these changes can lead to different trajectories. In every society there are norms as to what constitutes "correct times" for individuals to enter or exit from certain trajectories and to make transitions within trajectories. Under the traditional nuclear family, the transition to adulthood was compressed into a relatively short period; whereas in the 1980's we have experienced the deinstitutionalization of family, less dependent relationships between men and women, and culturally greater emphasis on companionship, individualism and gender equality. Their early life course transitions occur over a longer period of time. Children no longer leave the home as early as in the past, neither does formation (marriage) or extension (first birth) occur as early (if it does at all). Family transformation has resulted in varied and numerous life course trajectories of both men and women.

All of these trends impact social programs and are therefore of interest to policy makers.

## CONCERNS WITH CANADA'S AGING POPULATION

There are concerns that having an older population will impact us in the following ways.

1. It will place a burden on the working population who must bear the costs of funding public pensions and the cost of health care to a growing number of recipients.

2. It will encumber the health care system as older adults usually have greater medical needs than the younger population.

3. There will be such a demand by the elderly with a need for assistance with daily activities there will be insufficient resources (human and financial) to meet the need.

Much discussion revolves around the issue of meeting the health care costs of an aging population. However, some people believe that of equal concern is the changing demand on medical services brought about by higher personal standards of "wellness" and that the new generation of older adults will expect a more active lifestyle in their later years. To this end, they may demand more treatments, surgeries, medications, or therapies that support this "forever young" goal.

If a prediction had been made in the 1970's that our aging population alone would cause an increase in hospital days, it would be wrong. The average number of days that patients spend in hospitals has actually reduced because of new technology that shortens healing time and quickens the recovery process.

Population aging alone is unlikely to be the principal factor driving up the cost of health care. Many factors affect the future growth of health care expenses including:

- Population growth

- Rate of inflation

- Incidence rates in chronic illnesses

- Pharmaceutical costs

- Technological improvements

- Changes in the health-seeking behavior of individuals

- Inefficiencies in the delivery of services

In terms of whether there will be adequate levels of caregivers, although fertility rates have fallen, it is the average size of family that has changed most substantially and not the number who have remained childless. The greater issue affecting caregiving will be changes in social beliefs regarding what constitutes "good care". The impact of gender equality and dual-career trajectories is not yet fully known. It may be that a husband whose wife has always worked may believe that he is providing "best care" by hiring someone to assist his ailing spouse, rather than providing informal care personally. Similarly, a wife who has not stayed home in the historical "nurturer" role, may believe that the best care for her husband is achieved by "outsourcing" the responsibility to an agency supported through the public system. Or children who have been raised in institutional daycare settings may believe institutions are the best form of care for a parent who can no longer live independently. Currently, 80% of home support is provided by the informal caregiver (spouse, adult children and community volunteers). Informal (unpaid) caregivers are the backbone of today's home health care delivery system. A major shift in societal values could drastically impair the current delivery system particularly given the fact that the direction governments are moving is increasing reliance on informal home support. Will the government need to undertake a massive promotional campaign to change the shifting tides of societal values? Provinces are introducing programs such as *Wait at Home* and *Aging at Home* designed to extend seniors' independence in the community. While all agree this is what most seniors want, the success of the system rests heavily on the continued support of the informal caregiver network (spouse, children, community volunteers). Building on the strategy of "the right services at the right place at the right time", the goal is to push out the transition point from home to facility care so as to compress the years required in a publicly-funded institutional setting based on the premise that it costs less to provide care at home than it does in a long-term care centre (at least initially). Governments are recognizing our present institutional model will consume increasingly more public resources and there will be insufficient providers to accommodate the aging population.

During the post-war period, a number of important programs aimed at social security services and health care were implemented. These areas of government expenditures have grown rapidly over the last several decades despite modest changes aimed at reducing government spending. As the percentage of working population narrows, governments may turn to cost-sharing measures to make up the short-fall in tax revenue. This could be in the form of a user fee, or a two-tiered medical system whereby those who can pay personally are able to buy health services faster. The view that the Canada Pension Plan is a sacred trust and will always be there may also change. Presently, there is an unfunded liability in the Canada Pension Plan system of $516.3 billion[7] and an unfunded liability in the health care system of $1.2 trillion.[8] Old Age Security benefits introduced in 1952 to address the poverty levels prevalent amongst the oldest old, may be seen as no longer viable or relevant. Benefits commenced upon attaining age 70, while life expectancy at that time was 67 years. Today, life expectancy in Canada is 80.4 years (as reported in January 2008 based on the 2005 census) and regular benefits which now commence at age 65 are fully indexed. OAS is the foundation to the public pension system and has become the most widely accessible source of pension benefits, paying out over $27 billion dollars to 4.1 million seniors. In fact, 96% of older adults in Canada qualify for benefits through this program. Our government programs are based on pay-as-you-go financing systems largely supported by tax revenue generated by today's workforce. There were seven people in the workforce for every retiree in 1966. Now that boomers are beginning to retire, this will change dramatically. The first wave to hit age 65 will be in 2011. Within four years, the ratio of workers to retirees is expected to drop to three to one. This will create a serious shortage of tax dollars to support social programs, particularly given that Canada's life expectancy is increasing, as is the population of "oldest old". The age 80+ segment will double in 16 years and triple in less than 40 years bringing with it, significant increased pressure on social support programs, the health care system and public pensions. Is more tax the solution? If we were to try to solve the problem of unfunded liabilities in the health care system simply by increasing taxes, this would require a 70% increase in federal and provincial personal income tax rates[9] so clearly this is not the solution to a structurally sound future system. Some say that the solution lies in immigration. Yet studies indicate that the rate of immigration required to keep the ratio of retirees-to-workers at its current level would be colossal. Others say the solution is to eliminate mandatory retirement at 65 and allow workers to remain in the workforce longer. Some provinces have already taken this step. The average worker enters the

---

[7] *Annual Report of the Canada Pension Plan* (2007) HRSDC.

[8] Canadian Taxpayers, Healthcare's Long-Term Affliction (February 02, 1999).

[9] Ibid.

workforce at the age of 21, and retires at 61, so eliminating mandatory retirement is unlikely to have a major impact. Governments might turn to revamping their social programs to refocus on meeting the needs of a specific segment of the population by providing minimum security to older adults intended to keep this segment out of poverty.

## Dependency Ratios

The current Old Age Dependency Ratio, defined as the percentage of working-aged people (ages 15–64) to those who are age 65 or older, sits at 20 retirees for every 100 workers. Statistics Canada predicts this ratio will rise[10] to just over 30 by 2025, and to 45 by 2050. The Total Dependency Ratio, which is the percentage of working-age people to those who are dependent including both children and seniors, is currently about 44.0. It is likely to remain relatively level until around 2011 when it will start to increase, rising to 64.3 by 2050. The Total Dependency Ratio, which shows the degree of economic burden on the country as a whole, confirms the pressures future governments will face and the increasing emphasis on personal planning necessary relative to health care and pensions. While the reduction in the percentage of children in the population may result in some savings relative to government education expenditures, the increase in health care expenditures will far exceed the former.

## Retiring Boomers and Their Registered Pensions

Some argue that there will be little reduction in tax dollars in the foreseeable future and the "tax-shortage scare" is exaggerated or perhaps even unfounded. This theory is based on the premise that as boomers begin to retire and draw taxable pensions, this will generate a continued source of revenue to the government to offset the increases in health care spending. Given the demographic wave that will hit retirement, and the savings this generation has amassed through tax-preferred schemes, it could even be beneficial to the government as funds begin to flow from them. This may be further enhanced by the transfer of savings in the form of inheritances from the prior generation which may generate additional tax on investment earnings. When compared with other countries, Canada enjoys a closer balance between private and public pensions so this phenomenon would not necessarily be experienced by other countries.[11]

The pattern towards delayed formation (marriage) and higher levels of education may continue with future generations. As this normally results in delaying transition to full-time careers normal retirement may push out to age 70. This would not only soften the impact on the Canada Pension Plan, but also positively impact the Old Age Dependency Ratio which assumes an

---

[10] UN, World Population Prospects, 2004 revisions.

[11] *Population Ageing, Intergenerational Equity, and Growth: Analysis with an Endogenous Growth Overlapping Generations Model,* Fougère and Mérette, Department of Finance, Canada (January 1999).

age 65 withdrawal from the workforce. As a result, this may delay the effects of population aging.

At the root of this issue is whether current social benefits (primarily health and pension) are sustainable in the future. There is no standard measure or index that can be used to evaluate health care needs and expenses in the future. While some predictions may be made to estimate the future flow of tax dollars relative to today, even if there was no change in the level of available tax dollars, does this mean our future needs can be met with the same resources available today? Attempts at projections often assume age-related increases in health care utilization remain constant based on current utilization patterns. As discussed earlier, population aging is only one factor that affects health care utilization. Other future variables include inflation rates, changes in incidence rates in chronic illnesses (new solutions that keep people alive longer but living with chronic illness), pharmaceutical costs (expensive new medications that don't exist today), technological improvements, (new equipment), changes in the health-seeking behavior of individuals (higher expectations), and changes in the delivery of services. One must also bear in mind that trends measure the population as a whole, whereas planners deal with individuals whose personal needs and resources may be quite different.

Another variable that could affect future health care expenses is the risk of pandemics which could drive up the cost of medicine and health care. Emerging disease hot spots are more common in areas rich in wildlife, these areas being in developing countries. A rapidly increasing population drives wildlife into smaller areas, increasing human contact and hence the risk of developing and spreading new diseases. Some of these emerging infectious diseases such as HIV, Severe Acute Respiratory Syndrome (SARS), West Nile virus, and Ebola are on the rise. Antibiotic drug resistance has been cited as another culprit, leading to diseases such as extremely drug-resistant tuberculosis. Air travel has made the world a smaller place, and with global travel comes the risk of faster spreading diseases. Importing of exotic pets is also to blame. Scientists found that more new disease emerged in the 1980s than any other decade.[12] El Nino weather patterns in the 1990s may have helped to spread mosquito-born diseases.

## Health Care: Funding and Expenditures

### The *Canada Health Act*

Under the Constitution, the provinces and territories are responsible for health care delivery, education and social assistance. Their largest source of revenue is through the Canada Social Transfer (CST) and Canada Health Transfer (CHT), which provide cash transfers to support health care, post-secondary education, social assistance and social services. In April

---

[12] University of Georgia (2008, February 21). Emerging Infectious Diseases On The Rise: Tropical Countries Predicted As Next Hot Spot. ScienceDaily. Retrieved February 22, 2008, from http://www.sciencedaily.com/releases/2008/02/080220132611.htm.

2004, the former Canada Health and Social Transfer (CHST) was restructured to create two separate transfers with the goal of making transfers to the provinces more transparent. The CHT cash transfer was $21.3 billion in 2007-08 and will reach $30.3 billion in 2013-14. In addition to cash transfers, the provincial governments also receive CHT tax transfers. These are accomplished by means of a reduction in the federal income tax rates to allow for a corresponding increase in the various provincial income tax rates, an arrangement which dates back to 1977 when the federal government transferred 13.5 percentage points of its personal income tax and one percentage point of its corporate income tax to the provinces for a total of $2.7 billion. The value of tax transfers grows with improvements in the economies of various provinces, and consequently the CHT tax transfers for 2007-08 amounted to $13.3 billion.[13]

The federal government also provides funding to the provinces for Extended Health Care Services which includes health care services for nursing home intermediate care, adult residential care, ambulatory health care and the health aspects of home care. While the federal government does not dictate specific program delivery criteria for this funding, it falls under the *Canada Health Act* and is subject to the same governing principles.

Legislation such as the *Canada Health Act* lays out the criteria that provinces must follow in order to qualify for full CHT transfers. In addition to meeting five governing principles, provinces must also satisfy two conditions related to health services and extended health care services, and criteria related to extra-billing and user charges.

The practice of extra-billing in connection with hospital and physician services was becoming quite prevalent in the early 80s and as a result, the *Canada Health Act* came into force on April 1, 1984. The five governing principals the provinces must adhere to are: administration of the program by a public non-profit authority, universal benefits for all insured people, coverage for all medical-necessary services provided by doctors and hospitals, maintenance of coverage if the insured moves or travels within Canada or travels outside the country, and access to services regardless of income, age, health status, or gender. The practice of extra-billing and user fees used in various provinces was seen as limiting access to health care services based on financial reasons. Consequently, a dollar-for-dollar penalty was initiated to stop this practice. While most disputes between the federal and provincial governments have been resolved through dialogue without the need to resort to deductions in transfers, there have been situations where extra-billing and user fees have led to cash deductions from provincial transfer payments. For example, in March 2006 British Columbia received a deduction as a result of extra-billing and user fees charged by surgical clinics during 2003-2004 totaling roughly $29,000. The practice of extra-billing and users fees continues to be an issue. From April 1984, which marked the end of a three-year transition period, through to March 2004, extra-billing and

---

[13] http://www.fin.gc.ca/FEDPROV/chte.html, Department of Finance Canada Web site (February 19, 2008).

user fees charged by all provinces totaled $8,753,151. During the previous three-year transition window, fees charged by all provinces totaled $244,732,000. The latter deduction which was applied to transfers during that period was refunded to the provinces in accordance with the transition rules under the *Canada Health Act.*

## Compliance Issues

The Canada Health Act Division, together with regional staff, monitors the various provincial government insurance plans to ensure they are complied with. They do this through discussions with representatives, media reports, publications, correspondence, and complaints received from individuals. Penalties are only imposed when all other avenues have been exhausted and the issue remains unresolved. There was growing concern by late 1994 regarding emerging two-tiered health care and private health clinics that were charging facility fees for medically necessary services. Diane Marleau, who was the federal Minister of Health, issued a letter in January 1995 announcing a new federal policy on private clinics. It provided an interpretation of the *Canada Health Act* regarding facility fees for medically necessary services. "Hospital" was defined to mean any public facility providing acute, rehabilitative or chronic care. Therefore, if the province covered the physician's fee, it was also required to cover the facility fee. The private clinics involved services for surgery, ophthalmology and abortion. This resulted in deductions to transfer payments to Alberta, Manitoba, Nova Scotia and Newfoundland and Labrador.

As recently as 2005-6, private surgical clinics have been a concern in Quebec and British Columbia. Accessibility and long wait times are often to blame for their emergence, as well as a practice known as "queue jumping" by those able and willing to pay for medically necessary services. Diagnostic clinics have emerged for the same reasons not only in British Columbia and Quebec, but also in Alberta, Manitoba and Nova Scotia where individuals can pay for the privilege of "jumping the queue" and getting faster access to insured services. Another practice that gained attention in 2005-6 in Manitoba was supplemental hospital charges to patients for medical surgical supplies, a practice known as "tray fees".

Provincial health care systems are dynamic and evolve over time in response to changing demands and priorities. Governments are examining both the structure and the services with the objective of how best to deliver timely access to quality care within an affordable financial structure. Through various Health Accords since 2000, the federal government has committed additional funds to the provinces to support restructuring of health services and health care delivery. Some of these funds have been intended to target specific areas such as:

- Reform of primary care, home care and catastrophic drugs

- Purchase of medical equipment for diagnostic services and treatment

In 2000 a $1 billion Medical Equipment Fund was established for payout between 2000 to 2002 to assist the provinces in the purchase of medical equipment for diagnostic services and treatment. A further $1.5 billion Diagnostic/Medical Equipment Fund was established in 2003 with the goal of improving access to publicly funded diagnostic services. These funds were paid to third-party trusts for the provinces to draw from, and with the expectation they would report publicly on how they invested the funding. These funds were supplemental to other transfers for health care provided through the various Health Accords.

## Health Care Delivery and Services

The health care system in Canada is primarily a publicly financed, and privately delivered system. There are three primary groups involved — the federal government, provincial and territorial governments, and private physicians. Through this system, provision is made for universal prepaid coverage for medically necessary health services based on need, not based on the ability to pay. The various provinces and territories each develop and manage their own health insurance plans, all similar but not identical to each other. These programs provide universal coverage regardless of movement across the country. This system has evolved over ten decades from its initial beginnings in Saskatchewan in 1947 as a public hospital insurance program. The federal government started providing funds for this purpose in 1957, and by 1961 all provinces and territories had a public insurance plan in place for hospital services. Saskatchewan was the first to add physician services as of 1962, and by 1966 the federal government began to share in the costs of physician services. By 1972 all provinces' public insurance plans covered physician services in addition to hospital services. As early as 1979 there were concerns about extra-billing and the additional user fees charged by hospitals indicated that a two-tier medical system was developing in Canada. This led to new legislation defining the current five principles outlined in the *Canada Health Act* of 1984. Currently, physicians' fees are set through a negotiation process between the respective provincial medical association and the provincial government.

The federal government provides direct health services to some groups such as the Canadian Forces, the Royal Canadian Mounted Police, and inmates in federal penitentiaries. In addition, it is also accountable for disease protection and health promotion. The provinces have the greatest responsibility in health care delivery. In addition to managing their respective public insurance plans, the provinces and territories also manage their own pharmacare programs through which they provide prescription medication to seniors and other low-income residents, though this is not mandatory under the *Canada Health Act*. Pharmacare programs ensure access to medication regardless of income level. The province maintains a formulary listing of roughly 3,000–3,500 approved drugs covered by the pharmacare plan. While many are covered, newer drugs may not be listed. Plans provide for payment based on the "lowest-cost alternative". A small deductible is payable usually in relation to the insured person's income level.

Catastrophic drugs not covered by the plan may be applied for under separate programs such as Ontario's Trillium Plan.

The *Canada Health Act* stipulates that insured health services must include all medically necessary hospital, physician and surgical-dental services. While hospitalized, insured persons are covered for medically necessary services as either an in-patient or out-patient. Accommodation fees are covered at standard (ward) level, or if deemed medically necessary at preferred accommodation level (semi-private or private). Medical services include nursing care, physiotherapy, physician fees, diagnostic procedures, medication while hospitalized, operating room fees, anesthetics, and other related medical or surgical supplies during hospitalization. Surgical-dental procedures performed by a dental surgeon are also covered if it is medically necessary for the procedure to be performed in a hospital.

Insured physician services must include visits or procedures that are medically necessary as determined by the physician. Consequently, most doctors charge for non-insured services including paperwork or exams related to insurance claims, applications, school or camp enrolment, and drivers tests. Some physicians also charge fees for processing paperwork related to an application for supplemental government funding on catastrophic drugs not covered by the provincial pharmacare program, or for renewing a prescription by telephone. Most physicians follow the recommended fee schedule set by their provincial medical association for non-insured services. Fees are capped on insured services. From this physicians must pay their overhead, staff salaries, and draw a personal income. Consequently, physicians necessarily resort to rationing the amount of time they spend with a patient and this normally translates into roughly 10 minutes per person. Is it any wonder there has evolved an expectation by physicians that "one visit equals one problem" and multiple issues should be addressed through additional appointments!

The *Canada Health Act* makes provision for extended health care services as they relate to nursing home intermediate care and adult residential care services, as well as the health aspects of home care and ambulatory care services. Through transfer payments, the federal government provides financial assistance to the provinces, however the specific nature (extent and delivery) is determined by the provinces. Provinces are required to give public acknowledgement to transfer payments related to these services according to the *Canada Health Act.* While there have been discussions in the past about the need for a national home care program, it remains in the domain of the various provinces to determine how far they will go in covering costs associated with long-term facility care and home care.

The *Canada Health Act* also defines who is eligible to be an insured person. It provides for "a person lawfully entitled to remain in Canada who makes his home and is ordinarily present in the province, but does not include a tourist, a transient or a visitor to the province." Provincial public insurance plans stipulate the required waiting period (the maximum allowed being 90 days), and also define a limit regarding how long a person can be absent from Canada and remain insured.

### Interprovincial Agreements

One of the guiding principles of the *Canada Health Act* is that an insured person must be covered when they travel throughout Canada. This is achieved through a series of bilateral reciprocal billing agreements signed by all provinces except Quebec. The intent is that an insured person will be able to present their health card in any province and not have to pay out-of-pocket at the point of service. The physician or hospital will then directly bill the insured person's home province at the rate normally paid in the physician's province. Quebec on the other hand, pays only at the rates stipulated under the Quebec public health plan. Consequently, residents of Quebec who travel outside the province often must pay out-of-pocket for services rendered in another province and apply for reimbursement through their own government plan upon returning home.

### Critical Issues in Canada's Health Care

There are some common themes across the provinces regarding areas that need to be addressed to strengthen the health care system. They are:

- Addressing Wait Times

A key measure of a well-functioning health care system is how quickly people in need can get access to the right kind of care, whether it is a physician appointment, necessary surgery, a hospital bed, diagnostic tests, home care or facility care. The impact of wait times on the health of individuals is not always clear, but all agree this is a key area that needs to be addressed. Governments attempt to measure these various wait times to learn more about what structural changes can be made to improve efficiency and remove barriers to care. In a 2005 survey conducted by Statistics Canada, about 13% of Canadians reported waiting more than three months to see a specialist for a new illness or condition.[14] One of the primary reasons for delays is that there are not sufficient health care workers. The 2004 First Ministers Health Accord committed $41 billion to the health care system over the next 10 years which includes a Wait Times Reduction Transfer of $5.5 billion for the provinces to apply to their respective wait-time reduction strategies. Better methods and tools for managing wait times are essential, such as moving away from paper-based systems to electronic technology for sharing information, and addressing facility and equipment shortages.

- Home, Community and Long-Term Care

Governments are preparing for the increased number of seniors that will one day require personal care. Home care plays a significant role in their strategy for dealing with the increased demand for services.

[14] 2005 Health Services Access Survey as reported in Health Care in Canada 2007, p.24, Canadian Institute for Health Information

Improvements in the home care system together with community support can help to compress the years required for facility care. Current systems are fragmented and involve many hand-offs. There is a belief that many people today are not receiving the right care at the right time. This has led to initiatives aimed at realigning where people receive care in the care continuum. Hospitals are intended to deliver acute care, yet many beds are occupied by patients waiting placement in a long-term care facility. A number of new long-term care facilities were built in the late 90s when funding became available. Many were built by for-profit companies, who in order to obtain funding, had to meet certain occupancy levels. This led to admissions that may have been premature placements — people who could have been helped through home care or supportive living facilities. The average stay in a nursing home in Ontario for example, is about 3.3 years, whereas the goal is to compress this to 2.5 years through better alignment of the right care at the right time. To accomplish this many improvements have to be made to support aging at home. There needs to be better co-ordination between hospital discharge departments and home care services to support discharge from acute care and minimize risks. Another important component is improving respite care to ensure informal caregivers are getting the support they need too when they have exhausted their physical and emotional support. Consolidation of currently fragmented services are required to support aging at home such as transportation to appointments, meals-on-wheels, housekeeping services, personal care such as bathing, and assistance with medication. Changes must be made in the system to ensure seniors are not vulnerable as a result of lack of co-ordination.

- Human Resources in Health care

Physicians and registered nurses are the two largest groups of health professionals and form roughly half of all health care workers in Canada. In 2005, there were two physicians for every 1,000 Canadians and nine nurses. Between 2001 and 2005 the number of physicians and nurses grew by about 5% which roughly equates to the growth in population. However, the age profile is changing and this could impact whether there will be sufficient doctors and nurses to meet future needs. The number of physicians under 40 years of age dropped by 10% while those over age 50 years increased by 19%. The number of registered nurses who were 55 years or older increased by almost 20%.[15] There are also concerns for the future as to whether there will be sufficient radiation therapists and anesthesiologists. To address this, the rate of new entrants to the profession is being closely watched at universities where recruitment is a key issue. In addition to Canadian trained professionals, the health workforce is also accepting graduates from programs in other countries. Also, new professions are emerging in health care such as these five new professions: physician assistant, nurse endoscopist, clinical specialist radiation therapist, anesthesia assistant and surgical first

---

[15] Ibid. p.15-17

assist.[16] Incentives are offered to attract back physicians and nurses who have left, as well as encouraging the opening of practices in more remote under-serviced areas.

- Primary Health Care Reform

Primary Health Care Reform focuses on studying four areas for potential change:

1. Its organizational structure including governance

2. How it is funded

3. How physicians get paid

4. How services get delivered to the general public

The health care system has experienced rapid growth in its demands due to increased utilization of services and an aging population. The most expensive component of health care is institutional-provided care. Just as corporations get restricted by legacy systems that cannot readily support desirable product changes, so is Canada's health care delivery impacted by policy legacies developed by prior governments. The current model is largely a physician-centered model with only a small percentage of practitioners working in a multi-disciplinary practice. Most provinces are now focusing on how they may change the system to one that is client-centered. Physicians are still predominantly compensated on a fee-for-service basis through provincial health insurance programs with most operating as sole practitioners. New funding models are encouraging this to change. How the system gets funded plays a significant role in how medical practices are organized and the distribution of services provided. Primary Care has long been seen as the backbone of the delivery system, with general practitioners acting as gatekeepers to specialists' services. Is this an ideal model, or even sustainable? As the general population ages, so does the average age of health care workers with the result being an increasing number of retiring physicians. This will challenge the existing model of primary care delivery.

How provinces define "Primary Care" also impacts its delivery structure. Most agree that it involves more than just physician services and addresses the main health problems in the community including health promotion and prevention in addition to curative, supportive and rehabilitative services. Physicians play a major role in the co-ordination of all these services.

Cost containment is one of the major goals of health care restructuring. One approach used is to substitute "lower cost" service providers for certain services. For instance, some services currently provided by physicians may be provided by specialty-trained nurses. Similarly, some services provided by nurses may be provided by trained personal support workers. Some people

---

[16] Government of Ontario, HealthForceOntario Web site (February 21, 2008): http://www.healthforceontario.ca/Work/InsideOntario/OntarioHealthProfessions/ NewRolesInHealthCare.aspx.

argue that the cost savings are not supported because lesser-skilled staff take longer to perform the required service, or that the use of lesser-skilled staff sometimes results in relapses or complications that further impact health care delivery costs.

Current social policy restricts the amount physicians can charge for services and which services they can bill through government health insurance plans (GHIP). This, together with economic changes, has led to physicians identifying non-GHIP revenue sources to supplement their income.

A series of incremental changes is under way, and while most argue that radical reform is required, incremental change may be the most realistic solution to changing the system.

- Access to Pharmaceuticals

The *Canada Health Act* does not deal with the cost of outpatient pharmaceuticals. Some drugs, particularly those that deal with serious illness, can be quite expensive for individuals not covered by private insurance plans or those covered by plans with low annual limits. Formularies, particularly those under provincial pharmacare programs, do not cover all medications. Pharmacists in some provinces are given incentives to choose the lowest cost alternative from groups of drugs that have been deemed to have equivalent therapeutic properties, even though they are not chemically identical to the brand name drug prescribed. This is a controversial issue. With the cost of pharmaceuticals becoming an increasingly important component of the overall cost of health care, there will be more expectations by aging consumers to have these costs covered by government programs.

- Electronic Health Records

Despite the prevalent use of the Internet in business and society at large, the health care industry still relies on a paper-intensive system that moves paper files from doctors to hospitals, to clinics, to pharmacies, and from province to province as necessary. Patients tell their story to their physician, who refers them to a specialist where they must tell their story again, they may then be referred to a clinic or lab for tests where they may have to tell their story yet again. Manual notes are taken each step. Every minute there are 2,000 health care transactions in Canada. Over the course of a year there are[17]:

— 440 million laboratory tests

— 382 million prescriptions

— 322 million office-based physician visits of which 94% result in handwritten paper records

— 35 million diagnostic images

— 2.8 million in-patient hospitalizations

---

[17] *Backgrounder Document: The Case for Electronic Health Records in Canada*, Canada Health Infoway Web site (February 21, 2008): http://www.healthforceontario.ca/Work/InsideOntario/OntarioHealthProfessions/NewRolesInHealthCare.aspx.

All of these transactions must be documented, as many result in exchanges of information with other parties. These inefficiencies impact wait times, costs, and quality of care. Electronic records allow health care professionals to provide evidence-based information that patients rely upon for making personal health care decisions. Some people fear information may fall into the wrong hands or be used inappropriately. Provincial governments are mindful of these concerns and are investigating ways to use technology for improving the flow of information in ways that benefit everyone concerned. For instance, experiments have been conducted where physicians can electronically write a prescription on an electronic device such as a handheld computer which immediately transmits to the designated pharmacy who fills the prescription and delivers the medication to the patient's home. Projects such as this can have tremendous benefit to people who are ill or unable to get around, and offer time savings to everyone concerned.

- Public Health, Wellness, Prevention

A study conducted in 2002 in British Columbia concluded that 40% of all chronic conditions are from conditions that could have been prevented. Two-thirds of health expenditures during a lifetime are made after age 65, mainly from chronic disease that took 10 to 20 years to develop. The annual cost for treating chronic disease is roughly $39 billion nationally. If through education and public awareness that emphasizes prevention, it was possible to reduce the incidence by 10%, this would translate into $3.9 billion annually which could be available for other health care needs. Provincial governments are therefore setting targets to try and reduce these costs by moving from a disability-focused model to a wellness-focused model. Some provinces have gone so far as to consider "what-if" scenarios such as the potential improvement that might be possible by offering tax incentives for people to join fitness clubs (a tax-deductible membership fee), or other similar incentives for people who pursue wellness programs.

*Chapter 2*

# Memory and Learning

Consumerism, or the study of consumers, helps organizations to adapt marketing strategies, products and service delivery by taking the consumer into consideration. Many different issues are considered such as:

- The psychology of how consumers reach decisions

- Impact of influencers within their environment such as family and culture

- The process of information gathering, assimilation and decision-making

- Motivational issues that impact decision-making

Knowledge and beliefs are an important part of how people make decisions. The purchase of many insurance and investment products is often a high involvement decision-making process. That is to say, the consumer

**25**

undertakes more research and this engages the processes of learning and memory.

## MEMORY AND LEARNING

People do not stop learning when they grow old. Learning is an important factor in keeping one's mind active and agile. Nevertheless, as humans age, brain function changes in various memory tasks. These changes progress in a linear fashion with aging. Natural changes in brain activity due to aging occur gradually between the years typically thought of as middle-age (40–60 years) and old-age (65+). These changes are most evident during performance of memory tasks. As the brain ages, it becomes more vulnerable to distraction from irrelevant information[1] and this may explain why learning and processing information becomes more difficult as we age.

Tests on normal healthy middle-aged adults compared with results of tests administered to younger adults have been able to pinpoint specific areas of the brain where patterns show differences between the two age groups. These changes become even more pronounced after 65. The result is that as we age, the brain has less ability to filter out irrelevant data. Distractions may be things such as background noise, loud music, or excessive printed information. Multi-tasking becomes more difficult.

Different areas of the brain are active during the performance of difference tasks. For instance, tasks that require concentration, such as reading, are performed by a different area than a non-task related activity such as recalling episodic memories like a vacation taken several years ago. Younger adults can more easily shift between these two different mental activities while older adults have less ability to do so. Reducing distractions in the environment can aid memory and recall. While the ability to recall becomes more challenging, semantic and perceptual judgment remain strong. In other words, aging reduces the *efficiency* of memory.

## MULTIDIMENSIONAL NATURE OF MEMORY

Have you ever wondered why you can remember the name of your favourite grade school teacher but not the name of someone you were introduced to ten minutes ago? Or why you can still skate or ride a bike even though you haven't tried for years? The ability to create new memories, store them, and retrieve them after an extended period of time allows us to learn. There are three major processes involved in memory. These are encoding, storage, and retrieval. Encoding is what allows new memories to stay with us for retrieval at a later time.

Memory is not a single storage cell, it is multi-dimensional having many different aspects. In general, some aspects are of a temporary duration, and others are long-term. It is the former that are most impacted by aging.

---

[1] Baycrest, "Older Adults More Vulnerable to Distraction From Irrelevant Information." *ScienceDaily*, 7 February 2006. www.sciencedaily.com/releases/2006/02060206234253.htm. 27 April 2008.

*Sensory memory* is passive and lasts only for a second or two. It is the imprint left by a sensory perception such as a word, a sound, a touch or a smell. While full in detail, it lasts only a moment. Visual information lasts for only a half second, and auditory information lasts longer — for as much as three or four seconds. As our bodies age, sensory memory may be impacted by changes in vision, hearing, taste, and smell. For instance, in the nose, olfactory cells responsible for our sense of smell are replaced more slowly or not at all. Vision and hearing experience the most dramatic reductions. After 50, the number of taste buds on the tongue begin to decline with the eventual loss being as great as 20 to 60%. As senses become less acute, the person may have difficulty distinguishing details. These and other physical changes can cause reduced ability for proper encoding to take place.

*Primary memory* is another form of temporary memory. This type of memory is at work when reciting a new phone number. It typically can hold five to seven "chunks" of information at a time. In order to be retained longer than several seconds or a minute, "rehearsing" is required, which refers to the process of repeating it over and over to oneself. This type of memory is affected by distraction or interference during the rehearsal process.

*Working memory* refers to processes used for temporarily storing and manipulating information. In this respect, it interacts with information that is in primary memory. It is often compared to the RAM memory of a computer. Working memory enables simultaneous tasking such as listening to music while studying. It becomes less efficient with aging and is impacted by distraction or interference.

*Prospective memory* is at work when you remember to buy milk on your way home from work, or to take a medicine at bedtime. Unlike other types of memory that are past-oriented, this memory is future-oriented and is impacted by aging.

*Short-term memory* is a system for temporarily storing information required for executing complex cognitive tasks such as learning, reasoning, and comprehension. It is associated with the passage of information to long-term memory and involves encoding, storing and retrieving information. Short-term memory is affected by the aging process and consequently this is why learning becomes more difficult as people age.

*Long-term memory* is the permanent storage memory that enables information to lay dormant until a retrieval cue calls it up to working memory at a much later date, even after years have passed. However, when it is retrieved, it is a reconstruction and not a snapshot and is shaded by our current beliefs and perceptions about the past, present and future. Feelings in the present at the time of recall can alter how the memory is recalled. In addition to being the residence of our personal history, long-term memory is also where our knowledge-based skills reside.

*Declarative memory* is the aspect of memory that stores facts. It consists of semantic memories (factual knowledge which is independent of time and place) and episodic memories (memories of a specific time and place such as personal experiences). In addition to remembering facts and experiences, another type of memory is one that deals with procedures, known as procedural memory.

*Procedural memory*, also known as implicit memory is at work when we walk, ride a bike, swim, or play a musical instrument. Different parts of the brain are active for procedural memory than declarative memory.

Studies have shown that people can have two types of memories for one situation and this is particularly true if the situation involved strong emotions. For example, a person in a car accident will have explicit memories about the accident (facts about the other driver, the weather conditions, the location) and implicit memories (a memory of the emotions connected to the experience). These memories are referred to as emotional memories. They can be either positive or negative. Cues that trigger positive emotional memories can be valuable, and allow us to recall good times of our childhood, adolescence, and adulthood. They may be triggered by any of our senses such as the sound of music, or a fragrance, or touch of a hand. We encounter smells daily, often without even being aware of their presence. Some are pleasant while others are not, triggering within the person memory flashes of past and present times, rich in detail and feelings. They can be a way of unlocking the past and connecting with a loved one whose memory in other ways has begun to fade.

## Long-Term Memory, Encoding and Retrieval

Long-term memories are connected in associated networks similar to a spider's web. While short-term memory has a limit in terms of capacity and duration, long-term memory does not. Although some information may appear to be lost over time, it is not clear whether it is displaced, perhaps by more relevant information that gets assigned a higher level of importance, or whether it is still there but presently not accessible. Regardless, memories are stored in complex related networks. The brain seeks to find relevance between new incoming information and networks that are already in place. As people age, the brain craves even greater relevance to what it already has stored, a fact that marketers could do well to keep in mind when dealing with an aging clientele.

Encoding is the process of entering information into long-term memory. The ease of later retrieval is an indicator of how effective the encoding process has been. If the new information is connected by multiple paths, there is a much greater chance of easy retrieval later. For instance, if you meet someone who tells you they are from the city of Stratford, you may be more likely to remember it if you already have several associations formed with Stratford such as Shakespeare, parents' hometown, and last summer's vacation.

There are many techniques used by people to aid the encoding process. One of them is repetition. A student may use repetition to learn a poem for reciting. Marketers can also use this method to increase recall later by repeating a product name several times throughout the commercial. Mnemonic devices (memory aid techniques) can assist the encoding process to transfer new learning to meaningful associations and assist later recall. "Chunking" is one such device and is evident in the famous pizza commercial where someone sings, "9-6-7-11-11...". This highly successful marketing campaign is built on using one central call-in number. The jingle uses rehearsal and repetition to further aid encoding thus ensuring that the product will be at the top of the mind. Mnemonic devices work by deeply encoding into long-term memory with very little effort.

Retrieval is the process of calling up information into active memory. Retrieval can either be by recall or by recognition. Companies often maintain a constant "look" on a product's packaging label to aid recognition of the product by its customer base. As we age, it is easier to use recognition to retrieve information than it is to use recall. The process of retrieval begins with receiving a "cue" that is then traced back along one or more paths to bring the memory into awareness. Many studies have been done to test state-dependent or context-dependent learning. They suggest that people can more easily recall information if they are in the same sensory context and state, as they were at the time they first learned the information. Memories link people to their past and recalling them enables them to relive positive experiences thereby initiating good feelings. Visual imaging has been proven to enhance learning and accuracy. Marketers capitalize on this by incorporating photos with text in brochures.

Nostalgia is another technique used by marketers to tap into the power of past emotional experience by bridging to existing knowledge structures. It may be the use of music, clothing, cars, or other symbols from a past era.

The use of novelty has also been proven to increase recognition such as through the use of distinctive colour, size, brightness, or other stimulus dimensions.

## COMMUNICATING MORE EFFECTIVELY

A new age of senior consumerism is permeating almost every industry. While significant diversity means that marketers must increasingly refine their targeting approaches to appeal to this heterogeneous audience, there still are many common areas that can increase effectiveness to this group as a whole. A good place to begin is by communicating the proper benefits in language and approach that your prospect will appreciate. Also, understanding the physical changes that occur with normal aging must influence how you communicate with your audience. While it is important to understand the physical changes, it is imperative not to accentuate them. Focus communications on aspirational benefits such as maintaining independence, control, dignity — not inabilities, physical and cognitive limitations (existing or potential). Resist the temptation to flaunt statistics as supporting evidence, and concentrate instead on educating, communicating with sincerity and building rapport. If you enjoy the work you are doing, you will project to your audience an air of genuine credibility. This consumer is unlikely to make a snap decision, so patience is a virtue.

The aging process brings with it changes in cognitive abilities including how we learn, process and retain information. Message intake is further impacted by sensory changes in vision, hearing, taste and smell. Accessibility and utility can be impacted by changes in ambulation and dexterity. Chronological age is a less relevant measure of age. Cognitive or self-perceived age is more meaningful as our inner self sees a different self-image than what the world may see. It is a perception of age derived from how we feel and look physically, and the stage of life satisfaction we have achieved. Healthy seniors typically see themselves as being 10 to 15 years younger than their actual age. Contemporary seniors have changing expectations concerning quality of life and are re-inventing dated definitions of being old. This is creating a new age of senior consumerism.

When working with a senior clientele, it is wise to take these changes into consideration and their impact on such things as your choice of communication medium, message formulation, graphic style, physical layout of office premises, use of equipment, printed materials, forms, signage, accessibility, and even Web site design. When usability is enhanced for seniors in these areas, studies have shown that effectiveness is also increased with other audiences as well. Your business will benefit by adopting ageless marketing techniques.

## Cognitive Changes and their Marketing Implications

Don't mistakenly assume that the issue of cognitive changes within the context of marketing to seniors has to do with presenting to an audience who has Alzheimer's disease, Parkinson's disease, and other forms of dementia. Memory loss and mental disability are not a necessary outcome of aging, and in fact are considered unhealthy aging. Rather, healthy aging still involves cognitive change because as people age there is a reduction in working memory and capacity, and this means your aging boomer clients will begin to process information, solve problems and think more slowly. Because of this, not only does new information get absorbed at a slower rate, the quantity absorbed is less. Irrelevant information such as background sounds and other surrounding stimuli, is more difficult to filter. These changes can be thought of as inefficiencies, and are not indicators of organic disease such as Alzheimer's disease or Parkinson's disease. Studies show that over time six specific cognitive abilities will function less efficiently. They are:[2]

- Inductive reasoning

- Spatial orientation

---

[2] *Cognitive Decline: Strategies for Prevention* (London: Greenwich Medical Media, 1997), 12 by H.M. Fillit.

- Perceptual speed

- Numeric ability

- Verbal ability

- Verbal memory

Many theories have been proposed regarding why this occurs. Three such theories are:

1. Limited Mental Energy or Processing Resources

2. Age-Related Slowing

3. Failure to Inhibit

The theory of Limited Mental Energy or Processing Resources, suggests that seniors show declines on cognitive tasks when compared to young adults due to a diminished pool of mental energy that governs controlled cognitive processes in working memory.[3] There is less of a difference however, when seniors are given aids in encoding and retrieving.

The theory of Age-Related Slowing proposes that age-related cognitive declines are a result of reduction in the speed at which information is processed in the cognitive system.[4] Consequently, seniors require more time to absorb information being presented to them and time to respond accordingly.

The Failure to Inhibit Theory contends that seniors have faulty inhibitory mechanisms in working memory that result in attention to irrelevant contextual data and faulty interpretations of context.[5] This detracts from the processing of target information. Information should be presented in a manner that is clear, uncluttered, and free of unnecessary distraction from the primary message.

In summary, the communicator needs to take into consideration:

- The speed at which they present information

- The amount of time they provide during interviews so seniors can process information

- The format of how information is conveyed so that it optimizes the encoding process

Avoid unnecessary syntactic complexities in messages and stick with simple sentence structures and jargon-free language. Seniors tend to favour print media because they can read and absorb it at their own pace. Consequently, make brochures available that can be left with them. Divide text

---

[3] *The Handbook of Aging and Cognition* (New Jersey: Lawrence Erlbaum Associates, Publishers, 1992), 457, by Fergus Craik.

[4] *Ibid* p.460.

[5] *Ibid* p.462.

into short paragraphs as this aids comprehension. Avoid the use of reverse bold (white or transparent lettering layered on a dark background) as studies indicate low or no comprehension of such messages occurs.

Consider whether your current marketing tactics accommodate these changes, or whether they are more likely to alienate and confuse, preventing you from fully capitalizing on an increasingly profitable consumer group that needs your services. Understanding how to communicate with different segments of your clientele may be one of your greatest marketing issues. The world of advertising has evolved away from simpler structures to more abstract thinking and this is not an effective style for seniors. They consequently turn to relying on informal methods such as word of mouth from trusted sources including opinion leaders in their networks. Many have grown comfortable with the Internet and are turning to it to do their own research prior to making a buying decision. There are many senior lifestyle Web sites that represent good opportunities for free publicity or low-cost advertising opportunities. Seniors look for information on many topics. They are increasingly aware of health issues and seek information on preventative measures that will allow them to maintain good health. Nutrition and organics are related topics that seniors are interested in. They are also interested in information on travel, retirement living, housing, legal matters, investment planning, illness prevention, care giving, the effects of medication, leisure, volunteer and cultural activities. So consider your web presence as being a central focus of your marketing campaign, and not just as an electronic business card. It is your 24-hour brochure and showroom floor.

Ask yourself whether your message will appeal or offend your target audience. Does your method of delivery accommodate age-related changes occurring in your senior clientele without alienating other segments? Have you used a style that takes into consideration, as a marketing segment, that seniors are not a homogeneous group but a heterogeneous group? Look for what unites all your segments, and employ marketing methods that bridge age and youth.

For products that address lifestyle issues for healthy seniors, find ways to appeal to their increasing tendency to seek fun, excitement and new experiences. Be sensitive in communicating on issues that are associated with heightened fears that develop with age. If your product addresses lifestyle issues for the unhealthy years, find ways to show your solutions by focusing on their benefits rather than the age-related problems your product attempts to resolve. Keep in mind attitudes are key, not chronological age. Focus on the functional and offer realistic attainable aspirations and inspirations.

Use nostalgia as a marketing tool in communications to create a meaningful connection point. By bridging to existing knowledge structures and tapping the power of emotional memory, you will heighten the appeal of your product and make it more memorable.

## Tap Into the Power of Episodic Memories

Older adults have a greater ability to remember past personal experiences (episodic memories) than factual data that is independent of time and place context (semantic memories). Overall the power of recognition remains stronger than recall. Understanding how seniors process information can help you to create compelling messages that will reach and motivate your target consumers. Look at your seniors' segment through their eyes and consider whether you have created a senior-friendly marketing mix. It is just a matter of choice about how, when and where to communicate with your intended audience. It will create greater utility in the process for all.

## Evoked Sets in Seniors

What is an evoked set? Quite simply put, it is the limited range of seriously considered choices that come to mind first when making a purchase decision. For instance, if you were going to the grocery store for soup, you might think "Campbells" or "Knorr". Your product (or service) needs to make this short list if it is to be even evaluated for purchase by your target audience. Studies have shown that seniors hold tight to evoked sets. New incoming information does not get assigned as high of a priority as information already existing in the memory's associative networks. The brain seeks relevance with what it already knows. Communication programs need to build the right level of activation with the intended buyer. Language, image, and atmospherics need to match harmoniously. Seniors are cost-conscious buyers and have more disposable time than other buyer segments. The fact that they are willing to trade units of time in return for units of savings is a factor that may well be a motivator for changing evoked sets.[6]

Heuristics are "mental shortcuts" used in the decision-making process, such as previous experiences with specific products. Maintaining a consistent image is important to triggering recollection at the time of purchase (remember recognition is stronger in older adults than recall). Often, images are used by buyers and not names so it is important not to change logos and colours that have strong association with the brand.

Nostalgia can be an effective marketing tool to associate a product or service with a past positive image. Music from a prior decade can create the theme for a seminar and then tied to images in brochures, Web sites, and as follow-ups for mood congruence. By triggering positive past memories that can now be associated in the present through the event at hand, you will raise the level of activation in the buyer's mind.

Pricing strategies are a method of leveraging seniors' desire to save money by not paying a higher price than they perceive the service or product is worth. Being on a fixed income makes this a more price-focused consumer segment that is willing to shop around for a good deal, now that

---

[6] *Dimension and Characteristics of Time Perceptions and Perspectives Among Older Consumers*, by Guy, Rittenburg, Hawes, Psychology & Marketing Vol.11(1) Jan/Feb.1994:p. 44.

they have the freedom of time. In keeping with this theme, it is wise to avoid presenting the highest priced product loaded with bells and whistles as this is likely to cause the client to tell you they want to "think about it". Meanwhile, they then initiate a price-comparison shopping expedition of their own. A better approach is to demonstrate during your interview that you have carefully considered how best to achieve a solid program that meets their objectives while carefully considering methods for cost containment. Be prepared to back it up with concrete examples.

It is not only the product that matters to seniors, but the purchasing experience too. Mood congruence is the process of recreating the mood at the time of purchase that existed at the time the consumer first learned about the product or service. The theme should flow through subsequent marketing communications and thereby aid later recall.

Frequency marketing is an effective method of attracting and retaining senior clients. This refers to a program designed to generate loyalty and long-lasting relationships by encouraging and rewarding the ongoing use of the services and products. One of the earliest successful programs was the use of stamps for filling booklets at grocery stores that could be handed back in for a gift. It is important to maintain ongoing visibility in the eyes of the senior client and to find ways of saying, "I appreciate your business".

## Sensory Changes and their Marketing Implications

Changes in your senses can significantly impact how you perceive and experience the world around you. Your vision, hearing, taste, smell and touch communicate much information about your environment. Intake and learning about new products begins with a sensory impression. Aging causes the senses to become less acute with details being less distinguished. Before a sensation is perceived, a minimum amount of stimulation is necessary, and this minimum is called the threshold amount. It is this threshold level that increases with age and consequently means there is a greater level of activation required for new information to be understood and remembered. Hearing and vision are the two senses most impacted and likely to experience reduction first.

Some hearing loss is almost inevitable. Roughly 30% of people over age 65 have significant impairment, according to the U.S. National Library of Medicine. Deterioration of the ear structure occurs in the form of thickening of the eardrum and other inner ear changes that may affect balance. The ability to hear high frequency sounds diminishes. The sharpness of hearing may show signs of beginning to decline as early as age 50, and the brain may have less ability to translate sounds into meaningful communication. Tinnitus, (a persistent noise present in the ear) may begin to develop in older adults.

Some age-related eye changes may begin as early as age 30, however almost everyone older than age 55 will need glasses at least part of the time. All of the eye structures change with aging. By age 60, the pupils have decreased to about one-third the size they were at age 20. Sharpness of vision may decline gradually with the most common problem being difficulty in focusing. The eyes develop less toleration for glare. The lens of the eye becomes yellowed, flexibility is reduced and a slight cloudiness may also develop with age. "Floaters" may develop which impact vision. Older adults may also experience a reduction in their visual field and this can limit their social interaction due to reduced ability to see people sitting next to them clearly. These changes are considered largely to be normal age-related changes. Other changes that may occur and are not considered to be normal include glaucoma, macular degeneration and diabetic and hypertensive retinopathy.

Effective marketing and communications needs to take these changes into consideration. Following are some methods for doing this.

## Visual Aids to Enhance Learning and Memory

Use a white background with black print. The contrast makes it easier to read. Surround your text with white space — not just a little, but a lot! This makes it easier for the eyes to focus on your message. Avoid shiny paper or glaring surfaces as the glare that is cast makes it more difficult to read — an important point to remember when selecting paper for brochures and business cards. Avoid the use of character clip-art as graphics in brochures and Web sites. Instead, incorporate real images and real photos that depict seniors in healthy, happy settings. Studies have shown that senior consumers react more positively to these images than when depicted as frail, unhealthy older adults. When incorporating colour, make use of warmer, bright colours which help to compensate for lens yellowing that occurs in the eyes with aging. For people of all ages, it is harder to distinguish blues and greens than reds and yellows, but this becomes even more pronounced with age. Consider the point size, style and colour of the font you select for print and Web sites. In printed material, serif fonts such as Times Roman work best, while on Web sites, a sans serif font such as Arial and a minimum text size of 12 point works better. A serif font is one where the lettering contains "tails", while a sans serif font has smooth rounded lettering. The "tails" on a serif font are more difficult to read on a Web site, while the reverse is true in print media. The minimum point size recommended for print media is 14 point, however this may need to be adjusted depending on the actual font selected as some fonts print smaller and closer character sets than others. Avoid the use of italics as it has been proven to significantly reduce legibility. Also refrain from using solid CAPITALS for creating emphasis as it is the printed equivalent of shouting. Instead, when emphasis is required, consider using **bold** characters selectively. Avoid the use of dotted or wavy lines as spacers in brochures and Web sites because they make it difficult for the eye to focus. Soft grey solid lines work better and achieve the same result.

## Hearing

If you are producing marketing tools that incorporate sound, make use of simple uncluttered soundtracks that will enhance the ears' ability to distinguish between background and foreground sounds. Avoid speaking over music. Instead, if you are incorporating music, perhaps as a marketing tool for nostalgia, separate the two — music first, then fading to zero followed by the commentator's message.

Train yourself and your staff to speak clearly, using an unhurried speed. This is particularly important for telephone conversations as body language and other verbal cues are not visible.

## TRUMP YOUR COMPETITION

Marketing to seniors is more than merely offering products that seniors need. It is adapting your selling style, communications, marketing strategies and office environment to create a synchronized comprehensive senior-friendly marketing strategy. Your competitors may offer similar products and services, but you can differentiate yourself by adapting your overall marketing mix. Perhaps the best place to begin is by forming an advisory committee comprised of seniors. They can help you audit your current practices and provide feedback to guide your development of new materials and processes. Check your marketing materials and Web site to see whether you stereotype seniors as old, frail and disabled in graphics. Help your staff to operate in a more senior-friendly mode by documenting guidelines for serving seniors and by providing frontline staff with special training. Most offices today operate in high-speed motion rushing from one transaction to another. Allow staff to have extra time to deal with senior clients without rushing them through the process. Ensure that you and your staff do not speak in a patronizing manner or use a parent-child communication style.

"Seniorizing" your business goes beyond changing printed material to a larger font. Create a welcoming atmosphere if you conduct business with clients from your office. Consider the adequacy of parking, wheelchair accessibility of halls and doors, and lighting inside your office. Look around at your staff — do you hire seniors too? They have many skills to contribute. Review your telephone system to ensure it offers personal service and callers are not forced through a voice-recorded instruction loop.

Consider the best method of presentation to get your message across. Many seniors prefer to learn through communications that are both oral and visual. Providing back-up printed material is critical so they can review after at their own leisure.

Don't assume that seniors are not interested in learning about your services through your Web site. People over 60 are now the fastest growing segment of computer users. Advanced age is not an obstacle to computer or Internet use but poorly-designed Web sites can be. Consider age-associated changes and their impact such as declines in vision, cognitive abilities and what methods most support learning. Web sites are easier to read if the text is left-justified (aligned on the left side only). Reserve underscoring for links only as it can otherwise create confusion. Avoid patterned backgrounds as well as florescent lettering. Use a writing style that presents information in the positive, and avoid the use of negative statements. Write in an active voice with simple language and include an online glossary of any technical terms. Keep the use of animation, video and audio to a minimum as it can be distracting to the central message and reduce download time on older computers. Be consistent throughout your Web site in the use of navigation buttons using large text buttons where possible instead of graphics which may be confusing. Offer a telephone number in the header of your Web site that is always visible as the viewer moves through pages of your Web site. Provide an email address for questions or comments. And finally, don't forget to conduct usability testing by asking seniors from your advisory group to test your Web site.

# Chapter 3

# Societal Issues Affecting Seniors

When two adults meet for the first time, it isn't long before one asks the other the question, "What do you do?" Much of our identities and of how we see ourselves is tightly interwoven with what we do for a living. Is it any wonder why many newly retired people struggle at first to find a new sense of self-image? Retirement marks a shift from "doing" to "being" and historically societal norms have considered this as the entry to "old age". While youth is typically seen as the period of *potential* ("What might he be when he grows up?"), old age by contrast, is often seen as the period of *limitations* ("Look what he can no longer do. He used to be faster, more accurate — now he thinks more slowly. What can he expect, he doesn't have the energy he used to have.") The change does not occur overnight. As we pass through middle age (the sum of all those years that fall between youth and old age), we become more than just the manager, the plumber, the nurse, the teacher, the politician, the executive, or any of the other labels we may have claimed along the way. There is wisdom and the ability to continue to grow as a human being, and as a productive member of society.

Societal views of retirement as an apocalyptic passage to old age are gradually changing. We have already witnessed the end of mandatory retirement at age 65. Certainly, aging boomers will continue to redefine what it means to be a senior. Societal views of the "oldest old", however, still too often stereotype elders of society in a negative way. Ageism can be reflected in discriminatory practices in areas such as housing for seniors, employment practices or services provided to older adults.

## WHAT'S IN A NAME?

Many names have been used in society to refer to people over age 65:

- Seniors
- Senior Adults
- Senior Citizens
- Retirees
- Elders
- Elderly
- Older Adults
- The "Old"
- Geriatric
- The Aged
- The Golden Age

The problem arises when society associates a certain common set of characteristics with a name. A survey was conducted to determine how older individuals wish to be identified.[1] The results overwhelmingly confirmed the preferred term to be "seniors" and "senior citizens". The term "maturity" is seen as successful and healthy aging while "old" is a term associated with decay and loss. "Elderly" is perceived as frail and old, while "geriatric" is perceived as frail, old and sick. It then comes as no surprise that the least liked term by older people is the term "geriatric".

Group membership contributes to a person's social identity. The individual's sense of self is likely to be a reflection of the way the general population views members of the group, how the group members are valued and how they are treated in society by others.

There is an increasing focus on gerontology, the study of the aging process, because of the growth in the proportion of older people in the population and the need to consider medical issues and conditions that increasingly occur with age. Geriatrics has to do with related services and the specialty itself such as a geriatric ward, geriatric assessment, geriatric nurse and geriatric medicine. A geriatrician is a medical doctor with

---

[1] Crilly, Kloseck, Misurak, MacKenzie, Sheps, *Geriatric: A Name Clients Don't Like: What is the Preferred Language*, Canadian Geriatrics.com, FebMar2004, (May 09, 2008).

specialized training in health promotion, prevention and treatment of disease in later life. Older adults often have multiple conditions that affect them. Our bodies react differently to illness and disease as we age, so special consideration must be given to these issues. Geriatrics stresses a team approach because of the multiple nature of disciplines required to treat a person holistically.

Language usage evolves over time as attitudes change. Most people agree that the next generation of older people (boomers), will have their own views and terms like "geriatrics" and "elderly" will be replaced with more positive references less likely to conjure up stereotyped images. Of course, the utopian state would be reached when no label is required.

## DISCRIMINATION, AGEISM AND SOCIAL BEHAVIOURS

In 1969, Pulitzer Prize-winning author and gerontologist Robert Butler was the first to use the term, ageism, which he used to describe stereotyping and prejudice against seniors due to their age, taking his lead from existing terms such as sexism and racism. Butler was astounded by the attitude of many of his professors at medical school toward older adults, and their dismissive nature regarding illnesses in the elderly. His research led to establishing that senility is not an inevitable outcome of aging but, instead, is a consequence of disease.

Butler defines ageism as a combination of three connected elements:

- Prejudicial attitudes towards the elderly, old age and the aging process

- Discriminatory practices against the elderly

- Institutional practices and policies that perpetuate stereotypes about the elderly

The outcomes and practices that result from prejudicial attitudes are described as *age discrimination*, whereas the stereotypes and prejudices are commonly referred to as *ageism* (i.e., actions versus attitudes).

*Stereotyping* is a social behaviour whereby one assumes a group of characteristics occur together, such as aging and ill health. This negative perception is visible in language, media, and humour. Age-based stereotypes, or ageism can be harmful because they may lead to treating older adults in demeaning ways, denying basic necessities, or failing to provide appropriate medical care and elder abuse. Sometimes they result in pitying, marginalizing or patronizing seniors. This is referred to as *benevolent prejudice* because the pity is linked with seeing seniors collectively as "friendly and warm but incompetent". This type of stereotyping can have important, even if unintended, consequences in the form of age discrimination. Being seen as "friendly and warm" leads to greater public acceptance that seniors should have special or different treatment, but the perception of "incompetence" can result in the public having lower expectations of seniors and lead to the public's acceptance of discriminatory age-based laws such as mandatory driver's license testing. The end result is that older adults have reduced choice and control in their lives and their views are given diminished importance.

## Theories on the Causes of Ageism

Different theories have been put forth as to what contributes to ageism.

One theory is that society's fear of death leads to the fear of old age as it is seen as the precursor to death. Old age becomes synonymous with death and ageism attitudes insulate younger generations from their feelings of fear. From this grows a personal repulsion and distaste for growing old, disease, becoming powerless and useless followed ultimately by death.

Another theory is that society is overly fixated on youth culture. This is derived from the media including television, books and magazines that place emphasis on physical beauty and sexuality. Mature characteristics are portrayed as undesirable, distasteful and unpopular. This affects not only how youth view the aged, but how older adults see themselves. This leads to loss of self esteem as individuals grow older.

A third theory is that the strong emphasis in society on productivity, more narrowly defined as economic potential, leads to the view that both ends of the life cycle (youth and old age) place a strain on the country's economy. Youth are more positively viewed because they have future potential, but older adults are seen as a financial liability.

Another contributing factor is the nature in which research on seniors has been conducted by organizations studying older adults. This theory points out that researchers have often gone to long-term care centres to study seniors as this is where they are have been most easily found in groups. Consequently, the less healthy segment of the senior population has been studied which has focused on the unwell instead of the healthy. Those living in long-term care centres represent only a small fraction of the senior population so generalizations are not well founded.

Ageism can lead to *gerontophobia*, which is the irrational, morbid fear or dislike of older people or of growing old. Popular culture also contributes to these fears through media messages that advocate we can "age gracefully" by purchasing magic pills, potions and skincare beauty products. Governments and organizations are increasingly developing intergenerational programs to help change societal views and to nurture social connections with the senior population.

Not all cultures stereotype older adults negatively. Some cultures associate old age with wisdom, honour and respect. Society's views can change over time and the media can play an important role in influencing change.

## Age Cohorts

If you pay attention to statistics (it's hard to avoid them these days), then you are already aware that most of us will be a caregiver to an aging parent at some point in our lives. It is worthwhile to reflect on the generational differences. We can more fully appreciate these differences by looking at age cohorts, that is, groups of people who were born in the same period. People born between 1909 and 1945 are often referred to as the Mature Segment. Their value systems have been shaped by historical events and social institutions around them. Some of the more significant historical influencers included the world wars and the Great Depression. How they think and behave today is largely related to these past experiences. The Baby Boom Generation (people born between 1946 and 1965) see the world quite differently. They are not accustomed to distinguishing between want versus need, preferring to pay more to sport the right brand. Most are better educated than their parents and are more inclined to conduct their own research prior to buying products or services. Questioning comes naturally to boomers, whereas their parents were taught respect for authority without question.

This contrast in value systems sometimes prevents boomers from understanding their parents' viewpoint, such as their attitudes towards accepting help from others. The idea of hiring services to perform work they have traditionally done themselves is incongruent with their value system. The Great Depression taught the lesson of not paying for services that you can do for yourself. As the boomers did not live through this, their value system was not influenced by this historical event. The children of boomers are similarly being shaped by the events and circumstances they are experiencing today. One day they will be the caregivers of the upcoming generation of boomer seniors.

# RETIREMENT AS A LIFE STAGE

Retirement may have been long-awaited, or in some cases, individuals may have unexpectedly been thrust into it due to a corporate reorganization. While not everyone has worked up to retirement, those who have not still experience this life stage change but perhaps through their newly retired spouse. As time goes by, they pass through difference phases. The duration of each phase varies based on the individual.

## Phase 1: Disengaging

In the disengagement phase, individuals prepare for leaving the work force. This is also known as the *fantasy stage* because it is when the person begins to think about all the things they want to do once retired. This phase may last from one to three years.

## Phase 2: Transitioning

In the transitioning phase, individuals begin the business of retirement. Depending on how they faced the years leading up to retirement, they may approach it in one of three styles:

1. The *vacationer* is the individual who sees retirement much like being on vacation. They pursue leisure activities they previously never had time for and travel.

2. The *runner* is the individual who already set themselves a full agenda of activities prior to retirement. This individual "works at keeping busy", finding pleasure in being able to set their own tasks. Unable to slow down, they pursue recreation much like a job.

3. The *sleeper* is the individual who enters retirement with a period of low activity, relishing the new found ability of being commitment-free. However, after a few years of low activity, they eventually become more active.

## Phase 3: Disenchantment

Reality sets in. Eventually the novelty of being newly retired wears off and a period of disappointment may begin. Sometimes a triggering event occurs that initiates this phase such as the death of a spouse. There may be feelings of loss of identity associated with the transition from "being" to "doing". The person may find that even though they now have time to do all the things they dreamed of doing, financially they are limited now that they are on a fixed income.

## Phase 4: Reorientation

At this stage, people "take inventory" of their options and find ways to move forward. How well they adapt depends upon a combination of their health and how adaptable they are to change. The healthy/well-adjusted, may become more involved in the community or perhaps take up a new hobby. The unhealthy/poorly-adjusted have more difficulty trying to figure out what they will do. This stage may also involve a move to a smaller home with less upkeep either in order to free up time to focus on other interests, or because health is becoming an issue making it more difficult to manage home maintenance.

## Phase 5: Routine "Business"

Eventually the individual comes to terms with their new reality and establishes a routine. Life becomes "business as usual". Retirement has now become comfortable and a pattern of activity prevails. It is a time of reflection and for enjoying memories and simple pleasures like time with grandchildren. This phase may last for many years.

## Phase 6: Termination of Retirement

As time passes, the notion of retirement becomes less relevant. More significant health issues may have developed and the prevailing activity evolves around personal health care. A more introspective era begins, and there is a desire to "tie up loose ends". It is also a time for mending relationships, and reflection, "Am I ready?" The person may move to a facility providing assistance with daily activities of living.

# RETIREMENT AS A SERIES OF LOSSES

While retirement is the beginning of a new chapter in life, it is also a time of saying farewell. There is less structure than what people have been accustomed to during their working years. No longer is it necessary to rise at a set time, and weekdays are much the same as weekends. Initially it may bring welcome relief much like a vacation, but eventually the novelty wears off. Men tend to have more difficulty adjusting than women most likely due to the fact that women continue the structure of mealtime preparation and other home-related tasks they habitually performed over the prior years.

Income is now reduced and fixed and this may mean lifestyle changes based on a reduced budget. Social programs for seniors introduced over the past two decades have helped to significantly reduce poverty amongst the aged. These programs include Canada Pension Plan, Old Age Security Benefits, the Guaranteed Income Supplement and the Spousal Allowances. More seniors today have pensions from employment than the generation that preceded them. Despite this, there are many elderly women living on their own who struggle to make ends meet after the death of their husbands when company pension plans stop.

Personal identity is often linked to occupational roles and this change can affect a person's self-image and self-esteem particularly if the retirement was not planned and due to a forced situation. There may be residual feelings of lack of validation for the many years of loyalty given the former employer. The result can be feelings of mourning as the person struggles to redefine who they are. Work provides an opportunity for a social network. How quickly one adapts is impacted by whether they already have a social network outside the work environment in place when they retire. Personal relationships also change with time. There may be the loss of a spouse either due to divorce or death. Offspring that have grown up and left home may relocate to another part of the country.

Feelings of loss due to changes in relationships can be lessened by learning different methods of connecting such as email. There are many health clubs and service clubs that cater to seniors offering opportunities for excursions and events with peers who have similar interests.

Eventually as health begins to fail, the individual may have a need for assistance in performing activities such as meal preparation, laundry, home maintenance, or even with taking medication. Sometimes older adults are reluctant to let others know they need help for fear of losing their independence. However, the reality may be that a change would provide much needed assistance that would help the person to function more independently and in a safer environment.

Some seniors may be at risk of substance abuse, depression or even suicide as they increasingly begin to rely on medication for controlling chronic pain, or to aid sleep. Some of the common triggers include the loss of a spouse, their driver's license, or a general feeling that they have no further purpose in life. However, there may be other causes. As the body ages, a number of bio-chemical changes occur in the brain and this may be an indicator the person needs medical attention. Older adults are often taking multiple medications and there is a risk of mixing pills or taking incorrect dosages. Some seniors turn to alcohol and when mixed with medication, it can cause serious medical problems. There can be an increased risk of falls and an increased risk of depression.

Depression is not a normal part of aging and when symptoms appear it should be treated as any other medical condition with professional help sought. While many people believe teenagers have the highest suicide rates of any age group, in reality statistics indicate elderly people are at greatest risk, with males having higher incidence rates than women.

Elderly women may be particularly vulnerable to lack of access to medical supports and services for chronic conditions as many live on their own without transportation.

## THE SENIOR DRIVER — LOSING INDEPENDENCE

Marianne, age 79, started driving the same day she turned 16 years old. Other than a minor fender dent caused by backing up in a tight parking spot when she was 32, she has had no other accidents or tickets. In fact she has always joked about her cautious tendencies in life as being her best asset when behind the wheel.

Last month however, she was driving after dark during a light rainfall and accidentally side-wiped an empty parked car. Enough damage was done that she had to file an insurance claim and she reported in to the vehicle accident reporting centre where police wrote up an accident report. Marianne though not injured, was badly shaken up at the thought someone could have been hurt had they been in the parked car at the time. Marianne admitted to her family that she'd been bothered for some time now by glare at night limiting her vision. She vowed never to drive at night again.

Marianne's situation is not unique. As people age, changes in normal physical and mental health occur and these changes sometimes affect driving safely. For example, aging causes the lens in the eye to thicken and pupils become smaller, making the eye more sensitive to glare. Refocusing the eyes takes longer, such as changing the view from looking down at the speedometer back to focusing again on the road. The eye takes several seconds to adjust and to clearly see what lies ahead. Depth perception reduces with aging, so an older adult has more difficulty judging how fast other cars are moving. The retina becomes less sensitive to light with age making it necessary to have more light to see clearly than when we are younger.

Alcohol is metabolized by the system differently in older adults and it takes less of it to become intoxicated. Our body water decreases and body fat increases with age and these factors affect blood alcohol concentration; so an older adult who drinks the same as when they were younger will have a higher alcohol/blood level content in their system than when they were younger. They may not realize that alcohol is affecting them, and their driving ability, as their consumption is not greater than in years gone by.

Medication also plays a role in driving and safety. Just as alcohol affects the body differently with age, so does medication. Our sensitivity increases with age and the effects of medication become more exaggerated, such as drowsiness or disorientation, and this leads to slower reaction times. Two medications that cause no problem independent of each other, may have negative effects when taken together, making it unsafe to drive. Medication also interacts negatively with alcohol by increasing its effect. Many older adults take aspirin for chronic pain. When aspirin is taken with alcohol it causes the alcohol/blood concentration in the system to increase. So, the concern is not only with prescription medication, but with over-the-counter medication as well.

Reduced flexibility caused by arthritis, chronic pain and other conditions also affects safe driving. It can restrict a person's ability to turn and survey for oncoming traffic before backing out or lane changing, and it can also affect their concentration. Loss of hearing can put the driver at risk of not hearing warning signals, such as, at train crossings. Memory loss and dementia also put older drivers at greater risk.

Driving enables older adults to retain their independence longer. Without the ability to get to doctors' appointments, do errands, buy groceries and remain socially connected, their ability to remain living safely in their own home lessens. Many older adults continue driving safely well into their 80s, however some are at risk to themselves and others. According to one statistic, although seniors represent 13% of our national population, they account for 17% of road fatalities. They suggest that older adults typically drive less than younger people but get into more accidents. Conversely, according to Statistics Canada, there are 50% more young drivers involved in collisions than older drivers yet the 55 and over age group drove more than three times the kilometers than younger drivers.[2] Clearly there are mixed opinions regarding whether seniors as a group present a greater hazard driving when compared with young drivers as a group.

More importantly, what can be done to help older adults safely retain their driving ability longer? They can be encouraged to pursue various

---

[2] *New Program Pitched for Seniors Drivers*, CityNews.ca (May 8, 2008)

adaptations that enable them to continue driving safely. This could be anything from installing larger side mirrors for those with limited range of neck or waist movement to encouraging them to use more side roads that avoid hectic traffic areas. Also they can be encouraged to go for regular eye checkups and to have proper fitting sun glasses for driving. Sometimes couples have established driving patterns over the years that are difficult to change as may be the case where the husband has been the primary driver. While it may not be easy to convince "hubby" to give up some of the wheel-time to his wife, her confidence behind the wheel is important. It may turn out that he has to give up his driver's license before she does. When someone has not driven for a very long time, it can be  intimidating and highly stressful to resume driving after years of not being behind the wheel.

Some adults under age 80 may also be at higher risk particularly those who have Alzheimer's disease or another form of dementia. An indication may be unexplained dents in the car. The family physician will have experience in dealing with these matters.

Most provinces have aged-based obligatory medical exams for seniors. Newfoundland and Labrador, Quebec, Alberta, Northwest Territories, and Nunavut require seniors to have a medical exam at age 75, and 80, and then every two years thereafter. Yukon Territories require a medical exam at age 70 and 80, then annually thereafter. British Columbia requires a medical exam at age 80, then every two years, and a complete driver re-exam if deemed necessary based on the medical report. Ontario has the most stringent guidelines which requires adults age 80 and over to complete a vision, knowledge and group education session every two years; with a road test for those deemed to be at risk.[3] Books are available to help older adults prepare for their test. Ontario is currently considering a move to a graduated licensing system for older drivers, and tax concessions for care givers who act as a driver for a senior.

When seniors can no longer drive, their ability to remain living independent in their own home decreases. Programs such as Meals-on-Wheels and assistance from informal caregivers can help to support independent living. If transportation has become an issue, most communities have social programs offering transportation to seniors to aid independence.

## ETHICS IN MARKETING TO SENIORS

The first articles on ethical issues in marketing appeared in the 1960s in the form of philosophical essays but it was not until the 1980s that there was a major research thrust examining ethics in marketing. The concept of examining ethics in marketing is a relatively young discipline. Within its scope are product safety and liability, advertising truthfulness and honesty, fairness in pricing, power held by channels of distribution, privacy in Internet and database marketing and forthrightness in selling.

---

[3] CCFMTA Aging Driver Task Force Strategies 2006-2010; http://www.ccmta.ca/english/pdf/aging_driver_strategy_ppt.pdf (May 13, 2008).

As the seniors market continues to grow, it becomes increasingly attractive as a target market. One of the issues facing business professionals is what constitutes appropriate marketing ethics with this buyer segment. Marketing is viewed as human conduct and subject to public scrutiny. Ethics has to do with the moral principles that guide that conduct. Marketers must be aware of ethical standards and acceptable business behaviour as it relates to the seniors' market.

Many marketing associations exist that provide guidelines for members as to what constitutes ethical marketing. Some of these organizations are:

- Canadian Marketing Association

- Social Marketing Institute

- Word of Mouth Marketing Association

- Direct Marketing Association

Marketing ethics is generally associated with societal values. Ethical issues are often closely associated with legal issues. While some marketing practices may be viewed as "slightly grey", the line is quite clear when marketers or sellers cross from unethical to illegal behaviour. One growing problem is the issue of fraud perpetrated against seniors. Fraud affects thousands of Canadians each year resulting in the loss of millions of dollars. While some schemes involve small amounts of money, unfortunately sometimes entire life savings are wiped out by schemes that might have been preventable. The best way to prevent being scammed is by being aware of the schemes perpetrated by fraud artists and being vigilant.

## SENIORS AS TARGETS OF FRAUD

As fraud affects everyone, why is it that seniors are often specifically targeted by fraud artists? The reasons are many. They often have savings accumulated over a lifetime, a house fully paid for and credit cards with a good credit rating. This profile makes an ideal target for someone looking to pull off a fraudulent scheme. The era they grew up in stressed trust without question and politeness. Questioning others was not considered to be polite. Fraud artists are well aware of the trusting nature of this generation and how difficult or impossible it is for them to simply say "no" or to just hang up the phone.

Seniors are less likely to report a fraud. Sometimes this is because they do not know who to report it to, but often they fail to report it because they are too embarrassed to admit they were fooled. Some are concerned if their family discover it, they may interpret this as being unable to manage their own finances. The fear of losing their independence if they are perceived as not managing well on their own keeps them from telling others.

When they do report a crime, they are not the best witnesses, often forgetting details. Fraud artists rely on this in the hopes that they will not be able to provide police with enough information to track them. The questions are numerous — how many times did they call you? What time of day? Did they give you a telephone number or address? Was it always the same person that called you? Where did you send the money? What did they promise you? Did you write anything down? This can create confusion and feelings of loss of self-esteem when the senior experiences difficulty remembering. Sometimes weeks or even months have passed from the last contact with the fraudster and the meeting with the police and that would challenge anyone's memory at the best of times.

Seniors may be enticed by products that promise medical improvement, improved memory, virility, and cures for diseases. Those with low incomes may be enticed by the promise of easy windfalls and welcome the promises made by fraud artists on how they can relieve their financial woes.

## METHODS USED BY FRAUD ARTISTS

The methods used by fraud artists are many — telephone, fax machines, printed material, mail, in-person schemes and more recently, computer. As the number of seniors using the Internet continues to increase, this becomes a growing risk.

### Telephone and Fraud

Call display is often considered a safeguard in minimizing the risk of fraud. However, perpetrators have ways to disguise caller ID by displaying a false telephone number. Call display is *not* a reliable way to protect against fraud and may be used to give the appearance it is a bank calling to obtain personal account verification, a credit card number, or PIN. It is not wise to trust call display as verification that a caller is who they say they are; some other form of identification should be requested.

Businesses are increasingly making use of call centres to conduct telemarketing, sometimes under the category of being a courtesy service call. While not all businesses who use telemarketing are unscrupulous, there are some who use this method to trick individuals into thinking they have won a fantastic prize or low-cost vacation as a means of securing personal information such as a credit card. Personal information should never be given over the phone to unknown organizations. As the saying goes, if the offer sounds too good to be true, it probably is not true.

### Printed Material and Fraudulent Offers

A variety of offers are sent to unsuspecting seniors promising opportunities for work-from-home jobs, to sweepstakes, lotteries and low-cost home renovations. Some appear in the classified ads in newspapers giving the appearance they are quite legitimate. The perpetrators hide behind a post office box number and some elaborate schemes may even establish 1-800 lines to give the further appearance of legitimacy. Seniors should be cautious of such offers and investigate the reputation of the organization before investing any money in such offers.

## Fraudulent Offers through the Mail

Fraudulent mail offers take many forms such as a postcard, a certificate, envelopes that appear to be registered mail, free subscriptions, credit card approvals and invoice renewals. They appear legitimate because they are often addressed specifically by name to the individual. Perpetrators secure names in many ways, even by going through neighbourhood garbages and dumpsters. It is wise to use a shredder for destroying all documents and envelopes containing any personal information including address information. Maintain a list of billings and their due dates as this may act as an alert when an invoice is received at a time not consistent with the billing cycle. Be sure when posting mail that the box is a legitimate government mail box, and avoid using third-party "courtesy drop-offs". This opens the door to the possibility of mail being stolen that may contain cheques for bill payments.

## Fraud and Face-to-Face Schemes

Some perpetrators use door-to-door schemes to deceive unsuspecting victims. They may pose as a service repairman or inspector in the area. Some schemes involve fundraising for fictitious charities. With the changes in energy regulation, many people have received visits from callers who give the impression they are with the person's existing energy company and asking them to sign contracts. The best way for seniors (or anyone!) to avoid this risk is not to answer the door in the first place when no appointment has been scheduled in advance. References should always be checked in advance for anyone who is scheduled for an appointment, and identification should be requested prior to letting the person inside when they arrive.

Another in-person scheme involves looking over someone's shoulder while they are using a public bank machine or eavesdropping on a conversation taking place with a bank's customer service representative.

## Computers and Fraudulent Schemes

Seniors are increasingly using computers and the Internet. Their trusting nature may place them at risk when making Internet purchases that may involve fraudulent sellers. Internet shopping is a new experience and they may not recognize warning signals that all is not legitimate.

## Personal Identity Theft

Personal identity theft is on the rise. It occurs when an imposter assumes your identity by stealing your social insurance number, your credit card, health card, or other personal identification for their own use.

They may then use the identification to open a bank account and cash fraudulent cheques that leave you owing money. They may obtain a new credit card in your name and run up substantial debt. Some of the signs that your identity is being used fraudulently by another person are:

- You receive an invoice for a credit card you did not apply for.

- You receive bills for purchases you did not make.

- You no longer receive invoices for credit card statements you legitimately have.

- A credit agency is calling you to inform you they are collecting for a defaulted account you did not establish

Any suspicions you have that your identity is being used by someone else should be reported immediately to the financial institutions affected and the police through the PhoneBusters organization. They are a joint anti-fraud initiative by the RCMP, the OPP and the Competition Bureau. It was formed with seniors in mind. They can be contacted at 1-888-495-8501. They have created a downloadable form from their Web site for the purpose of notifying financial institutions when a personal identity theft has occurred. The two major credit bureaus should also be notified so they can place a "Fraud Alert" on your records so your credit rating will not be adversely affected. Their numbers are:

- Equifax: 877-323-2598

- Trans Union: 877-525-3823

Everyone should periodically order a copy of their own credit report whether they suspect identity theft has occurred or not. Errors do occur and this gives you the opportunity to rectify them.

Some organizations claim to sell special insurance to protect credit cards against fraudulent misuse. Insurance is not necessary because losses associated with misuse of credit cards is attributed to the banks or companies associated with the fraud. They have the responsibility to ensure the user of the card is the legitimate owner of the card.

## Minimizing the Risk

While no one can absolutely guarantee it will not happen to them, there are steps people can take to minimize the risk. Never volunteer personal information at stores that is not necessary. Many retailers routinely ask for personal addresses and telephone information. They cannot make you divulge this information if you choose not to. Many simply want to "build the data base" for later marketing purposes. Do not carry credit cards or identification that you do not need daily. Many people unnecessarily carry a birth certificate. If lost or stolen, this can be used by fraud artists to steal your identity. Thieves often break into cars looking for wallets and cash that have been left inside.

Secure your mailbox with a lock to prevent someone stealing your mail. During lengthy absences have your mail placed on hold and in short absences have a trusted neighbour pick it up daily for you.

Change passwords frequently and avoid using birth dates, house numbers and other passwords that may easily be guessed. Just as easily obtained, is your maiden name and telephone number. Make use of alphanumeric characters and other unique characters where possible such as +, ^, >, *.

When disposing of paper containing personal information, use a cross shredder. Identity thieves have been known to route through people's garbage to obtain personal identification information. Never give out your social insurance number when it is not necessary. Though it happens less often, some organizations still routinely ask for this information and for permission to use it administratively as your unique identification number in their database.

## SCHEMES USED BY FRAUD ARTISTS

There are many schemes used by con-artists to defraud people. Many of these schemes are listed below and can be found on the Phone Busters Web site with tips for safety and prevention. Variations and new scams are emerging all the time, so the best defense is awareness and exercising due diligence.

### 1-900 Scams

Fraud artists encourage the consumer to call a 1-900 line on the promise they have won a prize they need to claim. The offer will advise the cost of the call to be around $4.99, stating the charge per minute and the average wait time to be about seven or eight minutes. The caller is then locked into a loop of voice prompts so they cannot speed up the duration of the call. When they finally find out their winnings, the prize is usually no more than one or two dollars, but the cost they have incurred for the long distance is easily $35.00 or more. Some telephone companies offer a service of blocking 1-900 calls. This method can protect seniors from 1-900 scams. Note that new numbers also involve 1-976 numbers.

### Nigerian Letters Fraud

This scam has been in existence for a while and continues to surface. Letters are being sent out of foreign destinations to consumers by mail, email and fax. They stress the urgency to act quickly and confidentially to aid the sender in getting large sums of money out of the country usually from a prominent royal figure, a doctor or a large corporation. If the recipient responds, they are asked to submit an up front processing fee and or they are asked to meet personally to discuss it further. Emails often contain a virus that will damage the computer. The offers are bogus and

PhoneBusters should be contacted if the perpetrator has attempted to make personal contact.

## Advanced Fee Loans

Some seniors who are in need of funds may be attracted by the promise of low interest loans or guarantees of money to people who have poor credit history. The ads appear in magazines, newspapers, and voice mail messages. They usually require a fee up front. Once the fee is paid, you do not receive your loan and you never hear from the company again. In most jurisdictions it is illegal for a company to request a fee up front prior to obtaining a loan.

## Cheque Overpayment Fraud

This scheme involves a person receiving a cheque as payment for money that is actually owed to them. However, the cheque given is in excess of the amount owed. The scam artist then tells them to go ahead and cash it (it is a fake cheque) and to wire the excess overpayment back. Of course after they do so, the cheque is determined to be counterfeit and they are out the overage they paid to the perpetrator as well as bank charges. Never accept a cheque as payment if it exceeds what is owed you. Always ask for several forms of identification and avoid dealing with overseas wire services you are not familiar with. If money is owed to you, always request a certified bank draft and only accept it in the actual amount due.

## Sweepstakes Scam

This scam involves entering a sweepstakes contest and receiving a call that you have won. You may not even have entered a contest, but the caller relies on the person assuming they have just forgotten about entering a contest with the passage of time. The caller advises you in order to collect your winnings you must pay for the taxes up front. The caller sounds very official, representing themselves as a lawyer, judge or other official. After sending the money, there is no prize and the scammer has since disappeared.

A variation of this is that you are told you must purchase a small article of your choice, which entitles you to receive your cash prize. The fee charged for small article is much more than it is worth, and no cash prize is forthcoming.

## Puppy Scam

This scheme targets pet lovers by posting an ad in a newspaper or in the classifieds section of a Web site indicating a puppy for sale that the owner cannot keep. It offers to pay the shipping charges and may even show a picture of a puppy. The photo is fake, and so is the offer. After sending your money no pet is shipped. Always verify the identity of who you are dealing with and don't rely on just a telephone number and post office box. If you cannot verify the person's and puppy's existence, don't get involved.

## Pyramid Schemes

In pyramid schemes the emphasis is on attracting new entrants not selling products. No new money is generated. Instead, the early entrants, that is those at the top of the pyramid, collect the money and rely on a steady flow of new entrants at the base of the pyramid. Eventually when there are too few or no new entrants it collapses and those at the bottom receive nothing. Pyramid schemes are illegal and participating in one is a crime. Never invest money without thoroughly examining what you are investing in. If rates of return sound extremely high, keep in mind that high risk goes hand in hand with promises of high returns. If your investment turns out to be part of a pyramid scheme you may be facing prosecution.

## Recovery Pitch

This scheme involves targeting a person who has already been a victim of fraud by promising to get their money back in return for a fee up front. They may represent themselves as working with the police or a private investigation agency. Once they have your fee, you never hear from them again.

## Secret Shoppers Scam

This is an offer of employment as a mystery shopper that appears in the classified ads. The scammer sends a package which includes a cheque for about $2,000. Although it appears real, the cheque is counterfeit. After completing a small "test" assignment, the next assignment given is to send money using MoneyGram to a particular fake company and report on the shopping experience at MoneyGram. The fake cheque eventually bounces and the person is charged back the money by the bank.

## Dishonest Renovators

Seniors are often targets of dishonest renovators who may show up door-to-door. They may tell the homeowner they have observed the house needs a new roof, or a new chimney or other home repair. Their quote is usually low to get the job, and after taking a substantial deposit or completing only half the job, they are never seen or heard from again. The homeowner can lose thousands of dollars. Always ask for references, check them out, and verify their license is up to date. Contact local organizations such as the Better Business Bureau to check for complaints that may have previously been lodged.

## Health Scams and Miracle Cures

Seniors may be the target for miracle cures that promise to cure cancer, chronic pain, or other conditions. It may be through a classified ad, a multi-level marketing scheme, a Web site, or flyer. Researchers are working daily to find such miracle cures for dreaded diseases, and genuine discoveries will be public news. Seniors should always consult with their physician prior to purchasing any miracle cures, and be skeptical of sources that are outside the medical community.

## Mail Order

Seniors can be easy targets of mail order companies because they often have difficulty getting out to make purchases. Scam artists take advantage of this by targeting seniors with catalogues and flyers. While there are many good and legitimate companies who sell merchandise through catalogues, not all offers are legitimate. Seniors need to be vigilant when ordering through mail orders and catalogue offers.

## Automated Banking Machines

Seniors are becoming more comfortable with using automated banking machines. They offer convenience in locations where there may not be a bank branch. There are several risks that must be considered when using machines. Some fraud artists hang near ATMs and watch over the user's shoulder to get banking information. Some have attached devices to ATMs that record PINs and account details. Some machines are third party machines not owned by the bank and seniors may not be aware of the additional fees charged for using these machines.

## Internet Schemes

*Phishing* is a word that comes from an analogy that scam artists use email to "fish" for passwords and other personal or financial data. Sometimes the email contains very official looking bank logos that may fool the person into thinking it is legitimate. They may claim that the bank suspects their account is at risk or that someone has made numerous attempts to log into their online banking using a false password. They then instruct the individual to click on a link and verify their password settings or other such personal information. These links go to fictitious sites set up by the scam artists. Special software programs can help protect against phishing. Never reply to an email of this nature and never click on a link contained in an email.

## WARNING SIGNS A SENIOR MAY BE A VICTIM OF FRAUD

The following may be indicators that an older adult is being victimized by a fraud artist:

- Their mail contains an extraordinary number of "junk mail offers". Once someone has made the "hit list", their name gets circulated and the number of junk mail offers increase.

- They begin to have difficulty paying bills because of insufficient funds in their bank. Or they begin to ask you to lend them money. This may be an indicator someone has taken their money.

- Bank records indicate cheques made out to unusual business names or personal names.

- They appear quite secretive when taking incoming calls so as to avoid being overheard.

A senior who has been a victim of fraud already feels diminished and vulnerable. Rather than criticizing, the best approach is to offer them help by getting in touch with the police.

## ELDER ABUSE

Abuse and neglect of elders in the population is not a new problem. While it has existed in society for many years, silence, denial and isolation have kept it from becoming a known issue. However, growing awareness is causing attitudes to change.

Elder abuse refers to mistreatment of older people or lack of appropriate action by those in a position of trust, power or responsibility for their care. Elder abuse can take many forms from the withholding of favours to physical pain or injury. Some acts violate basic human rights, while others constitute a criminal act. In a health care setting, it may be the manner in which workers execute their tasks.

It can affect people of all social levels and ethnic backgrounds. While the greater percentage of victims is vulnerable women, men can be victims of elder abuse too. It can happen in an institution or in a person's home. Sometimes it is intentional, but in some situations the person may not even realize what they are doing constitutes elder abuse. Education can go a long way towards helping to reduce this problem. Two factors that can put an older person at greater risk of abuse are social isolation and dementia. However, a normally loving caregiver who is experiencing extreme prolonged stress, or what is referred to as "caregiver burnout", may unexpectedly behave in ways that constitute elder abuse. Sometimes in a home setting, elder abuse may stem from a poor long-term relationship within a family that has a past history of violence.

## Physical Abuse

Physical abuse involves inflicting or threatening to physically cause pain or injury to a vulnerable elder. Some examples are:

- Using or misusing physical restraints
- Beating, hitting, slapping or rough handling
- Forcing someone to remain in bed or in a chair or a room
- Excessive use of medication or alcohol to restrain by sedating
- Burning
- Failing to provide mobility aids for someone who requires them
- Neglect such as failing to provide adequate food, personal care, and other necessities

## Emotional Abuse

Emotional abuse involves inflicting mental pain, anguish, or distress on an elder person through verbal or non-verbal acts. The effect of this is that it reduces the elder's sense of self-worth and dignity. Some examples are:

- Treating the person like a child or a servant
- Isolating them socially from other people
- Frequently raising the issue of death
- Being overly familiar and disrespectful
- Intentionally scaring the person
- Threatening abandonment
- Threatening to withhold basic necessities such as food or other care
- Lying to the person or intentionally withholding information from them
- Insulting or swearing at the person
- Spiritual abuse which may include ridicule or preventing someone from participating in their religious practices

## Sexual Abuse

This involves non-consensual sexual contact of any kind as well as verbal or suggestive behaviour. It also includes:

- Assault
- Harassment
- Exploitation
- Not responding to personal privacy

## Exploitation

This involves the illegal taking, misuse or concealment of funds, property or assets of a vulnerable elder. Examples of exploitation are:

- Fraud, theft, forgery
- Stealing money or possessions
- Selling their home without their permission
- Misuse of a Power of Attorney
- Opening mail without the person's authorization
- Pressuring someone to change their will
- Pressuring the elder to move from their home against their will
- Sharing their home without paying a reasonable portion of the living expenses

## Neglect

This involves failing to provide food, shelter, social contact, health care, personal hygiene care or protection for vulnerable elders by those responsible. This may also involve self neglect.

## Abandonment

This involves deserting a vulnerable elder after assuming the responsibility for their care.

## Signals That Indicate Possible Elder Abuse

The following may be signals that suggest an elder is being abused:

- Withdrawing for no apparent reason from regular activities
- Sudden change in alertness, fear, anxiety or unusual depression
- Bruises, pressure marks, broken bones and other physical injuries
- Sudden unexplained changes in financial matters
- Bedsores, changes in personal hygiene, unexplained weight loss could indicate self-neglect
- Frequent arguments and strained relationships with the caregiver
- Over-sedation

The abuse may go undetected because older adults are often reluctant to disclose it. They may feel embarrassed, ashamed or fear repercussions if they say anything. Sometimes it is not reported because they simply do not know who they should go to.

Abuse or neglect may be chronic and occur over a long period of time, or may be situational. It may be intentional or unintended. Many communities are trying to increase awareness and through education help people to better understand this issue so older adults can live with dignity and safety. In addition to education campaigns they have programs that work directly with abusers and victims to end violence and nurture healing. A simple question can help to uncover possible abuse: *Is there anyone in your life who takes advantage of your good nature or who mistreats you in any way?* Seniors are more likely to discuss a situation if they feel their confidences will not be betrayed. Within the home and family members, most abuse that occurs is psychological abuse. Elders need to retain as much power and control as possible over their own lives, as this reduces the risk of abuse. It is also important that elders know their rights.

As the senior population continues to increase and change, this will have an impact on the trends and risks of abuse for older adults.

# Chapter 4

# Healthy Aging

## THE AGING PROCESS

Most of us don't change very much inside as we age. A morning person generally remains a morning person and night owls remain night owls. For the most part our disposition is firmly set as well. Therefore the upbeat young person will usually become an optimistic older person. The reverse is also true! It is however those physical changes that we notice in others and ourselves. By middle age, you begin to need those bifocal eyeglasses to read the fine print, as your arms aren't quite long enough to hold that paper at a readable distance. You might also notice that you can't quite accomplish the same amount of work in a 12-hour period that you did in your twenties and thirties. You need more "down time" to recuperate. Changes in our bodies do not occur all at once but rather "sneak up" on us. We tend not to notice those outer changes such as wrinkles and hair loss until one day we look at our reflection and wonder who is that older person in the mirror? But inside we generally feel the same as we did at thirty! We have the capacity to learn new things, have an adventure and fall in love all our lives.

## AGING AS DEVELOPMENTAL STAGES

From birth until death psychoanalyst Erik Erikson (1902–1994) reminds us that we experience many developmental stages. Even in later adult years we undergo changes in how we think, feel and behave that are characteristic to that time in life. It is worthwhile to review these changes so we can better understand our senior clients, and identify the signposts related to our own lives.

### Signposts in Late Adulthood

Late adulthood is defined as changes occurring after age 65. These changes include the following:

1. Adjusting to changes in physical strength and health

2. Forming a new family role as an in-law and/or grandparent

3. Affiliating with one's age group

4. Adjusting to retirement and reduced income

5. Developing postretirement activities that enhance self worth and usefulness

6. Adjusting to the death of a spouse, family members and friends

7. Arranging satisfactory physical living quarters

8. Conducting a life review

9. Preparing for the inevitability of one's own death

## Why We Age

For centuries, scientists have attempted to answer the question, "Why do we age?" Surprisingly, despite all we have learned about the human body there is still not agreement on what causes aging, though many theories exist. What is certain is that over time, deterioration occurs in many tissues and systems no matter who we are or how well we take care of ourselves. Aging (*senescence*) is inevitable. In general, there are no anti-aging agents that have significant and clinically demonstrated effectiveness. However, it is widely believed that some lifestyle things we do such as exercise and good dietary habits increase human life span by staving off chronic disease.

There are two broad categories of aging theories — one holds that aging follows a biological timetable (*Programmed Theories*), and the other holds that aging occurs from environmental impacts that cause things to go wrong (*Error Theories*). Within each of these are numerous hypotheses as to how this happens.

One Programmed Theory holds that senescence occurs at the cellular level and is known as the Hayflick Limit Theory after one of its proponents. Drs. Leonard Hayflick and Paul Moorehead discovered there is a specific number of times fibroblast cells will divide after which they will divide no further. Examined under a microscope, these senesced cells bear a similarity in appearance to the visual signs of aging we see externally. The maximum number of times a cell will divide varies by species and is about 50 times in humans. Cells taken from an older adult divide less than this. They also discovered that some cells have unlimited life and are mutations that later result in tumours.

Another Programmed Theory holds that with aging, the hypothalamus and pituitary gland send out signals, which affect the release of hormones by various organs in the system and this occurs according to a biological clock. Known as the *Endocrine Theory*, it is believed this causes the system to be less functional leading to high blood pressure, impaired sugar metabolism and sleep abnormalities. This has led to studies that focus on the insulin hormonal pathway, which could explain the increased rate of diabetes as we age. Stress hormones are also released into the system, which are associated with increased morbidity.

A closely related theory holds that a programmed reduction occurs in the effectiveness of the immune system (*Immunological Theory*). As the immune system weakens it leaves the body more susceptible to infectious disease eventually leading to chronic illness and death.

Dr. August Weismann, a German biologist, first introduced an Error Theory in 1882 hypothesizing that wear and tear occurs in cells and vital organs due to toxins in our diet and the environment (*Wear and Tear Theory*). These environmental assaults include intake of excessive fat, sugar, caffeine, alcohol and nicotine as well as ultra-violet rays from the sun. Regardless of whether you maintain a low-fat diet, never drink, and never smoke, simply using the organs causes wear and tear, but abuse causes the cells to wear out even faster.

The oldest theory explaining why we age is the *Rate of Living Theory*, which links aging to energy consumption that limits longevity, pointing out that species with higher metabolic rates, have shorter life spans. There are exceptions that have been used as evidence to dispute this theory (Why does a parrot live as long as an elephant?) Consequently current researchers no longer believe this to be a valid overall explanation for why we age, but still consider it one of several factors that sometimes contributes to the aging process.

Many other hypotheses exist; some have eventually been proven to be false. Testing theories helps researchers to learn more about the mechanisms affecting aging and this can lead to treatments for dealing with the effects of chronic illness and strategies that help us to live longer lives.

## TRUTHS AND FABLES ABOUT AGING

There are many popular beliefs about changes that occur as people age. Some of these are true, while others are not. Some of the more popular concerns are explored below.

### Aging and Sleep Patterns

*Is it normal to change your sleep patterns as you age?* Sleep "efficiency" changes and we wake up more often through the night as the amount of deep sleep reduces. We go to bed earlier and rise earlier. Our internal clock (circadian rhythm) changes and sleep is spread across the 24-hour period instead of being concentrated in the night hours. Some changes in sleep patterns are due to chronic pain felt during the night or may be symptoms of an underlying condition that needs to be addressed. But for most of us changes in our internal clock are simply a sign we are getting older.

## Teeth Loss

*Is it normal to lose all your teeth with age?* The need for dentures is not an inevitable outcome of aging. Proper dental hygiene and regular visits to your dentist can maintain natural teeth for a lifetime. Fluoride has helped to maintain healthy teeth and gums.

## Depression

*Is it normal to be depressed much of the time?* Depression is not a normal part of aging and can be treated. If ignored, it can lead to suicide. The rate of depression in seniors is highest amongst those living in nursing homes (roughly half) as compared with those living in the community. Depression does not have to be an inevitable outcome of aging.

## Memory Loss

*Does everyone experience memory loss as they age?* Memory loss and mental disability are not a necessary outcome of aging and in fact are considered unhealthy aging. Healthy aging still involves cognitive change because as people age there is a reduction in working memory and capacity and this results in new information being absorbed more slowly as well as a reduction in the quantity of information absorbed. It is the efficiency of memory that changes with age. As we age it is easier to use recognition to retrieve information than to use recall. It becomes more difficult to filter out background noise and this interferes with encoding new incoming information. But humans are life-long learners and do not lose the ability to learn new things as older adults.

## Aches and Pain

*Does everyone get chronic joint pain with age?* Some people believe that chronic join pain is just an expected result of growing older and nothing can be done about it. Stiffness associated with pain and swelling is not a normal part of aging and is likely an indicator of an underlying condition such as arthritis. There is medication and treatment available and a person bothered by chronic joint pain should see their physician, as this is not a routine part of growing old.

## Incontinence

*Does incontinence occur in older adults as a consequence of aging?* While roughly one in ten people over age 65 have a problem with incontinence, it is associated with an underlying condition, not simply "old age". Conditions that might cause urinary incontinence include urinary tract infections, weakened bladder muscles or it may be a side effect of a certain medication. Medical consultation can help to determine the cause and it may well be treatable.

## CONDITIONS ASSOCIATED WITH HEALTHY AGING

No matter how well we take care of ourselves, getting older is a natural part of life. Your body will undergo many changes, gradually at its own pace. Lifestyle choices you make can slow down some of the effects of aging, but not stop or reverse the process. Family history can also play a role. In this section, we consider what changes occur as part of the normal aging process. Development of chronic conditions is considered unhealthy aging and is dealt with in a separate chapter.

*Eyesight.* By age 40, reduced elasticity in the lens of the eye may cause difficulty focusing resulting in headaches from eye strain. There is loss of peripheral vision, sharpness of images (visual acuity) and decreased ability to judge depth By age 55, most people require reading glasses at least part of the time. By age 60, the pupil has reduced in size to about one-third the size it was when you were in your 20s. It responds more slowly to changes in light. The retina functions less efficiently which impacts spatial discrimination, black and white contrast, and increases sensitivity to glare. Aging also causes colour intensity to become more difficult to distinguish, particularly discerning between blue-greens due to yellowing of the lens making these colours appear faded or washed out. Night vision often declines and there is an increased need for light in order to see clearly.

*Hearing.* A number of changes occur in the ear as a normal part of the aging process. Membranes become less flexible, the small bones in the middle ear become stiffer. By around age 55, high frequency sounds are harder to hear. After age 60, there is about a 10dB reduction in hearing sensitivity each decade. There is also less ability to distinguish sounds when there is background noise.

*Smell.* Age reduces the number of olfactory receptors and this decreases our threshold for smell. It begins to reduce more rapidly after age 55 and by age 80 our sense of smell is about half of what it once was. This can make it more difficult to detect odors like spoiled food or gas.

*Taste.* Taste buds are continuously being replaced. The rate at which this occurs slows down with age so your taste sharpness declines. This can lead to increasing the dosage of salt or sugar a person use as they get older and this can impact a person's health in other ways. Taste and smell are closely related, and as our sense of smell diminishes with age, this also impacts our taste.

*Touch.* The number of touch receptors reduces with age and this affects our sense of touch as well as our response to painful stimuli. This can create an increased risk of being burned, particularly if the temperature of hot water is set too high.

*Skin.* Skin loses its elasticity and loses its moisture. Lines and wrinkles appear. Nail growth slows and skin heals more slowly. As skin is more delicate and likely to burn it becomes more important to protect the skin from UV rays with sunscreen and protective clothing. Extremely dry skin can cause cracking and lead to infection. Skin cream applied routinely can help.

*Muscles.* Muscle mass declines, especially with lack of exercise. It is important to maintain a physical daily regimen.

*Height.* Compression of joints, spinal bones, and spinal discs and normal changes in posture occur and this can result in a reduction of as much as two inches in height by age 80.

*Hair.* Hair pigment cells decline, and grey hair appears. It also is normal for hair to gradually thin.

*Bones.* Mineral content reduces gradually beginning around age 35 faster than they are replaced and bones become less dense. Bone density decreases faster for women after menopause. Weight-bearing exercise helps to slow down bone loss, as does daily intake of calcium with vitamin D. Strength training is particularly important to stave off conditions such as osteoporosis.

*Arteries.* Arteries stiffen with age and fatty deposits build up in the blood vessels over time, eventually causing arteriosclerosis (hardening of the arteries). Maintaining a healthy low-fat diet can help.

*Bladder.* There is an increase in the frequency of urination.

*Body Fat.* There is an increase in body fat until middle age at which time it generally stabilizes until later in life when it decreases.

*Brain.* The brain loses some of the structures that connect nerve cells, and the function of the cells themselves is diminished. It is common to have less recall of recent memories and to have a greater challenge remembering things like people's names. However we can continue to be life long learners because despite these changes there is an increase in connections between nerve cells.

*Heart.* The heart is a muscle that thickens with age. The maximum pumping rate and the body's ability to extract oxygen from the blood both diminish with age. You may find you now have to work a little harder than you once did at physical activity.

*Kidneys.* The kidneys shrink and become less efficient.

*Lungs.* Around age 20, lung tissue begins to lose its elasticity, and the rib cage muscles shrink progressively. Maximum breathing capacity diminishes with each decade of life.

*Metabolism.* Medicines and alcohol are not processed as quickly. Prescription medication requires adjustment. Reflexes are slowed while driving and therefore an individual might want to lengthen the distance between their car and the car in front and drive more cautiously.

*Immune System.* The immune system is impaired with age and this explains why seniors are more vulnerable to infections that can lead to health complications and even death.

Some changes may indicate an underlying medical condition that needs to be addressed, and symptoms should always be checked with a physician. Chronic illness and pain are not inevitable outcomes of aging and adopting a healthy lifestyle can reduce the risk of disease. Some of the ways you can take an active role in staving off chronic illness and pain is through physical activity, consuming a healthy diet, not smoking, and correct use of medications that your doctor has prescribed for you.

## SENIORS AND NUTRITION

There is much evidence that a good diet in later years helps both in reducing the risk of chronic illness and in managing the diseases' signs and symptoms. Specifically a low-fat diet rich in grains, fruits, and vegetables lowers the risk for many age-related conditions like cardiovascular disease, high blood pressure, and diabetes. It can also reduce risk for a variety of cancers.

Like exercise, good nutrition contributes to a higher quality of life, enabling older people to maintain their independence by continuing to perform basic daily activities, such as bathing, dressing and eating. Poor nutrition, on the other hand, can prolong recovery from illnesses, increase the risk of institutionalization, and lead to a poorer quality of life. Malnutrition weakens the immune system, increasing the risk of pneumonia and other serious infections and exacerbating existing health conditions. During the SARS (Severe Atypical Respiratory Syndrome) crisis of 2003 many older adults were in the high risk group for not surviving the illness.

A nutrient-poor diet accelerates the loss of muscle mass and strength that normally comes with aging. Eventually, the chronic lack of nourishment leads to increased frailty and dependence, which in turn can trigger depression — itself a major drain on appetite.

### Why Might Older Adults Not Eat Well?

Reasons for poor eating habits are many, all of which can significantly affect an older adult's health.

#### Loneliness

Loneliness can lead to poor eating habits. Those who have lost a life partner may find it difficult to be alone, especially at mealtimes. They may become depressed and lose interest in preparing or eating regular meals, or they may eat only sparingly. Widows may view food preparation as a job that no one is around to appreciate. This can lead to the "tea and toast" habit that leaves out so many important nutrients. Widowed men may be inexperienced with cooking and may tend to eat snacks rather than meals or eat out often.

### Depression

The reasons for depression can be many and interrelated such as: a mixture of grief, isolation, failing health, lack of mobility, chronic illness, medications and malnutrition itself, which makes depression worse.

### Difficulty Chewing and Swallowing

Poor dentures, gum disease and missing teeth can have an impact on chewing. Older adults may have gastrointestinal disturbances related to an excess of gastric acid or be prone to constipation. Many important foods such as fresh fruits and vegetables, which are important sources of vitamins, minerals and fiber, may be avoided. Also a dry mouth (a side effect of many drugs) can affect the nervous system and interfere with swallowing.

### Diminished Taste and Smell

Taste and smell often diminish later in life; and can diminish the pleasure surrounding their favourite foods. It may be tempting to season food more heavily than before, even though older adults should have less salt.

### Medications

Drugs including some antidepressants, certain blood pressure and osteoporosis medications, and even common analgesics such as aspirin can suppress the appetite. Another effect of medication is that it may alter the way food tastes, causing upset stomach. It is worthwhile to have a pharmacist review the medications to ensure that mixing of medications is not causing additional problems with digestion and absorption.

### Chronic Conditions

Chronic conditions such as arthritis, stroke or Alzheimer's disease, can interfere with good nutrition. It may be difficult for example, for people with arthritis or who have had a stroke to cook, shop, or even lift a fork to eat without assistive devices. Dementia associated with Alzheimer's and other diseases may cause them to eat poorly or forget to eat altogether. Chronic conditions may suppress the appetite even as they increase the body's need for nutrients.

### Financial Concerns

Some seniors with limited incomes go hungry, especially if they are taking expensive medications not covered by provincial pharmacare plans. It's not uncommon for older adults to have to choose between drugs and groceries at the end of the month when government pension cheques are stretched thin.

### Restricted Diets

Some restricted diets can be so bland and unappealing that older adults simply stop eating. For that reason, it is worthwhile consulting a dietitian, as malnutrition is more detrimental to overall health than are rich or salty foods. Balance is the key.

## Malnutrition In Seniors

At 84, Judith looks great — slim and charming as always. She still attends her weekly church service and volunteers her time one day a week at the community centre. All appearances suggest she is fit and healthy, yet during her recent physical, her doctor shared concerns that she is clinically malnourished.

According to Canadian statistics, as many as 60%[1] of adults in nursing homes or hospital settings suffer from malnutrition and significant numbers of functionally dependent seniors living in the community also show signs of malnutrition. Poor nutrition or malnutrition (low or dangerously low levels of protein and other nutrients) is more prevalent amongst functionally dependent seniors, and identifying those at risk is not that difficult. The problem is with finding the growing number of active, independent older adults who like Judith, are malnourished. They are generally women who live alone and low-income seniors. Though they may appear well nourished this is not always the case.

The consequences can be significant. Body strength is reduced, there is lower resistance to infections and disease, and ultimately a reduced quality of life. Fractures can result and the risk of institutionalization goes up dramatically.

Why is this happening in a country that has an abundance of food? In some cases, there may be an underlying medical condition preventing nutrients from being absorbed. But often the reasons are more complex. Sometimes finances are responsible. Seniors with low incomes may opt for skipping meals or substituting less nutritional sources such as canned products instead of fresh produce. It may be related to social factors such as the inability to get out to purchase groceries. Some seniors are simply not motivated to prepare a full meal for just themselves and opt for non-nutritious fillers eating a bowl of cereal and a cup of tea.

### Signs To Watch For

The best evidence comes from spending time with the older adult, especially during normal meals at home, not just in restaurants or on special occasions. If the older adult is in a hospital or long-term care facility, make a point of visiting during mealtimes. Note the fit of clothing that now appears baggy and visible signs of weight loss. Also look for physical problems such as poor wound healing, easy bruising and dental difficulties as they also may be indicators of poor or malnutrition. Know what drugs the older adult takes

---

[1] Aging and Seniors Website (Public Health Agency of Canada), *Prevalence of Malnutrition*, http://www.phac-aspc.gc.ca/seniors-aines/pubs/workshop_healthyaging/nutrition/nutrition4_e.htm (Accessed May 29, 2008).

and how they affect appetite and digestion. Be aware of what is normal for them, and their general daily routines.

Many older adults are well informed about Canada's Guide to Healthy Eating and are only missing company to enjoy eating again. Others may have had lifelong poor eating habits that require outside help. For tips on healthy eating, see the section below.

## A Healthy Diet for Older Adults

A healthy diet follows the Canada Food Guide for Healthy Eating. For full details, you can visit the Health Canada website at: http://www.hc-sc.gc.ca/fn-an/food-guide-aliment/index_e.html. Food fads that exclude whole food groups are suspect. It is always important to investigate scientific research to support validity of these diets.

### Focus on Good Carbs

Older adults may have tried many different grains in their youth and may enjoy them once again. Items such as brown rice, whole wheat bread, rolled oats, barley, millet are good choices.

### Focus on Fiber

Older adults may have grown up with brown beans and they are a great source of fiber and  an inexpensive source of roughage. Raw fruits and veggies are loaded with fiber, vitamins, minerals, and enzymes to aid digestion. Apple or carrot can be cut into bite-sized pieces. Or try a green salad with grated zucchini. Raisons and dried fruit also contain fiber and are delicious. Berries are rich in fiber and contain valuable antioxidants.

### Include Calcium Rich Foods

Milk, cheese and yogurt retain their calcium content. Some non-dairy choices include the following foods: salmon, tofu, rhubarb, sardines, collard greens, spinach, turnip greens, okra, white beans, baked beans, broccoli, peas, brussels sprouts, sesame seeds, bok choy, and almonds. A calcium supplement might be necessary to meet calcium requirements. An older adult who suffers from poor nutrition or malnutrition would be well advised to have a discussion with their doctor who may arrange for them to visit with a nutritionist or dietician.

### Include Some Fat

It is important to include some fat in your daily diet. The key is to get the right kind and in the right quantity. "Good fats" are found in oils such as olive oil and sunflower oil, avocados and avocado oil, nuts and seeds.

### Drink Plenty of Water

In addition to drinking enough water each day, aim to consume foods that have a high water content. High water content foods include melons, grapes, cucumbers, onions, apples, cabbage, and, of course, soup! Staying properly hydrated flushes toxins from your body, relieves constipation, helps keep joints flexible and your mind clear. Drink water after meals rather than before or with meals to avoid diluting important digestive enzymes.

**Flavour Enhancers**

Use flavour enhancers to further encourage eating the right kinds of foods. These may include olive oil, vinegars; garlic; onions; spices, including cinnamon, cloves, ginger, and turmeric — which also aids digestion.

**Frequent Small Meals or Snacks**

Peanut or other nut butters can be spread on toast and crackers, on fresh fruits such as apples and bananas or on raw vegetables. Add a sprinkling of nuts or wheat germ on yogurt, fruit and cereal; or add extra egg whites to scrambled eggs and omelets; try melting cheese on sandwiches, vegetables, soups, rice and noodles. A smoothie shake with frozen berries and plain yogurt is healthy and delicious.

**Nutritional Supplements**

A good diet is the first defense against malnutrition. However older adults may well be deficient in vitamins B-6 and B-12, folate, niacin, vitamin D, calcium and zinc. Supplements can help supply missing nutrients but it is important to ensure that supplements will not interfere with medications. Talk to the pharmacist!

## Consider Outside Help

Investigate Meals-On-Wheels and other community services, including home visits from registered dietitians. Some churches or community centers have congregate dining that is open to older adults and provides company as well as a nutritious meal. Some grocery stores will deliver right to the home as well. Contact the local Senior Center or YMCA, and ask about senior meal programs. Another possibility is to hire a homemaker who can do the shopping and meal preparation for you. Community Adult Day Centres provide both companionship and nutritious meals for older adults who are isolated and lonely, or unable to prepare their own meals.

The overall benefit of good nutrition will be an improvement in their quality of life, mobility, and independence.

## HELPING THE BODY STAY FIT

*I feel like my body has gotten totally out of shape, so I got my doctor's permission to join a fitness club and start exercising. I decided to take an aerobics class for seniors. I bent, twisted, gyrated, jumped up and down, and perspired for an hour. But, by the time I got my leotards on, the class was over.*

©2006 The Saturday Evening Post with Permission.

The idea that exercise helps people stay healthy is not new. But past images excluded older adults; visualizing them instead sitting on the sidelines with grey hair in rocking chairs. Little was done to encourage, promote and support active living amongst seniors. Fortunately today, this has changed. Exercise may well be the fountain of youth for living a long and healthy life.

## What is "Active Living"?

"The biggest threat to healthy aging in Canada is sedentary living" according to the Active Living Coalition of Ontario. And the World Health Organization, of whom Canada is a member, affirms active living as: *A way of life in which physical, social, mental, emotional and spiritual activities are valued and are integrated into daily living.*

Exercise plays a key role in quality of life. It seems the word "exercise" can sound like a bad word to adults who have led a sedentary lifestyle. Activity may be seen as frivolous, and not as valuable as the need to work and be "productive". After all older adults lived through the Great Depression when "work" was hard won. Some people may assume they have "earned the right to rest"; it is also likely ageism influences what activities are considered appropriate for older adults, favouring activities such as lawn-bowling and fishing. Yet the benefits of active living are invaluable. Activity can improve quality of life by inducing a better mood or sleep, more energy and increased strength. It can lessen aches and pains and stimulate increased alertness. Even for those living with a chronic condition activity can decrease the chance of complications related to the illness.

So where to begin? It helps to open a dialogue about areas of activity and to identify any barriers that may be present in the older adult's mind. Be prepared to hear barriers such as "I can't exercise because I am too busy, too old, too sick or don't feel like it!" When raising the topic, the key is to pick the right time to have a meaningful dialogue. Just listening is the first step, then exploring activities that may not have been considered. A balanced exercise regimen consists of endurance activities for improving the cardio-vascular system, strengthening exercises to build muscle mass and prevent muscle atrophy, stretching exercises to remain limber and flexible, and balance exercises to reduce the risk of falls.

## Fitness Tips For Seniors

What long-term goal does the older adult want to achieve? What small goals are needed to achieve that "big" goal? An example might be "I wish to have more energy and sleep better so I will walk 15 minutes a day at least five days a week." It is important to start slowly and review any new exercise plan with a medical practitioner who will affirm the plan's appropriateness as a starting point for the person's situation.

## Stretching and Strength Training

So much can be gained from stretching and strength training. Low level aerobic exercise can be added little by little. Once balance is improved and muscles are stronger fear of falling declines and confidence increases.

## Warm Water Exercise

Exercising in warm water is a very safe and effective activity even for frail adults. Walking in water improves balance and stability while using paddles or resistance bands in the water increase muscle strength. In addition the warmth of the water improves pain for those living with conditions such as arthritis or fibromyalgia.

## Low-Impact Aerobic Activities

Consider such low-impact aerobic activities such as swimming, walking and dancing. Aerobic exercises strengthen the heart and improve overall fitness by increasing the body's ability to use oxygen.

## Indoor Walking Clubs

In the cold weather older adults can join the local indoor walking clubs that start before storing opening in malls. With a good pair of walking shoes, walking is easy on the joints and gets the heart rate and respiratory rate up, which is important to health. The social benefits of meeting others while walking are rewarding as well.

## Chair Exercise Programs

Even those who are more restricted activity-wise can participate in a chair exercise program. There are video programs that take the individual through a complete workout for all the muscle groups and joints of the body with both stretching and strengthening exercises. This is also a good place to use resistance bands as well.

## Dance, Tai Chi, and Yoga Programs

Balance exercises are important to keep legs and arms strong so as to aid the person if they should stumble. Balance is an important element of fitness, as is flexibility and maintaining muscle mass because when muscles become weak the risk of falling increases and recovery takes longer.

## Visit The Doctor First

It always makes good sense to begin by discussing activity plans with the doctor first and be familiar with any limitations that are recommended.

## Risk of Falls

Falls can happen to anyone at any age, but as we get older, falls becomes more dangerous. Seniors are at increased risk of hospitalization and ultimately admission to a long-term care facility as a direct result of falls. Removing environmental hazards plays as significant role in falls prevention, as does living an active life. Annually, one quarter to one third of all seniors experience at least one fall.[2] Falls are the most common cause of injury for older adults.[3] Falls cause more than 90% of all hip fractures in seniors.[4] The fear of falling is very high amongst older adults and this in itself leads to greater instances of falls.[5] Roughly 40% of nursing home admissions are the result of a fall.[6]

Broken hips can ultimately lead to death because immobility affects circulation thereby affecting major organs. Muscle atrophy occurs and joint stiffen and quality of life is significantly impacted.

Exercise plays an important role in preventing falls.

## Practice Medical Prevention

Regular visits to your physician and follow-through on recommended treatment plans can help to maintain quality of life in one's senior years. Preventative health screenings and immunizations are important components of self-care after age 50. Preventative screening is available for blood pressure checks, cholesterol testing, colorectal cancer screening, hearing and vision tests, and dental examinations. In addition to this, men should have an annual prostate check and women should have a regular breast examination, pelvic examination and Pap test. Early diagnosis can enable effective treatment.

Be an active participant in managing your health and medical conditions. Educate yourself regarding any conditions with which you have been diagnosed and learn about various treatment options available. Ask questions of your physician and where appropriate, ask for second opinions. Know your options.

---

[2] Tinetti, M.E., Speechley, M. (1989), *Prevention of falls among the elderly*, New England Journal of Medicine, 320(16), 1055-1059.

[3] Raina, P., Dukenshire, S., Chambers, L., Toivonen, D., & Lindsay, J. (1997), *Prevalence, risk factors, and health care utilization for injuries among Canadian seniors: An analysis of the 1994 National Population Health Survey* (IESOP Research Report No. 15). Hamilton, ON: McMaster University.

[4] Zuckerman, J.D. (1996), *Hip fracture*, New England Journal of Medicine, 334(23), 1519-1525.

[5] Tinetti, M.E., Speechley, M., & Ginter, S.F., (1994) *Fear of falling and fall-related efficacy in relationship to functioning among community-living elders*, Journal of Gerontology, 49(3), M140-M147.

[6] Rawsky, E. (1998), *Review of the literature on falls among the elderly*, Image — the Journal of Nursing Scholarship, 30(1), 47–52.

# HEALTH EMERGENCY ADVANCE PLANNING

If we were to examine the incidence rates of death due to four main causes (hypertension, heart disease, cerebrovascular disease and diabetes) as compared with the incidence rates of living with impairment, the results would show that over the past two decades we have traded mortality (death) for morbidity (disability). We are living longer lives thanks to improvements in medical technology. However, it is not all good news — we're doing so by living with chronic conditions that prior generations did not survive. As new drugs are developed it changes the way illnesses are treated. There are better techniques such as the use of lasers in surgery; smaller incisions means quicker healing times and the result being less time is spent in hospitals and more time is spent recovering at home and in the community.

Family structure has changed since the prior generation. In the past extended families lived closer and could help each other. There were fewer women in the workplace. Another important difference is that families today have fewer children. Our society is more mobile, and many times parents live in different cities or provinces than their adult offspring. Current estimates indicate that almost half of seniors over age 65 will need some kind of home care at some point in their lives. Normally the first to assume this role are spouses who may be dealing with health issues of their own. Ultimately once one parent has passed away, the adult children assume this responsibility often as distance caregivers. Siblings have always played an important role within the informal caregiver network, but since families are now smaller and live at greater distances, there is more reliance on the broader community than in the past.

## Informal and Formal Care

Informal caregivers include the spouse, adult children, friends and volunteers. They are the backbone of the health care delivery system. In fact informal caregivers provide more than 80% of all care needed by people with long-term health problems. The boundaries regarding the roles performed by informal versus formal caregivers are blurring. Formal caregivers include licensed specialists such as doctors, nurses and non-licensed trained workers such as personal support workers. Informal caregivers are being asked to perform tasks that in the past were handled by paid trained caregivers. This is due to the extensive hospital cut-backs that resulted in downloading care to home care and nursing homes before appropriate increases in resources were allocated to handle the increased volume.

The result of this is that the number of calls being made to 911 for medical emergencies is increasing. Seniors make $2^1/_2$ times more calls to EMS responders than non-seniors. Those over age 65 account for 30% of all calls even though they only represent 6% of the population, according to the Ottawa Paramedic Association. Paramedics often have to deal with making treatment decisions that could make the difference of life and death in a matter of seconds or minutes — often in an information vacuum. Normally two paramedics arrive at the home in response to a call from 911; one takes the spouse aside to ask a barrage of questions while the second goes immediately to the ill person to provide medical assistance. Under this type of pressure it is difficult to think clearly and essential facts may not be communicated to responders.

Some seniors live on their own with no one to advocate on their behalf. "Invisible" disabilities such as osteoporosis may mean fragile bones that could be broken when transferring if emergency responders are unaware.

Canada has opened its doors to people of many new nationalities who now call Canada home. English is not their first language and communication barriers could exist during a medical emergency. Some medical conditions place individuals at greater risk. Conditions such as heart disease, diabetes, Parkinson's disease and many more chronic conditions affect 82% of older adults. Falls affect 35 to 40% of older adults every year with more than half occurring in the home. As many as 29% of older adults live alone and therefore have no one to speak on their behalf in a medical emergency. Therefore, it is important to consider what would happen if sudden illness was to occur at home.

## Planning Ahead: Health Emergency Advance Planning

Advisors can be an advocate to clients helping them to appreciate the importance of planning ahead for a medical emergency.

Health Emergency Advance Planning is the process of documenting personal information well in advance of a medical emergency. The focus is on information that would be important and relevant in the event of a medical emergency. It is not about listing every medication or condition you have ever taken in your life, or every visit you have ever made to your doctor. But it does deal with both past and present medical information. Just as important and sometimes overlooked is taking time to document future wishes so that health care providers will know what you want in a health crisis.

Health Emergency Advance Planning not only helps the person who is ill, but planning ahead also shows consideration of loved ones who may be called upon to deal with the medical emergency. It can lessen their stress when they are dealing with the emergency at hand. Documenting key medical facts helps to ensure the person receives the best medical response at the earliest point because paramedics and hospital staff will know essential details. This could save their life.

## Steps for Medical Safety

There are four steps your clients can take that can lessen risk during a medical emergency.

## Medical Alert Bracelets

Ensure the person wears a medical alert bracelet listing allergies to medications. Paramedics will check for a bracelet, however they do not have time to place telephone calls to a third party. Time is of the essence in a medical emergency.

## "I.C.E." Your Mobile Phone

Most people regardless of age have mobile phones today. Many people store their contacts' numbers in the directory. Emergency responders will check a directory to find their "key contact" during an emergency if the phone is labeled with an "I.C.E." label. The acronym, "I.C.E." stands for "In Case of Emergency." The concept of storing an emergency contact in the mobile phone directory was conceived by a London, U.K. paramedic during the subway bombings. He needed to find contacts to notify next of kin, and realized that there was no way to determine which of 50 or 60 names in a cell phone directory was the "key contact" to notify. The concept involves not only labeling the phone itself with an "I.C.E. Label", but also entering the contact's name in the telephone directory preceded by the acronym. Thus, a spouse whose name is Mary, would be entered in the cell phone directory as follows: "I.C.E. — Mary — Spouse — 902-111-1111". More information on this safety concept is available at http://www.icelabel.ca.

## Home Emergency "Panic" Buttons

Programs such as "Lifeline" are available to provide a personal response service that lets the person summon help any time of the day or night — even if they cannot speak. A personal "Help Button" is worn in the form of a wristband or pendant. When pressed, a trained Response Centre Associate ensures help is sent quickly. This system is ideal for older adults who live on their own.

## Storing Information: "Grab-and-Go Pouch" Programs

Programs such as My-MEDIC-Notes™ provide tools to document and store medical history, personal wishes, and other essential medical background paramedics should know during a medical emergency. An exterior door label alerts paramedics where to look for the My-MEDIC-Notes™ pouch (which is included in the kit). The pouch has a magnetic back to affix it to the fridge door. Most paramedics are familiar with the fridge as a central place where emergency medical information gets posted. The medical forms and an instruction booklet are provided as well as access to a website for obtaining replacement forms and supplemental tools such as a Medication Chart, Blood Pressure Diary, Blood Sugar Diary, and Physician's Appointment worksheet to help prepare prior to a visit to the doctor thereby ensuring you get the most out of your visit to the physician.

The storage pouch acts as a central depository for all key medical documents such as copies of test readings (ECGs, EEGs, or MRIs) and medical directives. This is a valuable tool for planners and caregivers. More information about this program is available at http://www.My-MEDIC-Notes.ca.

## Documenting Information

When gathering information, the pharmacy may be a key resource for obtaining a summary of all medications that have been prescribed. If your client has purchased all their medication from one source, many pharmacies today can produce a printout summarizing their medications and dates they were issued.

Once a Health Emergency Advance Plan has been set up, it is important to remind clients to keep their program up to date as information changes over time.

As important as documenting past and present medical information, is getting your client to give consideration to their wishes if end of life were near. Naming someone as a substitute decision maker ("proxy") to act on their behalf ensures their wishes will be understood and voiced in situations where they cannot advocate for themselves. A Power of Attorney for Personal Care is a document that appoints someone to act on your behalf in medical decisions during your incapacity. You can indicate within this document your wishes regarding *heroic measures*, i.e. the use of life-sustaining technology such as a feeding or breathing tube at end of life. A "Do Not Resuscitate" (DNR) directive can instruct others regarding your wishes in the use of CPR. Another area to be considered is that of organ donation.

Instructional documents regarding medical treatment wishes should be filed with other medical forms for quick access during an emergency such as in a "grab-and-go" storage pouch (like the My-MEDIC-Notes™ version) mounted to the fridge door where it will be easy to bring along to the hospital.

Once information has been documented the person should arrange a family meeting to ensure everyone in their circle of care knows their wishes, values and beliefs. As these may change over time, and in the course of personal health — this discussion is not a one-time meeting but an open dialogue.

## Relevant History

What exactly is "relevant" in a medical emergency? There needs to be current personal information that would identify the individual as well as their limitations. For example, it is important that emergency responders know the languages the person speaks, where to find their health card, and identifying traits. Perhaps the individual is blind in one eye, or deaf in one ear. Do they have a pacemaker? Do they normally use a mobility aid to get around such as a cane or a walker? What other special considerations should emergency responders be aware of that would impact transferring them safely. Perhaps the person has a hip fracture or pins that others should be aware of when lifting or moving them.

Allergies to medications are very important. With the passage of time, essential information can be forgotten and this could make the difference of life or death in a critical situation. When listing medical conditions, the focus is on those that are significant such as hepatitis, HIV/Aids, anemia, asthma, cancer, diabetes, dizziness, epilepsy, heart — or any major organ condition, stroke, abnormal EKG readings. An individual who has an abnormal EKG can and should request a copy of their printout and make it available for access by emergency responders. This becomes their new "norm" against which health care providers can measure current readings.

When listing medication, the details should include the name of the drug, when it was prescribed or last changed, the dosage, frequency, condition it treats, and where it is stored. It is not unusual for a medication typically prescribed for one condition to be used for other less-typical conditions; therefore emergency responders cannot assume what condition the medication is being used to treat.

Other important details include listing prior hospitalizations, the name and number of specialists, and details regarding health insurance coverage.

While it can be tempting for people to set the issue aside, it is important to take time in the present to gather the missing data, as memory fades with the passage of time. Just as important, is ensuring regular updates are made as information changes over time.

Layout details clearly so they can be quickly and easily scanned in seconds by emergency responders. Paramedics will not access other computer devices such as memory sticks in an emergency. This is one time when old-fashioned paper-based documents will serve best!

## Barriers to Planning

According to a study conducted by one hospital in Alberta, most of their patients do not have advance directives. Since this is such an important part of health planning, what are the barriers that get in the way?

### No Time

Some people may feel they simply don't have the time to document. Keeping in mind that the focus is on *essential* medical background, the process only takes about one hour to write out medical history, one physician appointment to gather any missing background details, one visit to the pharmacy to get a printout of medication history, and an evening to consider advance directives.

### No Need

People who say they have "no need" are often the same people who overestimate the level of their own health. Some of the predictors of ill health include changes in blood sugar level, fluctuations in weight, elevations in blood cholesterol level, and smoking status.

## No Hurry

Some people simply have no sense of urgency. The future remains a mystery; therefore it is better to be proactive than to wait until it is too late.

## Empowerment

Information is power, and ignorance is not bliss. Planning helps by reducing stress in an emergency situation. It brings peace of mind to distance caregivers who have parents living in a different city. It is empowering especially for the frail, elderly and people who live alone. And it is an unselfish act because it helps those who must deal with the medical emergency when the time arises.

*Chapter 5*

# Chronic Conditions and Pain Management

## CHRONIC CONDITIONS AND PAIN MANAGEMENT

Aging is a process that involves biological, emotional, social, as well as financial changes, all of which affect a person's overall health. It is not as simple as counting the chronological years but is a complex combination of factors affecting the overall functioning of the person. The aging process varies from person to person. Many people age 65 and above run marathons even into their 80s while others are crippled with arthritis and other debilitating diseases as early as their 60s. According to Statistics Canada, by age 65, 77% of men and 85% of women have at least one chronic condition.[1]

Genetics plays an important role in the aging process. Just as eye and hair colour runs in families, so do chronic diseases such as heart disease, cancer, diabetes, and high cholesterol. While genetics plays an important role, it is not the only cause. Lifestyle also impacts the likelihood of acquiring a chronic condition. A study conducted in 2002 in British Columbia determined that for 60% of people having a chronic condition, the cause can be attributed to factors they have no control over such as heredity and other factors, while 40% are due to lifestyle factors that are controllable.

Emotional and psychological issues can also play a major role in healthy aging. A person can be physically strong and develop Alzheimer's disease, depression or anxiety. Social and financial changes are often not considered as impacting healthy aging. However, seniors living on a fixed income with increasing living costs can find themselves having to decide between buying groceries or medicine and medical treatments. Similarly, their nutrition may suffer for the same reason if they feel forced to budget food costs as this often leads to skipping meals or becoming a "tea and toast granny". Stress can cause radical changes and may occur following the death of a spouse. This stress causes excessive wear and tear on the body and someone predisposed to heart disease may find it triggers an attack. The World Health Organization defines health broadly as a person's physical, psychological, and social well-being.

Chronic illness is one of the major causes of mortality and morbidity among the old and consequently has a direct impact on the quality of life and the costs of health care.

## DISABILITY-FREE LIFE EXPECTANCY

*Life Expectancy* is a measure of the number of years a person is expected to live from the day he or she is born. It is interesting to consider to what age a person is likely to be "healthy" and free of disability or limitations and outside of a health care institution. In this respect, *Disability-Free Life Expectancy* introduces the concept of quality of life. As can be seen from the chart below, Canadians can expect to live with one or more chronic conditions for about the last 10 years. While women can expect to live almost 5.8 years longer than men, only 3.3 of those years are disability-free.

---

[1] *Dependency, Chronic Conditions and Pain in Seniors*, p. 21, Supplement to Health Reports, Vol. 16, Statistics Canada, Catalogue 82-003. (2003).

| Disability-free life expectancy, Canada | | | | |
|---|---|---|---|---|
| **1996**[1] | | | | |
| | **Life expectancy at birth**[2] | **Disability-free life expectancy at birth**[3] | **Difference between life expectancy and disability-free life expectancy** | |
| | | Years | | % |
| **Canada** | 78.3 | **68.6** | 9.7 | -12.4 |
| **Males** | 75.4 | **66.9** | 8.5 | -11.3 |
| **Females** | **81.2** | 70.2 | 11.0 | -13.5 |
| **Difference between females and males** | 5.8 | **3.3** | | |

1. The estimates are based on the three years of death data, 1995 to 1997. The reference period associated with these data reflects the mid-point of the three-year period, 1996.

2. Life expectancy is the number of years a person would be expected to live, starting at birth on the basis of mortality statistics for a given observation period.

3. Disability-free life expectancy introduces the concept of quality of life. It is used to distinguish between years of life free of any activity limitation and years experienced with at least one activity limitation. The emphasis is not exclusively on the length of life, as is the case for life expectancy, but also on the quality of life. Disability-free life expectancy is calculated using Sullivan's method (Sullivan, Daniel F., 1971, "A single index of mortality and morbidity", Health Services and Mental Health Administration Health Reports, 86(4), 347-354).

**Source:** Statistics Canada, CANSIM, tables 102-0018 and 102-0019, and Catalogue no. 82-221-X. Last modified: 2007-04-13.

http://www40.statcan.ca/l01/cst01/health38.htm. Accessed July 29, 2004.

Having a chronic condition increases the likelihood of eventual dependency, that is to say, the need for assistance with activities of daily living (ADL) and with instrumental activities of daily living (IADL). ADLs are activities considered vital to retaining independence such as bathing, eating, dressing, transferring from a bed to a chair, and toileting. IADLs include activities such as shopping, preparing meals, paying bills, banking, and housekeeping. A person who needs assistance with these tasks is considered to be IADL-dependent. While almost everyone who is ADL-dependent is also IADL-dependent, the reverse is not always true. ADL-dependency has a more devastating impact as it involves personal care tasks and this almost always results in the need for the person to move to a long-term care centre. Many chronic conditions associated with an increased likelihood of dependency are also accompanied by chronic pain. Seniors with chronic illness need a wide range of support if they are to avoid institutionalization and to continue living at home. A supportive environment includes both physical as well as social support. This requires a multidisciplinary approach and strong collaboration amongst community service providers and professionals. It also places significant demands on family members who fulfill the role of informal caregivers.

## What is a Chronic Condition?

A chronic condition is one that is permanent, and while it cannot be cured, care is directed at treating and managing symptoms. Hypertension is an example of a chronic condition, while a urinary track infection may or may not be a chronic condition (depending on whether there is an underlying condition that is always present causing frequent reoccurrences). Some chronic conditions can be well controlled with medication and/or diet and the individual can lead an otherwise healthy normal lifestyle for many years. The problem for seniors is that the incidence and severity of chronic illness increases with age, and may eventually impact the person's ability to perform normal activities of daily living and their ability to remain living independently on their own. Not only does chronic illness affect the lives of those who have it, but also the family support network that surrounds them. Often this network includes their spouse and adult children.

There are many chronic conditions that are associated with aging. A person may be affected by more than one condition at the same time. Some conditions alone may have little or no effect on the person's quality of life. Co-morbidity or several chronic conditions occurring simultaneously, is more likely to occur in older people. In fact, they many suffer from three or more chronic conditions. When this occurs, one condition may increase symptoms and risk of another underlying condition. Whereas each condition on its own may be manageable, when two or more occur simultaneously there may be an increased risk of dependency.

## Prevalence of Chronic Conditions Amongst Canadian Seniors

A survey was conducted in 2003 (Canadian Health Survey) that provides a breakdown by illness of conditions affecting Canadians over age 65 living in households. The results are based on self-reports from a checklist of diagnosed conditions. It reveals amongst those living in the community, arthritis affected more seniors than any other condition, followed by cataracts, back problems, heart disease and diabetes.[2]

---

[2] Statistics Canada information is used with the permission of Statistics Canada. Users are forbidden to copy this material and/or redisseminate the data, in an original or modified form, for commercial purposes, without the expressed permission of Statistics Canada. Information on the availability of the wide range of data from Statistics Canada can be obtained from Statistics Canada's Regional Offices, its World Wide Web site at http://www.statcan.ca, and its toll-free access number 1-800-263-1136.

| Prevalence of Chronic Conditions by Gender, Household Population Aged 65 or Older, Canada, 2003 | Men % | Women % |
|---|---|---|
| Arthritis/Rheumatism | 37.7 | 54.7* |
| Cataracts/Glaucoma | 19.6 | 28.7* |
| Back problems | 21.6 | 26.1* |
| Heart disease | 21.8* | 18.1 |
| Diabetes | 15.6* | 11.9 |
| Thyroid condition | 5.3 | 18.7* |
| Urinary incontinence | 8.9 | 12.0* |
| Asthma | 6.9 | 8.1* |
| Bronchitis/Emphysema/Chronic obstructive pulmonary disease | 7.6 | 7.3 |
| Mental illness | 4.4 | 7.5* |
| Cancer | 7.1* | 4.2 |
| Migraine | 3.6 | 6.8* |
| Effects of stroke | 5.2* | 3.9 |
| Stomach/intestinal ulcers | 4.2 | 4.5 |
| Bowel disorder/Crohn's disease/Colitis | 2.8 | 4.9* |
| Chemical sensitivities | 1.5 | 4.0* |
| Alzheimer's disease/Other dementia | 2.4* | 1.7 |
| Fibromyalgia | 1.1E | 2.6* |
| Chronic Fatigue Syndrome | 1.3 | 2.3* |
| Epilepsy | 0.7E | 0.6E |

Data source: Statistics Canada, 2003 Canadian Community Health Survey, Catalogue No. 82-003-XPE, Vol.16, Special Issue 2006, Page 25, Table 3.
Note: Based on self-reports from a checklist of diagnosed conditions
*Significantly higher than estimate for opposite sex (p < 0.05)
E Coefficient of variation 16.6% to 33.3% (interpret with caution)

## TYPICAL CHRONIC CONDITIONS: SYMPTOMS AND TREATMENT

There are many conditions that can affect people of any age, but occur more frequently in older adults. Some of these conditions are explained below.

According to the Canadian Study of Health and Aging,[3] late-life dementias, which include Alzheimer's disease, affect 8% of older adults over the age of 65 and more than 25% of those over the age of 80. Alzheimer's disease is not considered a normal part of aging but is a progressive neurological disease that concerns the brain. When someone has dementia, brain cells are damaged and die faster than they would normally. Functions including language, intellect and spatial orientation are affected. Once the brain loses

[3] Canadian Study of Health and Aging Working Group: Study Methods and Prevalence of Dementia, Canadian Medical Association J 1994, 150: 899-913.

the capacity to regulate elementary body functions, people with Alzheimer's disease or related dementia die of malnutrition, dehydration, infection or heart failure. It normally runs its course over an average of 7–10 years but life expectancy for someone with Alzheimer's disease can be between two years and 20 years following the onset of symptoms.

There are roughly 70 to 80 different types of dementia but the most common forms are associated with Alzheimer's disease, Parkinson's disease and Vascular Dementia. Vascular Dementia occurs when nerve cells are deprived of blood. The damage causes nerve cells to die, as occurs with strokes or trans-ischemic attacks ("TIAs"). After Alzheimer's disease, this is the most common cause of dementia. Two other examples of dementia are Pick's disease and dementia with Lewy bodies. Each form of dementia has its own predominant symptoms. For instance, with Pick's disease behavioural changes usually occur before memory loss, while with Alzheimer's disease memory loss is one of the first symptoms. Dementia with Lewy bodies is characterized by fluctuating periods of alertness/confusion, visual-spatial problems, vivid hallucinations, memory loss of long-term memory and repeated falls. Signs and symptoms differ with each form because different areas of the brain are affected. Specific regions of the brain are responsible for different functions. For example, the area responsible for generating thoughts, solving problems and planning is located in a separate area from where voluntary movement is controlled or where forming and storing memories occurs.

Because Canada's population is aging and Alzheimer's disease is predominantly a disease affecting the older population, there will be a substantial increase in the number of people who have Alzheimer's disease. In fact, by 2030 it is predicted that one out of three people will have a dementia by age 85. Women are more often affected than men. Presently there is no cure or prevention but research is being conducted to learn more with the hope that one day a cure or prevention will be found. There are some forms of medication available that help in aiding memory for one or two years if taken in the early stages, but they do not actually slow down the progression of the illness itself. A person with Alzheimer's disease experiences chemical changes in the brain and this affects their cognitive abilities. Medications help to improve cognitive performance and may delay nursing home placement for a year.

Some forms of dementia are reversible or treatable, such as those whose symptoms are caused by the side effects of medication, depression, a vitamin B deficiency, chronic alcoholism, brain tumors, fluid buildup in the brain (known as normal-pressure hydrocephalus), and infections. Metabolic imbalances can also cause similar symptoms as may be caused by thyroid disorders, kidney or liver disorders, bladder infections or dehydration. Consequently, it is important to first eliminate other possible causes of symptoms so a proper diagnosis can be made and treatment plan prescribed. A misdiagnosis can lead to improper medication usage and aggravate the underlying condition.

Alzheimer's disease is distinguished from other forms of dementia by its irreversibility, the characteristic patterns of progressive degeneration and the types of changes that occur in the brain. While it most often affects people after age 65 (referred to as late onset), it can affect people in their 40s or younger (referred to as early onset). While researchers do not know exactly what causes Alzheimer's disease, it is known that there is no single gene for it and that genetic factors are responsible in only a small number of families.

**Warning Signs**

Who hasn't experienced an episode of mild forgetfulness or problems with remembering peoples' names? At various times anyone can identify with a few of the symptoms associated with Alzheimer's disease. The difference with Alzheimer's disease is that the person affected will display many of the symptoms frequently. The symptoms include:

- Memory loss that affects day-to-day function

- Difficulty performing familiar tasks

- Problems with language

- Disorientation of time and place

- Poor or decreased judgment

- Problems with abstract thinking

- Misplacing things

- Changes in mood and behaviour

- Changes in personality

- Loss of initiative

Some of the changes in mood and behaviour that occur include wandering, pacing, repetition, depression, aggression, sundowning and shadowing.

There is a tendency for someone with Alzheimer's disease to merely wander off. This creates a serious risk to the individual. People have been known to leave nursing homes where they reside in the middle of winter without as much as a coat or boots. Because of this risk, many nursing homes have controlled entrances not only at the main floor entry, but also on floors where residents with dementia reside. When visiting someone who resides in a nursing home on a controlled-entrance floor, be careful when you leave. Alzheimer's disease patients have been known to fool visitors into thinking they are allowed off the floor. One lady for instance, followed a woman who she identified as a visitor because she was wearing a coat. She donned her own coat and put her purse over her arm, and simply said to the visitor who was exiting, "Could you hold that door for a minute for me ...?" The Canadian Alzheimer Care Wandering Registry Program was established as a joint initiative by the Alzheimer's Association and the RCMP to protect individuals as a result of wandering. The person's name, address and contact information is placed on a list with a registration number assigned. You can then mark their name and registration number in their clothing (such as in their collar) so if they are found wandering they can be identified.

*Sundowning* is a term used with Alzheimer's disease patients to describe their tendency to show behavioural problems in the later afternoon or evening. Experts speculate about the reasons this may occur. Some say it is related to dim lights causing confusion with objects or perhaps their biological clock may not be able to distinguish between night and day, or they may simply be less able to cope with stress when they are tired.

*Shadowing*, another term associated with Alzheimer's disease patients, refers to their tendency to follow the caregiver and mimic their actions. There may be an underlying reason for this agitated behaviour that can be addressed by examining patterns such as the time of day it normally occurs, the activities in the environment, how long an episode lasts, and what eventually appears to calm the person.

One of the most difficult changes affecting the person is the loss of their driver's license. Driving with dementia is dangerous because it affects a person's ability to react quickly, to use good judgment, and to anticipate in advance what other drivers may be about to do. Family members often turn to the physician who knows the person's condition and will act to have the license permanently suspended for everyone's safety.

## Diagnosis

Medical practitioners begin by gathering information about the person's general health, past medical history and current limitations with activities of daily living. They gather information from family members who can provide feedback concerning mood changes, emotion and other behavioural changes and they complete a battery of tests (blood tests, urinalysis, spinal fluid test etc.) in order to eliminate other possible causes of the symptoms exhibited. Neuro-psychological tests are conducted to measure cognitive skills. CT scans, MRIs and PET scans are also used. This latter test allows for earlier diagnosis and has a higher accuracy rate than other methods (as high as 90% compared with 60 to 70% rate of accuracy with other methods). The only method that provides 100% accuracy is by examining the brain through autopsy following death. So it still remains predominantly a diagnosis by process of elimination of other possible causes.

## Connecting with the Person

Dementia is not a global condition. There is not a complete deterioration of memory, intellect and personality until the late stages of the illness. A person with Alzheimer's disease can continue to experience joy in life. For someone whose memory and language skills are affected, they can enjoy music from a past decade that helps them experience warm feelings of a past era. If auditory memory is affected, visual memory can be experienced through photos. If long-term memory is better than short-term memory, a person may experience greater pleasure from re-reading books from their adolescent years better than new books they have not yet read due to the challenge of absorbing and recalling details they just finished reading a few short paragraphs ago. Sensory memories can hold many pleasures and be triggered by sounds, smell and touch. For example, someone who enjoyed baking may find pleasure in the scent of home-baked bread or fresh peanut butter cookies. A person who enjoyed gardening may welcome the scent of fresh-cut flowers. Happiness can be found in the present, when memories of the past have faded. A person with dementia is still someone deserving of dignity and love.

## Arthritis

Arthritis is a general term that means inflammation in the joints. While arthritis is not life threatening it can have an enormous impact on quality of life. It consists of more than 100 different forms ranging from mild forms of tendonitis and bursitis to crippling systemic forms such as rheumatoid arthritis. The following are all various types of arthritis:

*Ankylosing Spondylitis* is a form of arthritis that affects the spine. The vertebrae fuse together and this results in a rigid spine, often exhibited by a curved, bent-over posture. It is systemic, and therefore symptoms may not be limited to just the joints. A person with the disease may have a fever, fatigue and loss of appetite. Sometimes eye inflammation occurs as well. In rare cases, it may also affect the lungs and heart. It affects only a small percent of the population, more often men than women and symptoms appear in their early 20s or 30s. While the exact cause is not known, it is believed to have a strong genetic link. There is no cure, but medication, exercise and physical therapy can help to reduce the symptoms.

*Bursitis* is an inflammation of a bursa, a sac containing lubricating fluid that decreases friction and rubbing located between tissues such as bone, muscle, tendons and skin. It can become inflamed from an injury, infection or an underlying rheumatic condition. An injury can occur from something as simple as carrying a bag of groceries, doing gardening, raking or shoveling. It mainly affects adults over age 40, usually at the elbow, shoulder, hip, and knee.

*Fibromyalgia* is a chronic condition most common among women ages 35 to 55 that causes pain throughout the body and is accompanied by stiffness and tenderness in muscles, tendons and joints. The cause is unknown. There is no inflammation or joint damage as is associated with arthritis, or damage to internal organs as occurs with lupus. It is identified by a collection of symptoms some of which include chronic muscle pain, leg cramps, sleep problems, severe fatigue, anxiety, morning stiffness, headaches and intestinal problems.

*Gout* is a type of arthritis more common in men and usually occurring in the big toe, foot, ankle or knees. It causes burning pain, stiffness and swelling in the joint from too much uric acid in the blood which forms hard crystals in the joint. An oral medicine is normally prescribed to address the uric acid in the blood, and a pain medication may also be prescribed. A change of diet may help to prevent a recurrence by reducing the uric acid in the blood. In the case of acute gout arthritis some people may develop uric acid kidney stones. Interval gout is the next stage, whereby progressively shorter periods occur between attacks, they last longer, are more severe, and involve more than one joint. It can become a chronic condition if left untreated and eventually destroy the cartilage and bone.

*Inflammatory Bowel Disease* is a term that encompasses a number of chronic inflammatory disorders that can lead to damage of the gastrointestinal tract. The most common of these are ulcerative colitis and Crohn's disease. These two conditions have no medical cure. Once they begin, there are periods of remission followed by relapses. Women and men are equally affected. It can begin during adolescence, early adulthood or later in life. While the exact cause is not known, speculation is that it is caused by an infection. Diet may affect the symptoms but is not the likely the cause of Crohn's disease. The immune system becomes chronically activated resulting in chronic inflammation and ulceration. It can also be associated with reddish tender skin nodules and inflammation of the joints, spine, eyes and liver. There is a genetic connection and it therefore runs in families (brothers, sisters, children, parents). The disease can be quite painful and there is no cure for it so the goal of treatment is to minimize the effects and maintain remissions. Anti-inflammatory medications may be used to treat symptoms as well as other types of medication and in severe cases surgery may be required to improve the quality of life.

*Lyme Disease* is a bacterial illness which can be spread by ticks found on deer. When these ticks bite into the skin the bacterium infect the body. It causes abnormalities in the skin, joints, heart and nervous system. It is in the later stages of the disease arthritis, or inflammation in the joints occurs, beginning with swelling, stiffness and pain. The most common joints affected are in the knees and it can become chronic.

*Lupus* is a disease of the immune system where the immune system attacks tissues in various parts of the body leading to tissue damage and illness. It more often affects women than men between the ages of 14 and 45. Some of the symptoms include painful swollen joints, fever, fatigue, skin rash, ankle swelling, pleurisy, hair loss, a butterfly-shaped rash across the cheeks and nose, seizures, light sensitivity, and mouth sores. The cause of it is not known but factors that are believed to contribute include viruses, environmental chemicals and genetic makeup. Hormones may also play a role given that women of child-bearing age are most often those that are affected.

*Osteoarthritis* is also known as degenerative joint disease and is the most common form of arthritis. Cartilage, a firm rubbery material that covers the ends of bones in the joints and acts as a shock absorber breaks down. When this happens, tendons and ligaments stretch and this causes pain. In severe cases, the bones can rub against each other. While it can occur in almost any joints, those most often affected are the weight bearing joints such as the hips, knees and spine. The likelihood of getting osteoarthritis increases with age. Most people over age 60 have it to some extent, affecting women more often than men. Some of the symptoms include aching joints, pain after long periods of inactivity, enlargement in the middle and end joints of the fingers, and fluid accumulation in the joints. Heredity, obesity, injury and excessive joint use all play a role in the risk of getting osteoarthritis. Someone with scoliosis or curvature of the spine is likely to develop it, as is someone who is carrying excess weight which places more pressure on the knees and hips. Athletes with knee injuries or people who have broken a bone near the joint are also at risk, as is someone whose job has required repetitive motion such as bending at the knees. Strengthening exercises including swimming and physical therapy can help. As well, hot and cold compresses that can be applied to the painful joints and various medications like creams and steroids, are also available. In severe cases surgery may be necessary. Arthroscopy is a surgical procedure that may be used to clean out damaged cartilage and joint replacement surgery may be used to replace a damaged joint with an artificial one.

*Psoriatic Arthritis* is a form of arthritis that only affects people who have psoriasis. Psoriasis is a condition affecting the skin caused by a malfunctioning of the immune system. Those who also develop psoriatic arthritis, have stiff, painful and swollen joints that if left untreated can cause bone loss and joint deformation. The age group most commonly affected is the age 30 to 50 group. Just as psoriasis is caused by a problem with the immune system, so is psoriatic arthritis caused by an overactive immune system that causes pain and swelling of tissues around the joint. Pain medication is used to relieve the symptoms.

*Rheumatoid Arthritis* is characterized by its symmetry as it usually simultaneously affects the same location on both sides of the body such as both hands, wrists or knees. It can also affect the skin, eyes, lungs, heart, blood or nerves. Some of the symptoms include pain in the joints, swelling, stiffness and fatigue that develops gradually over several years but symptoms can vary from one person to another. Some people may suffer from symptoms for a period of time after which it goes into remission while others may find that severity increases very rapidly. Women more often then men are affected by it, and onset is normally in middle age, though there is a form of juvenile rheumatoid arthritis. While the exact cause is not known, it is believed to be due to a combination of genetic, environmental and hormonal factors, where something (perhaps a virus or bacteria) appears to trigger the immune system to attack the joints and occasionally organs throughout the body. A blood test can help to diagnose this condition along with self-reported symptoms of pain, joint stiffness in the morning, and the presence of nodules under the skin. Oral pain medications or other drugs may be prescribed to help relieve the symptoms, as well as topical creams, or corticosteroids. Rest during flare-ups and specific exercises may help and when necessary surgery may be required to repair a damaged joint.

## Cancer

Cancer is a disease characterized by an abnormal growth of cells. After a while, groups of abnormal cells can form lumps or tumours, or can spread through the bloodstream and lymphatic system to other parts of the body. Tumours can be either benign (non-cancerous) or malignant. (cancerous). Benign tumour cells stay in one place in the body and are not usually life-threatening. Malignant tumour cells are able to invade the tissues around them and spread to other parts of the body. Cancerous cells that spread to other parts of the body are called metastases. The first sign that a malignant tumour has spread is often the swelling of nearby lymph nodes, but cancer can metastasize to almost any part of the body. It is important to find malignant tumours early and treat them.

Cancers are named after the part of the body where they start. For example, cancer that starts in the colon but spreads to the liver is called colon cancer with liver metastases. There are over 100 types of cancer. The four most common cancer sites are prostate, breast, colorectal and lung. Different types of cancer have different symptoms and treatment. Some spread faster than others. The focus here will be on the four most common cancers.

*Prostate Cancer* is the most common cancer in Canadian men. Prostate cancer is often slow-growing and can be managed successfully when caught early. To look for signs of cancer, in addition to a physical exam, various tests are conducted including a blood test which checks for a substance called PSA (prostate specific antigen). If the PSA score is higher than normal for your age, a more detailed battery of tests are performed which may include a biopsy. A biopsy involves removing cells or tissues that are checked under a microscope. If the cells are cancerous, they may be studied further to see how fast they are growing. Various imaging tests that may be used include x-rays, ultrasound, CT scans (computerized axial tomography), MRIs (magnetic resonance imaging) and bone scans, each of which enables tissues, organs and bones to be examined in more detail. Treatment may include surgery, radiation therapy, and hormone therapy.

*Breast Cancer* is the most common cancer in Canadian women. Almost all breast cancers start in the glandular tissue of the breast and are known as adenocarcinomas. Cancer cells may start within the ducts (ductal carcinoma) or lobules (lobular carcinoma). Ductal carcinoma is the most common type of breast cancer. Breast cancer is usually first suspected one of three ways:

- Through self-examination

- Through a physician's examination

- Through a screening mammography

Imaging studies that may be used include x-rays, ultrasound, CT scans (computerized axial tomography), MRIs (magnetic resonance imaging) and bone scans. These tests allow tissues, organs and bones to be examined in more detail. In the case of breast cancer, a diagnostic mammogram (a special x-ray of breast tissue) will be done. A biopsy is usually necessary to make a definite diagnosis. If cancerous cells are found, they are tested to find out what kind of breast cancer it is and if it has hormone receptors (estrogen or progesterone). Testing will also identify the grade of the cancer cells. Low grade cells are slower to divide and the cancer is generally less aggressive. Higher grade cells divide more quickly and the tumour is more likely to spread. Surgery, chemotherapy and radiation therapy are the most common treatments. Other treatments may include hormone therapy.

*Colorectal Cancer* usually starts in the cells that line the inside of the colon or the rectum. Cancer of the small intestine is very rare, so when people talk about bowel cancer, they usually mean colorectal cancer. It is the third most common cancer for both men and women in Canada. It can develop over a long time without showing any signs because the lower abdomen has room where the tumour can grow unnoticed until it eventually blocks or constricts the bowel. Some of the symptoms that may appear include a general discomfort in the abdomen, changes in bowel habits, blood in the stool, nausea or vomiting, feeling very tired, weight loss, and anemia. The treatment may involve surgery, radiation therapy and chemotherapy.

*Lung Cancer* starts in the lung tissue. It can occur in both men and women. It is the leading cause of death due to cancer in Canada. Smoking causes most lung cancers. Unfortunately no amount of tobacco use is safe. Other risk factors include exposure to cancer causing substances (carcinogens) in the workplace and the environment. Symptoms that may indicate lung cancer include coughing, breathing problems, changes in phlegm, pneumonia, hoarseness, hiccups, chest pain and pleural effusion (a collection of fluid between the layers of tissue lining the lung and the wall of the chest cavity). Various tests may be used for diagnosis including a complete physical examination, blood test, chest x-ray, biopsy and visual image scans. A treatment plan may include surgery, chemotherapy, radiation therapy, or laser therapy.

There are many support organizations that provide information and support for people who have cancer and their families.

## Cataracts

A cataract is a condition that appears as a cloudy film over the lens of the eye making it difficult to read, drive a car, or see detail. While they affect vision, normally they do not cause any pain. While many seniors eventually get them, removal is normally a safe and effective surgical procedure. They, therefore, generally do not present as an ongoing chronic condition. Most cataracts develop slowly and initially vision can be enhanced with stronger lighting and corrective eyeglasses. The following symptoms may be indicators of the presence of cataracts:

- Blurry, dim or cloudy vision

- Increasing difficulty with night vision

- Sensitivity to bright light and glare

- Halos appearing around lights

- Finding it necessary to increase light for reading

- Numerous changes in vision correction prescriptions

- Fading or yellowing of colours

- Double vision

Cataracts do not normally cause other problems such as redness, itching, burning or discharge. If other symptoms are present, this normally is an indicator of some other eye problems. While normally cataracts are not damaging to the eye, there is a condition called a hypermature cataract that can cause inflammation, pain and headache. Removal can rectify this.

Cataracts associated with normal aging usually appear symmetrically in both eyes. Surgery is usually performed in one eye at a time, and may be recommended at such time as the reduced vision is affecting the person's quality of life or their ability to perform daily activities. The recovery process is quite fast and surgery is performed on an outpatient basis under local anesthesia.

Eye exams are recommended at two-year intervals for people over age 65. While the risk of getting cataracts cannot be eliminated, there are a number of ways to help minimize it. Eliminate exposure to smoke as this removes exposure to free radicals. Eating a balanced healthy diet is also believed to have a modest effect, though scientific evidence has not actually proven this to be the case. Protection from ultraviolet rays of the sun such as protective eye wear and hats can help to protect the eyes.

## Chronic Obstructive Pulmonary Disease (COPD)

Chronic Obstructive Pulmonary Disease is a lung disease in which the lungs have been damaged and this makes it hard to breathe. Cigarette smoking causes 90% of COPD. It can cause anxiety for the person affected with it because their capacity to breath is so reduced that it can feel like breathing through a straw. Airways and air sacs in the lungs lose their shape and elasticity. The walls between many of the air sacs are destroyed and the airways become thick and swollen. Cells in the airways create more mucus than normal and this leads to blocked airways. Some of the symptoms include shortness of breath, increased mucus and coughing. Physicians can determine whether a person has COPD based on the presence of these three main symptoms. They may also use a device known as a spirometer that determines the presence and severity of airway obstruction. Complications may occur as a result of COPD. For example, the person may have recurring chest infections including pneumonia or flu and abnormally high blood pressure in the arteries of the lungs. Heart complications may occur such as enlargement, irregular heartbeat or strain on the right side of the heart. There may be dependence on mechanical ventilation and oxygen therapy, and in severe cases, respiratory failure.

### Living Better with COPD

A person who suffers with COPD can take several steps that may help them live better.

### Eat Healthy

- Eat small frequent meals instead of three larger meals
- Rest before eating
- Eat slowly and chew food well
- Avoid drinking fluids until after eating is through
- Try liquid meal preparations when too tired to cook a full meal
- Arrange for services such as Meals-on-Wheels

### Exercise

Stretching and breathing exercises can help and a daily walk. A physiotherapist or physician should be consulted prior to beginning a new exercise program.

### Assistive Devices

There are several assistive devices that can aid someone who has COPD such as:

- Using a bath stool and a hand shower and non-skid mats
- Install grab bars or rails that attach to the walls or bathtub
- Use a small mop for wiping up spills to save bending
- Use pick-up tongs to pick up articles from the floor

## Depression

Depression is not a normal part of aging but unfortunately it is very prevalent in the older population. All too often, however, it goes untreated despite the fact that it is a very treatable condition. It often occurs in combination with other chronic conditions and increases the risk of death as a result. Heart disease is twice as likely to develop in someone who is clinically depressed and recovery following illness is slower. If not dealt with, it can lead to suicide. The rate of suicide is higher amongst the "oldest old" than in any other age group and particularly amongst men. Positive outlook and engagement in life may help keep depression at bay.

### Causes of Depression in Older Adults

There are a number of changes and losses that can affect the mental health of an older adult. When major illness with resulting disabilities occur later in life, individuals who were involved in working, socializing and traveling may suddenly face lower incomes, reduced mobility and dependence on caregivers and assistive devices. Retirement, loss of a life partner, or a shrinking circle of friends can all contribute to increased levels of stress and depression in older adults. Certain types of medication can cause depression, as can other illnesses, chronic pain, and fear of death. There may be a family history of major depression. Seniors who are caregivers to an ailing spouse can find themselves socially and emotionally isolated and may develop mental health problems such as alcohol abuse, substance abuse and sometimes suicide. Older people who are depressed are three to four times more likely to have alcohol-related problems than are older people who are not depressed.

Other feelings and behaviour changes that may occur include:

- Being easily upset
- Not having the energy to do things
- Changing sleep habits
- Increasing forgetfulness
- Being afraid of things
- Changes in eating habits
- Neglecting housework
- Frequent episodes of crying
- Having trouble managing money
- Low self-esteem
- Being confused
- Getting lost frequently
- Staying alone a lot of the time
- Spending little or no time with friends
- Feeling hopeless or overwhelmed
- Thinking life isn't worth living
- Thinking about hurting oneself

## Treatment

Older adults are among the most undertreated populations for mental health. In the over-65 age group, about 6% suffer mild to severe depression in any given year. Of those who have chronic illness, this number jumps to around 25%, and a startling near 50% of residents in long-term care facilities are affected by depression.

A key to correctly identifying and treating depression among older adults begins with education. Older adults, like many others, hold negative attitudes that stop them from seeking help. Some of the treatment options include antidepressant medication, professional counseling, and support groups.

## Reasons Depression May Go Unrecognized in Older Adults

Older adults may believe the myth that depression is just a natural part of the aging process. Some may see depression as a normal consequence of losing their independence and not want to speak up as a result. In some cases, the person may already have other physical or mental illnesses such as dementia or diabetes and they may not have been properly diagnosed with depression as a separate illness that can be treated. Depression can be a side effect of medications such as certain drugs taken for high blood pressure, and this connection may not have been identified. Many older adults feel embarrassed or ashamed to even discuss it. The fact that they cannot see any life events that could have brought the depression on may cause them to feel it must be a personal flaw; alternately, they may have so many life events going on that could trigger a depressive episode that the person feels going to a doctor would serve no purpose. Culture can also play a role in not seeking treatment for depression.

When treatment involves cost, the person may not have the funds to buy the necessary medication or pay for transportation to appointments if family support is not available.

## Medication Concerns

The most common medical approach to anxiety and depression in older adults is to prescribe drugs. Medications can be very helpful in managing depression and in assisting with grief and loss. It is important that medications are managed well so they do not lead to accidental misuse or intentional overdose.

According to Statistics Canada, nine in ten older adults take at least one type of medication — most take three types of medication. More than a quarter of senior women are taking more than five. More concerning is that according to the Canadian Public Health Association, nine out of every ten outpatients take their prescriptions improperly or not at all. Another concern is that the most widely prescribed medications for older adults are known to be addictive and may cause numerous side effects. It is important to have a complete list of medications, to deal with only one pharmacy, and to get as much information as possible about drug interactions and side effects.

Some common possible side effects include confusion, poor muscle coordination, drowsiness, impaired performance, and decreased cognition.

## Other Coping Strategies

Counseling can be a very effective tool in managing depression and grief. Older adults may also benefit from information about alternative methods of dealing with emotional and stress-related illnesses. There is value in expressing feelings such as grief, anxiety or frustration and in receiving understanding about these difficult times. They may also benefit from:

- Learning relaxation techniques from CDs in library

- Taking meditation classes or learning from a book

- Joining a support group

- Grief counseling

- Spending time with people who bring joy into their lives

## How Caregivers Can Help an Aging Parent Maintain Good Mental Health

Staying connected is very important to maintaining good mental hygiene. The following are ways to encourage an older adult to stay connected:

- Keeping up with friendships and social connections.

- Making new friends — helps prevent feelings of isolation and loneliness that can lead to later-life depression.

- Volunteering is another way to bring people into your life.

Exercising the brain through mental activity helps keep the mind sharp, just as physical activity keeps the body strong. The following are ways older adults can remain mentally active:

- Learning to play a musical instrument

- Playing Scrabble or doing crossword puzzles

- Starting a new hobby, such as crafts, painting, biking, or bird-watching

- Staying informed about world events

- Reading

## Diabetes

The incidence of diabetes is rapidly increasing in Canada, with serious financial implications on health care programs. If left untreated, it can lead to a heart attack, stroke, kidney or heart failure, limb amputation, vision loss, digestive problems, thyroid disorders and skin problems. It makes having surgery for other conditions very risky. The risk of getting heart disease or stroke is exceptionally high amongst diabetics. Eighty percent of diabetics die because of a heart attack or stroke. The prevalence of diabetes increases with age. Older adults face some challenges in dealing with this chronic condition. Economic barriers caused by living on a fixed income can cause seniors to skip meals, and this seriously puts the diabetic at risk of health complications. Transportation is not always readily available to seniors which can make it difficult for them to attend physician appointments regularly to monitor their condition. Many seniors have mobility issues that prevent them from exercising as much as they should. Inactivity impairs proper blood circulation. Lack of an emotional social support network may complicate their condition further by adding anxiety and depression to their health problems. The rate of depression is twice as high amongst people with diabetes as it is in the general population.

Some seniors may have been diagnosed with Type 1 Diabetes (which requires insulin) as a child and dealt with its challenges through most of their life. Others may be amongst the 90% that have developed Type 2 Diabetes (which does not require insulin) in adulthood. This occurs when the pancreas does not produce enough insulin or when the body does not effectively use the insulin that is produced. Glucose then builds up in the blood instead of being used for energy.

There is an increased risk of getting Type 2 Diabetes if any of the following risk factors are present:

- Being overweight
- Being age 40 and over
- Having a parent or sibling with diabetes
- Having high cholesterol and elevated lipids (blood fats)
- Having an unusual blood glucose level
- Having high blood pressure

Diabetes is more common among seniors who have low income. This may be due to a number of reasons including less access to necessary medication and supplies, poorer nutritional habits due to income, and less exercise. Some, but not all provinces provide full access through their pharmacare programs to the most current treatments and supplies for managing diabetes. Many seniors rely on these programs to cover these costs.

Education plays an important role in successfully managing diabetes. Through knowledge about proper diet, exercise and how to use blood glucose monitoring devices, people are better able to manage their condition wisely.

### Warning Signs and Living Healthy With Diabetes

Many people who have Type 2 Diabetes may display no symptoms. Signs and symptoms that may indicate the onset of diabetes include :

- Unusual thirst

- Frequent urination

- Weight change (gain or loss)

- Extreme fatigue or lack of energy

- Blurred vision

- Frequent or recurring infections

- Cuts and bruises that are slow to heal

- Tingling or numbness in the hands or feet

The two main tests that measure the presence of blood sugar problems are:

1. The direct measurement of glucose levels in the blood during an overnight fast, and

2. The measurement of the body's ability to appropriately handle the excess sugar presented after drinking a high glucose drink. Blood is tested before the drink is taken, again 30 minutes later, then one hour, two hours and three hours after drinking the high glucose solution.

A diabetic can live a long and healthy life by keeping blood glucose levels (the amount of sugar in the blood) in the target range set by their doctor. Things that help are:

- Eating healthy meals and snacks

- Enjoying regular physical activity

- Taking diabetes medications (including insulin), if prescribed by your doctor

Type 2 Diabetes is a progressive, life long condition. Over time, it may be more difficult to keep blood glucose levels in the target range. A health care team can help by working with the person to adjust the food plan, activity and medications. Poorly managed blood glucose levels can cause serious and even life-threatening complications.

## Heart and Stroke

### Heart Disease

Heart disease is a group of conditions affecting the structure and functions of the heart and has many underlying causes.

The build-up of fatty deposits (known as plaque) leaving arteries less elastic and narrow causes atherosclerosis or clogged arteries. This blocks or slows the smooth passage of oxygen-rich blood. The heart itself may slow down or even stop when a blockage or a coronary artery temporarily contracts or goes into a severe spasm, effectively shutting off the flow of blood to the heart. The length of time the blood supply is cut off will determine the amount of damage to the heart.

Managing this condition means knowing and controlling blood pressure, diabetes if present and blood cholesterol. It is also important to lead a healthy lifestyle by being smoke-free, physically active, eating a healthy diet that is lower in fat, especially saturated and trans fat, achieving and maintaining a healthy weight, limiting alcohol use and reducing your stress. Certain medications may be used to reduce fats and cholesterol in the blood, as well as medications to control blood pressure. Anti-platelets or anticoagulants may be prescribed to reduce the risk of developing a blood clot. Surgery may be necessary if these measures do not produce the expected results. Stents can be inserted in the narrow part of the artery to prop it open and allow blood to flow freely. In some cases, coronary artery bypass surgery is performed.

### Warning Signs of a Heart Attack

The Heart and Stroke Foundation advises that people should pay attention to the following warning signs that may indicate a heart attack:

- Pain

  — sudden discomfort or pain that does not go away with rest

  — pain that may be in the chest, neck, jaw, shoulder, arms or back

  — pain that may feel like burning, squeezing, heaviness, tightness or pressure

  — in women, pain may be more vague

  — chest pain or discomfort that is brought on with exertion and goes away with rest

- Shortness of breath

- Nausea

- Sweating

- Fear

- Anxiety

- Denial

### Women and Heart Attacks

Heart disease is the leading cause of death in women. Post-menopausal women are more at risk for heart disease. The most common symptom in women is reported as chest pain. Both women and men may experience typical or non-typical symptoms such as nausea, sweating, pain in the arm, throat, jaw or pain that is unusual. However, women may describe their pain differently than men.

### Stroke

A stroke is similar to a heart attack in that it is caused by a blockage of blood vessels in the brain thus depriving the brain of oxygen. A stroke can also occur if a weakened blood vessel in the brain spontaneously bursts causing a sudden loss of brain function. Cells or neurons without oxygen die. The effects of a stroke depend on where the brain was injured, as well as how much damage occurred. A stroke can impact any number of areas including your ability to move, see, remember, speak, reason and read and write.

### Warning Signs of a Stroke

Stroke can be treated. That's why it is so important to recognize and respond to the warning signs.

- **Weakness** — Sudden loss of strength or sudden numbness in the face, arm or leg, even if temporary.

- **Trouble speaking** — Sudden difficulty speaking or understanding or sudden confusion, even if temporary.

- **Vision problems** — Sudden trouble with vision, even if temporary.

- **Headache** — Sudden severe and unusual headache.

- **Dizziness** — Sudden loss of balance, especially with any of the above signs.

If a stroke victim receives a clot-busting drug called TPA within **three hours** of initial symptoms the physical and mental damage can be greatly minimized!

## PAIN MANAGEMENT

Pain not only hurts but interferes with a person's quality of life. In this day and age with so much information and help available, no one should have to live with unremitting pain. If pain is left untreated, it can affect personality, mood, and even relationships. It can also develop into a chronic pain situation. Pain is our body's way of telling us something is wrong and where it is. There are two types of pain — emotional and physical. Emotional pain is just as real as physical pain and needs to be taken seriously. This section deals with physical pain.

The "Pain" we associate with physical pain is defined as *an unpleasant sensory experience that also effects our emotions and is associated with actual or potential tissue damage.* Pain is generally categorized as Acute, Chronic, or Recurrent. "Acute pain" is associated with acute injury or disease, whereas "chronic pain" refers to pain that has persisted for longer than three months or past the expected time of healing following an injury or disease. "Recurrent pain" is associated with tension as in headaches and in certain types of chronic diseases. Recurrent pain means that there are episodes of pain alternating with pain free periods.

## Why Older Adults May Not Seek Help

Surprisingly, an older adult may not be open to getting relief from pain. This may be due to not permitting themselves to ask for help as may be the case with someone who grew up in a "stiff upper lip" environment. Insufficient knowledge about pain relief, as well as fear of addiction can be other issues as well. Some individuals fear they may not be able to function while on pain medication. Another reason for not seeking help is the fear that doing so means acknowledging that the increased pain they are experiencing might mean a worsening of the condition they have. They may feel that ignoring it might make it go away through the power of "positive thinking". Given that older adults have such a deep respect for physicians and their time it is tempting for them to behave like a good and complying patient that does not complain of pain.

It is so important to have a good understanding of the condition your loved one is living with. Research can help in this respect. Is the pain related to a chronic condition such as arthritis or is the pain related to disease such as cancer? Then have a thorough assessment done by a qualified physician or pain management specialist. It could be helpful to bring forward the person's fears about pain management so that they can be discussed with the doctor. Treatment recommendations that come from a respected source such as a physician can go a long way toward encouraging the person to explore methods of pain management. He or she can discuss the various types of medications available, the expected outcome of the medication use and ease any fears the older adult may have. The pharmacist is also an important partner in medication therapy.

## Managing Pain

Managing an older adult's pain requires a partnership between the individual, their informal caregiver, and their formal caregiving team. When an individual is in pain they will react in different ways. Some will moan or even cry, others may become very quiet, still others may not move a muscle or not want to eat. Some older adults attempt to mask their pain as they fear the treatment itself will cause even more pain. Or they may be trying to protect their informal caregivers from worry. Nevertheless, talking about it is important. This lets the person know that the person has options that may lessen the pain and improve their quality of life.

### Pain Scale

Pain is not that easily measured however introducing the concept of a pain scale can be helpful in communicating level of discomfort. You might ask "If on a scale of one to ten, ten being the worst pain you have felt and one being the least pain you have felt what is your number right now?" Now there is some idea of pain perception. When a treatment plan is introduced the pain scale can be revisited to see if there is a lessening of pain perception.

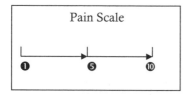

Ask: "If on a scale of one to ten, ten being the worst pain you have felt and one being the least pain you have felt, what is your number right now?"

Good pain management may not mean alleviating all pain but rather the management and lessening of that pain. It is important to deal with pain rather than to learn to simply "tolerate" it because when a body part hurts we tend not to want to move it. This can lead to disability and loss of function of that part. For instance, pain may be an indication of insufficient blood flow to the area. This can ultimately affect major organs. Pain management can help reduce that risk. In addition, helping to ease the *emotional distress* related to pain is also a worthy goal and goes a long way toward improving *quality of life*. When we feel pain we tend to avoid doing things we normally do, and our quality of life is significantly diminished.

## Medication for Relief of Pain

The type of medication recommended by the physician or used by a specialist will vary based on the situation or procedure.

### Minor Procedures

Some procedures will require the use of a local anesthetic. This often involves the injection of a small amount of numbing medicine under the skin. After a couple of minutes the medicine takes effect and the individual undergoing the procedure will not feel anything. This type of pain treatment may be used for instance when someone requires stitches for a minor cut. Numbing cream can sometimes be applied to the area before the local anesthetic is injected.

## More Involved Procedures

Some procedures require more than local anesthesia to prevent pain. A trained specialist may administer sedation that causes drowsiness, but does not make a person unconsciousness. Monitoring equipment is used to monitor vital signs throughout the procedure.

## Surgery

Operations that last for longer periods of time will require the use of deep sedation or anesthesia. An anesthesiologist will "put them to sleep" for a period of time. As most operations cause some pain thereafter, use of medication for prevention and pain management is administered following surgery. Medication is reduced over time as healing takes place.

It is important to remember that pain medication should be given to keep pain away (prevention), not as a "catch-up" for pain that is already severe. All pain should be treated. Medicines for lesser pain can usually be given by mouth, though some cases require administration rectally. The most common type of oral medication is acetaminophen. Other pain relieving medication frequently given by mouth includes anti-inflammatory medications such as ibuprofen. When these medications are not enough to prevent or relieve pain, the physician may prescribe the use of narcotics. When narcotics are used to manage real pain for a short period of time, they can safely be taken without fear of it leading to addiction. This type of medication should only be taken under the direct supervision of a licensed physician.

Sometimes during hospitalization, pain medication is administered through an intravenous line. This is a patient-controlled method of delivering analgesia by pushing a button attached to a computer on the IV so that a specially prepared IV pain medication is delivered in small doses. The computer will not deliver more than the safe amount of medication as determined by the physician. It records the number of times the patient pushes the button for pain medication, so it can be determined if the patient's pain is being managed properly.

## Medications and Allergies

Some people may be allergic to certain types of medication. It is very important to maintain a record and advise hospital staff and the physician well in advance of any such allergies before undergoing surgery. They will find a safe alternative.

## Alternative Solutions to Medication

There are a number of non-pharmacological pain management approaches that can be helpful in the treatment of chronic pain. Below is a brief list. You can find more resources through your local pharmacy or physician's office.

### Transcutaneous Electrical Nerve Stimulators (TENS)

This device is often used in chiropractor or physiotherapy office. Also available are hand-held self-administered machines which can be an affordable and helpful home solution. A small, battery-operated device delivers painless low-voltage electrical current through the skin via electrodes placed near the source of pain. TENS stimulates nerves in the affected area and sends signals to the brain that "scramble" normal pain perception, thus relieving pain.

### Acupuncture

Acupuncture therapy is based on the idea that the body has energy centers at various strategic points. This therapy involves insertion of very thin, stainless steel needles into various parts of the body. It is thought that pain impulses are blocked from reaching the spinal cord and the brain. Acupuncture is believed by some to aid headache, orofacial conditions and myofacial pain by activating naturally occurring endorphins in the body.

### Thermal Therapy

Pain related to spacisity can respond to cooling such as a reusable jell pack while joint stiffness can be improved by application of heat such as heating pad. A combination of therapies such as massage and heat or cold can also be helpful. There are various products available on the market that offer both cooling or warming applications.

### Exercise Therapy

An appropriate exercise program can aid in pain management. Studies show that there is no benefit to extended bed rest . The key is to keep moving! By maintaining muscle strength and conditioning there is less risk of a fall and a better chance to recover should an injury occur. How often exercise occurs, and at the right intensity, are of importance. This therapy also helps to improve mood, energy levels and self esteem. The other key is to find that enjoyable activity which produces early gains and is comfortable to do.

### Chiropractic or Manipulation Therapy

Manipulation can affect pain by freeing up a restricted joint by manually applying a controlled force into the joints. Manipulation, or adjustment of the affected joint and tissues, restores mobility, thereby alleviating pain and muscle tightness. Chiropractic therapy promotes tissue healing. Although chiropractors has an excellent safety record, no health treatment is completely free of potential adverse effects. A physician should be consulted prior to initiating a treatment plan to determine if it is a safe treatment for the condition involved.

## Massage Therapy

Massage is a gentle hands on therapy that can relieve pain, decrease inflammation, decrease stress and increase overall feelings of well being. For those who have been inactive due to illness, massage is important in bringing relief to aches and in improving the health of the skin, muscles and connective tissue by increasing circulation.

## Therapeutic Touch

Therapeutic Touch is a non-invasive, holistic and hands-on approach to healing which stimulates the receiver's own recuperative powers. It is a modern form of laying-on-of-hands and is based on principles of an energy exchange between people. Therapeutic Touch promotes relaxation, reduces anxiety, and often alters a person's perception of pain. It can promote healing, and elicit a relaxation response. Therapeutic Touch allows people to comfort without the need for talking. It is particularly useful in end of life care.

## Reflexology

Reflexology is the application of pressure, stretch and movement to the feet and hands to affect corresponding parts of the body. Reflexologists view the feet and hands as a mirror image of the body. By applying appropriate pressure using the thumbs, a reflexologist can break up patterns of stress which manifests itself as pain in other parts of the body.

There are many theories as to why it works, but the premise is that it uses the body's nervous system. Pressure applied to the feet generates a signal through the peripheral nervous system. From there it enters the central nervous system where it is processed in various parts of the brain. It is then relayed to the internal organs to allocate the necessary adjustments in fuel and oxygen. Finally a response is sent on to the motor system which adjusts the body's tone or overall tension level. If applied properly, the tone will reset itself to a lower operating tempo. A lower operating tempo means a lessening of stress and pain.

## Behavioral and Cognitive Therapy

By helping to modify one's thoughts, feelings and beliefs about pain, one can shift the attitude about pain from overwhelming to manageable. This therapy assists with developing coping techniques and skills to help adapt to pain. Its aim is to empower the person and can include relaxation and breathing techniques.

## Pain and Depression

Pain is more likely to be a part of the lives of people who live with depression than it is for those who are free from depression. Studies also show that among individuals who have chronic pain, those with depression will report more severe pain and worse functioning, and use more medications than do non-depressed people. This underscores the importance of screening for depression when treating someone who has chronic pain.

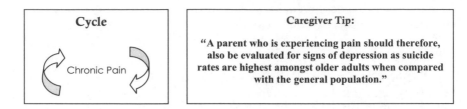

| Cycle | Caregiver Tip: |
|---|---|
| Chronic Pain | "A parent who is experiencing pain should therefore, also be evaluated for signs of depression as suicide rates are highest amongst older adults when compared with the general population." |

Furthermore, individuals with depression who also experience pain are known to have worse depression outcomes than those without pain. A person who is experiencing pain should therefore, also be evaluated for signs of depression as suicide rates are highest amongst older adults when compared with the general population.

# Chapter 6

# Care for Older Adults

# PROFILES OF TODAY'S INFORMAL CAREGIVERS

## Meet Bonnie

**Bonnie is 42 years old, married with two small children.** In addition to providing her parents with assistance, she manages to work full-time as a dental assistant. Her father's health is failing and she provides her mother (dad's primary caregiver) with emotional support by phone as she lives several hours from her parents. Dad's memory is failing due do his Alzheimer's disease but they still spend time reminiscing on the phone and talk about cyclical activities like today's weather, what they ate for dinner, and whether they got out of the house today. Bonnie wishes she could do more, but helps as much as she can at a distance through the week by using the telephone to arrange appointments for her parents and to follow up on their results. She is very stressed by trying to juggle raising her own children, spending time with her husband, and being the secondary caregiver to her father. She is considering giving up her full-time work in favour of part-time so she can help her parents more.

## Meet Marla

**Marla is 55 years old, married, with 23-year-old twin daughters.** One still lives at home part-time while attending university. Marla works full-time as a marketing manager. Her mother, who lives in the same city is now 84, and has continued to live in her own home after Marla's dad passed away last year. Marla's mom refuses to move even though her arthritis makes it difficult for her to do the housework. The house now needs a new roof, the bathroom faucets leak, and her mom cannot afford the repairs as her only income is from her modest CPP widow's pension, OAS and GIS. Marla takes time off work to take her mom to doctor's appointments and spends weekends helping out with grocery shopping. Her mother needs assistance with washing her hair, and Marla has applied to the Community Care Access Centre to get her mother personal help. But the case worker advised Marla her mother doesn't qualify because Marla lives close by and can help her. Marla recently had to pass up a promotion at work and is now experiencing stress and symptoms of chronic fatigue. She has asked her doctor for medication to help her sleep at night. She argues with her husband who feels she is already doing too much and resents Marla spending their strained finances towards support for her mom.

## Meet Vivian

**Vivian is 79 years old, and primary caregiver to her husband Joe,** who just celebrated his 87th birthday. Joe has not be able to keep up with repairs to the home they have lived in for the past 50 years because of their limited income from CPP and OAS, so now the furnace needs to be replaced and the badly worn carpeting is affecting Vivian's allergies. Joe hasn't driven a car since his license was taken away at age 84 and a parishioner from their church helps out occasionally with driving them to doctor's appointments.

Vivian worries about Joe's heart condition, their limited finances and has asked the doctor to give her medication to help her sleep at night. She knows Joe should be moved to a nursing home but she feels they can't afford the expense with her still living in their home.

Bonnie, Marla and Vivian are typical of today's caregivers and care recipients. The stresses they face and the financial burdens are real, only their names are fictitious. Many primary caregivers are spouses who in addition to providing help to their spouse, are themselves dealing with one or more chronic conditions. Many middle-aged women are secondary caregivers — part of the sandwich generation who are simultaneously providing care to an aging parent while raising their own family. In 1996, 84% of seniors received some type of assistance. Only 10% of this support came from a home care agency while the other 90% came from family members. As many as 70% of informal caregivers (so-called because they receive no pay and have no formal training) are family employed in full-time careers yet still managing to provide an amazing average of 23 hours per week of informal assistance.

## ECONOMIC AND NON-ECONOMIC IMPACTS

The glass ceiling of caregivers has become a widespread reality as many Canadians (mostly women) forego promotions in favour of taking on care giving duties in their spare time. While increasingly more men are counting themselves amongst the growing number of caregivers, there are still 3.5 women for every man fulfilling the caregiver role. According to the Ontario Women's Directorate, women spend 17 years caring for their children and 18 years helping an elderly parent. The role is not a new one but what has changed is the "multi-tasking" nature. There are hidden "job opportunity" costs when providing eldercare for a caregiver who also maintains a career outside the home. These include financial earnings losses, vacation time lost, sick days lost, social opportunities lost such as the need to go home immediately versus going out with the office, job advances lost due to inability to relocate or to take training courses. Many eventually cut back their work hours to increase care giving duties and the economic cost of doing so not only impacts current earnings but may also impact future benefits like *Canada Pension Plan*. Reduced work hours can also impact other employee benefits such as extended health care, dental and disability insurance. Informal caregivers often incur out-of-pocket expenses as well. There may be respite care expenses and "out-sourcing" expenses such as childcare, housework, and yard work to free up personal time for taking on increased duties.

The year 2006 was a milestone for the boomer cohort; the eldest of the "forever young" generation now hit age 60. While the first wave was small, their numbers will swell with tsunami force; impacting social programs and health care. They are a generation learning to navigate new relationships with aging parents. As if they don't already have enough on their plate, they now must get ready to help mom and dad live longer, stay healthy, and prepare for the eventual medical issues they will inevitably face as a natural part of the aging process. When the need to provide help occurs, it can be sudden and unexpected. There is no time to research; decisions will have to be made quickly. Even when a relative is moved to a long-term care facility, the role as a caregiver does not end. The role merely changes to a new one that the provider must adapt to.

Informal caregivers provide assistance to seniors who suffer from a wide range of conditions with the two major groups being physical limitations and dementia-related conditions. By definition, an informal caregiver includes anyone who provides unpaid assistance and who does not have formal training in the field of long-term care. This includes a wide range of individuals such as the spouse, children, volunteers, friends and neighbours. Volunteers from the community include church parishioners, charities, and other groups who volunteer hundreds of hours each year to help support seniors living in the community. Society has relied on informal caregivers for many decades, but with fewer children, and greater tendencies for adult children to live in other cities, there is fear that there will not be enough informal caregivers to care for the next generation of seniors whose number will drastically exceed the generation of seniors before them.

## WHO IS RECEIVING CARE?

Most seniors live at home, not in institutions. For instance in 1996 only 254,000 seniors lived in an institution, which equates to about 7% of the population. Of the 93% living in private households, many live alone. By comparison, 29% of seniors live alone as compared with 8% of the under-65 population. Seniors who live alone are at greater risk for safety during a medical emergency and advance planning for such an emergency is vital. This is an essential area where both caregivers and advisors to seniors can be a valuable resource by providing assistance in helping them to prepare ahead. Amongst seniors age 75 to 84, as many as 49% live alone according to a 1996 survey,[1] while amongst those over age 85 there were 58% living alone. The majority of seniors take some form of prescription medication or over-the-counter medication on a regular basis. One in five meet Statistics Canada's definition of low income. Senior women are far more likely to be living alone and are more likely to have low incomes than are men. Many older adults hesitate to ask for help for fear it is interpreted by others as their inability to manage on their own. They are concerned this might lead to being placed in a nursing home against their wishes.

## THE CAREGIVER'S ROLE

When an aging parent, spouse, or sibling becomes ill, thousands of Canadians, many of them women, will become caregivers literally overnight. Causes may range from a broken hip due to a slip on ice-covered pavement to a stroke, heart attack, or cancer.

---

[1] *Canada's Seniors* (1999), Statistics Canada, Division of Aging and Seniors.

The caregiver's role may range from providing emotional support and guidance on a long-distance basis by telephone to local daily assistance in person. The individual that requires assistance may be living independently, in a facility, or with the caregiver.

## Am I a Caregiver Yet?

Knowing when you have crossed the invisible boundary is not always apparent at first. Being a caregiver is often associated with providing physical assistance with activities of daily living such as transferring from a bed to a chair, getting dressed, or eating. But many seniors receive help in much more subtle ways. A report published by Statistics Canada (1999) indicated family members provide support most often in the following ways:

- Housework and household maintenance:                    67%

- Shopping, transportation, banking, bill payment:        51%

- Personal phone call to check on parent:                 39%

- Emotional support:                                      23%

- Assistance with personal care:                          12%

There is a good possibility many people are caregivers but have not yet thought of their role in this way.

## Risks and Rewards Associated with Being a Caregiver

Being a caregiver is a demanding role that carries its own risks to the caregiver such as:

- Clinical depression

- Loss of privacy

- Restrictions upon one's social life

- Personal stress that leads to illness

- Suffering in the form of grief

- Depletion of income and savings

- Feelings of isolation and loneliness

- Added responsibilities such as legal/ethical issues including power of attorney, substitute decision making

Some people find joy in adopting the caregiver role such as:

- Risks and Rewards Associated with Being a Caregiver

- A sense of accomplishment

- An opportunity to develop new skills and knowledge such as advocacy abilities

- Increased compassion and personal growth

- A chance to give back to someone who has cared for themselves

The greatest obstacle that caregivers face, is learning to stop grieving for what used to be and to find joy in the present.

It is not easy for either the caregiver or the care recipient. No one wants to be cared for all the time, dependent upon another person for getting up out of bed, or dressed, or getting to and from the toilet. There are many daily tasks we all take for granted such as eating, going places, and even simple things like going to bed when you feel like it. There is loss of esteem that goes with loss of control, frustration, and fear of what the future holds.

It is hard to be a caregiver because coping with today's health care system is not easy. Government funding is simply not adequate to provide all the care needed by seniors, or even some of the support needed to assist caregivers in doing their job well. Rarely is the caregiver seriously considered as part of the care team. They often have to "chase down" information and this takes time away from caregiving duties. Caregivers lack training to deal with many of the expectations placed upon them by the health care system. People are being released sooner (and sicker) from the hospital to recover at home. This often leads to relapses, increased calls to 911 and increased visits to the Emergency Department.

Caregivers often suffer in silence. Their loss is a collection of quiet sorrows. A spouse loses companionship, a partner in decision-making, someone to share good times and laughter, and support during sad times. Their needs do not disappear just because someone else's needs are greater, and they are too often overlooked.

## Caregiver Adaptation to Change

There are seven emotions that caregivers commonly go through upon first receiving the news of a loved one's diagnosis. These are:

1. **Denial** — the feeling that nothing is seriously wrong and a mistake has been made, or that nothing is going to change in a major way.

2. **Anger** — outrage at the unfairness of the situation, misdirecting this anger towards others.

3. **Guilt** — a feeling that the caregiver is somehow to blame for the situation, regrets regarding past problems in relationships or discomfort with making care giving decisions.

4. **Acceptance** — eventual recognition that the circumstances cannot be changed and that the present still holds moments of happiness and joy of being together.

5. **Anxiety** — concerns about what the future holds.

6. **Sadness** — unhappy feelings about the losses being experienced.

7. **Loneliness** — a feeling that others do not understand the pain the caregiver is going through.

Women in particular find themselves in the role of caregiver whether by choice, instinct, or by process of elimination. Of all the caregivers, almost 80% are women, and more than half of them are in the workforce balancing a career role with that of caregiver.

The role of caregiver may be brief, lasting several months or may extend over many years. Caring for someone with a dementia such as Alzheimer's disease can be particularly stressing, as the disease is chronic and on average, lasts about nine years. While the person may look healthy physically, the cognitive impairment associated with this illness requires the caregiver to exercise patience, understanding, and creativity in expressing and communicating with the elder. As the person's abilities decrease, the caregiver must increase the assistance given in day-to-day tasks. Eventually, as the disease progresses to its final stages, the elder will require assistance with daily living including bathing, toileting, grooming, eating, and transferring.

## UNDERSTANDING ALZHEIMER'S DISEASE

Alzheimer's disease is the leading cause of dementia, representing 64% of all dementias.[2] It gradually destroys nerve cells in the brain and is not a normal part of aging. There are 316,500 Canadians that have some form of dementia.[3] This is expected to grow by the year 2031 to over 3/4 million people.[4] Canadians spend approximately $3.9 billion each year on persons with Alzheimer's disease and related dementias.[5]

Alzheimer's disease is progressive, degenerative, and irreversible dementia. The nerve cells in the brain break down and cannot be repaired. There is presently no known cure, however medication is available to treat some of the symptoms. The effect of Alzheimer's disease on each person varies.

It can strike at any age, however the majority of people with Alzheimer's disease are over 65. While there is no single test for it, the diagnosis is made through a systematic assessment that eliminates other possible causes. Evaluation includes a review of the person's medical history, mental status exam, physical exam, lab tests, and psychiatric and psychological evaluations.

The disease is characterized by three stages — early, middle and late. The early stage can last for two to four years with the person showing mild forgetfulness and experiencing difficulty in learning new things. There may

---

[2] www.alzheimer.ca/alz/content/html/disease_en/disease-whatisit-eng.htm — Alzheimer Society of Canada Web site (10/14/99).

[3] Ibid.

[4] Ibid.

[5] Ibid.

be difficulty finding words and using proper grammar. This may be accompanied by mood shifts, depression, passiveness and mild coordination problems. During the middle stage that lasts from two to 10 years, the caregiver has increasing day-to-day demands. The person affected may begin to wander, become disruptive, even hostile, may have delusions, and require assistance with daily tasks such as dressing, bathing, and using a toilet. The last stage is referred to as the late stage, and usually lasts from one to three years. The person may exhibit symptoms such as the loss of ability to communicate, severe disorientation about time, place and people, and display physical inabilities such as difficulty eating, swallowing, dressing, and speaking.

The degree of assistance required varies as the illness progresses. Initially, home care may be sufficient for assisting the person. Adult day support programs exist that are dementia-specific and they can offer the caregiver additional assistance in providing meaningful structured activities including socialization, exercise and routine as well as offering the caregiver themselves a well-needed respite. Eventually, long-term skilled medical assistance is required and the caregiver must seek appropriate long-term care facilities that have dementia-specific care sections. The decision to move the person to a medical facility is one of the most difficult and agonizing decisions the caregiver must make. Providing in-home care for a person with Alzheimer's disease is a 24-hour responsibility. Not only is the caregiver faced with the stress of this personal time commitment, but often friends and family begin to remove themselves from regular contact for fear of being asked to take on some of the responsibility. This can result in the caregiver feeling isolated, angry, resentful, and then guilty for their feelings. When home care has been chosen, it is important for the caregiver to get involved with a support group that understands the nature of the loved one's illness, and that the caregiver becomes familiar and utilizes community care support systems available.

## LONG-DISTANCE CAREGIVING

The mobility of society today means that often parents live in a different city or country than their adult children. As our population continues to age, many adult children will find themselves in the position of needing to fulfill the caregiver role to elders at a distance, while simultaneously raising children of their own — a characteristic known as "the Sandwich Generation" — or shortly after their own children have become independent. Nearly half a million Canadians (470,000) moved in 1996, either to provide care to someone with a long-term health problem or to be looked after by someone else.[6] American statistics indicate that nearly half of all adults over the age of 85 and nearly one quarter of those over the age of 65 need assistance performing one or more activities of daily living (ADLs).[7] These

---

[6] 1996 General Social Survey (GSS), Statistics Canada, *Canadian Social Trends*, Winter 1999, Catalogue No. 11-008, Page 11.

[7] *www.careguide.com*, (January 6, 2000).

activities include eating, toileting, transferring to and from beds and chairs, bathing, dressing, grooming, and changing adult diapers or briefs.

Some of the challenges of providing long-distance care include:

- Frequent travel to check on status of parents

- Financial, physical and emotional strain

- Feelings of guilt, anger, frustration and anxiety

The first thing the caregiver must do is to accept the situation as it is and know that they are not responsible for the elder's condition. They must avoid role reversal and the temptation to "become the parent". Elders want and need to continue to be respected and to maintain their dignity.

## Establishing Local Assistance and Local Contacts

An individual who has just assumed the role of caregiver should begin by identifying the kind of assistance required. A local case worker can assist in this evaluation and provide access to the many home care programs available in the area. The caregiver should not assume the only solution is to relocate the elder parent to live with them. This may not be the best solution for all concerned. A home care program can enable the elder to remain in their home for an additional one or two years.

| Caregivers Involved in a Move Pay a Higher Price for Helping | | |
|---|---|---|
| | All Caregivers | Caregivers Involved in Move |
| Helping others resulted in: | | |
| Changes in social activities | 45% | 76% |
| Changes in holiday plans | 25% | 45% |
| Repercussions at work | 50% | 61% |
| Changes in sleep patterns | 29% | 46% |
| Extra expenses | 44% | 59% |
| Changes in health | 21% | 30% |

Source: Statistics Canada, General Social Survey, 1996 *Canadian Social Trends* Winter 1999, Catalogue No. 11-008, p. 12.

Establish open communication with the case worker who is assigned to the elder. Speaking directly with someone who has face-to-face contact with the elder will provide some comfort. Determine whether there is a neighbour or a member from the local church community that can briefly visit the person weekly to report personal observations.

## Personal Observation

One of the best ways to find out how the senior is managing and whether they need more support is to visit and observe them in their home environment as they tend to their daily regimen.

- Does the elder appear to be losing weight?

- Are utilities and other bills being paid on time?

- Do clothes appear to be clean?

- Is the home odor-free?

It may be necessary to make some minor changes in the home to ensure a safe environment:

- Are there loose scatter rugs that should be removed?

- Should stronger wattage bulbs be installed to eliminate shadows that are confusing?

- Is there a need to widen passages between furniture for easier access?

- Does the elder require hand rails to be installed in the bathroom for using the toilet and tub?

- Would a microwave be safer for warming food than risking a stove that might not be turned off thereafter?

- Do small appliances such as the iron and the coffee machine have a safety switch to automatically turn off if left on?

- Is there a neighbour who might like to be a walking companion to ensure the elder has daily exercise?

It may be possible to have bills for routine expenses redirected to the caregiver for payment or set up on a pre-authorized payment through direct bank debit or credit card charge. A Power of Attorney will enable the caregiver to handle many  routine banking transactions and thereby lessen the burden on the elder.

# PREPARING FOR THE ROLE OF CAREGIVER

When a first-time informal caregiver takes on the role of helping an elder, they enter new and unfamiliar territory. Their role may be to provide assistance with activities of daily living, or instrumental activities such as buying groceries, preparing meals assisting with homemaking and bill payment. Perhaps the most important role they must fulfill is that of advocate. Someone must be able to speak on behalf of the elder when they cannot do so for themselves. There are several ways new caregivers can prepare in advance that will make their role a little easier.

## Learn Everything You Can about the Condition

The goal is not to become the expert in treating the condition, but to become a better advocate by knowing the questions to ask and being better equipped to identify when something is not quite right. Many associations exist that can be a valuable resource tool such as the Arthritis Society of Canada, the Canadian Cancer Society, the Alzheimer Society of Canada, and the Heart and Stroke Foundation of Canada.

## Get Personal Support

You cannot go it alone, nor should you try. There are many support groups that can help with emotional support and information. Learn from the experience of others, but get your medical advice only from medical experts.

Support groups are groups of caregivers that meet regularly to share information and discuss practical solutions to common problems. Many groups are available that consist of caregivers providing assistance to elders with common illnesses, such as cancer or various forms of dementia. They provide the caregiver with an opportunity to give and to receive support from others with whom they have something in common. The benefit of knowing that the caregiver is not alone can itself help the caregiver to deal with the emotional stress associated with their caregiver role. It can also be a source of information and helpful ideas. Groups can be found through the hospital and by searching the internet. Local community services are also a good source for finding support groups, and associations that represent a particular condition such as the Heart and Stroke Foundation, the Alzheimer Society of Canada, etc.

## Educate Yourself About the Health Care System

You could miss valuable support opportunities if you haven't explored what the health care system offers.

## Investigate Community Support Services

In addition to the health care system, many valuable resources exist through the social support network and are available at a nominal cost. Some of these services include Meals-on-Wheels, foot care clinics, pharmacy home delivery service, and much more.

## Develop a Plan of Care for the Elder

Create a binder to use as a daily log where you can store everything in one central place. You can use this  information to share progress reports and other details with siblings who may be living at a distance. It is a baseline from which to measure changes in functional abilities. Include photographs with dates that also help to depict changes as measured over longer time periods. When the time comes to approach the Community

Care Access Centre or Single Entry Point to community services, this will be a valuable resource tool to help you obtain the additional support you need.

### Develop a Plan of Care for Yourself

You will need support and breaks periodically if you are to be the best that you can be. There is no hero award for running yourself into the ground by neglecting your own needs. Schedule routine breaks and source out in advance supports that allow you to get respite relief. It may be a combination of informal and formal back-up such as a combination of neighbours, other relatives and community services like adult day support centres.

## ASSISTING AN ELDERLY RELATIVE TO PLAN FOR THE FUTURE

In 1931, only 6% of Canadians were over age 65. By 2021, one quarter of the elder population will be over 80 years of age.[8] This longevity revolution means that most Canadians will be in a caregiver role at some time in their lives.

The following checklist may be a useful tool for anyone who may be likely to assume a future role as a caregiver. A few hours of organization today can save countless days of frustration down the road when information and documents may be required suddenly to deal with a medical issue. The subheadings can be arranged as separate files for information.

## CHECKLIST

**Family Records**

❏ Birth certificates, adoption papers and passports

❏ Marriage certificate, divorce/separation papers

❏ Citizenship, Landed Immigrant Status

❏ Social Insurance cards

❏ Driver's Licenses, car ownership

❏ Military records

**Health Records**

❏ Names, addresses, telephone numbers of physicians, dentists, optometrist, pharmacist, specialists

❏ List of major illnesses, surgeries, hospitals attended

❏ List of allergies

❏ List of current medication

❏ Health Card

---

[8] Mireille Marcil, Corporate Work/Life Services Web site (January 6, 2000).

**Financial Records**

❏ addresses, telephone numbers of bankers, investment planners, stock brokers, accountants, insurance advisors

❏ Name, address, telephone number of lawyer

❏ Wills

❏ Power of Attorney

❏ Advance medical directives, organ donor cards, etc.

❏ Pre-paid funeral, plot, etc.

❏ Trust agreements

**Miscellaneous Information**

❏ Location of safety deposit boxes

❏ Church affiliations

❏ Tax records

❏ Burial instructions

The caregiver should take time to talk with the individuals they are most likely to provide care for. They should be sure they know their attitudes and preferences concerning care, accommodation, and medical treatment. They should know where to find legal papers, professional advisors, a list of fixed expenses and obligations, their income sources and assets, and what insurance they have in place. They should have an open discussion regarding Power of Attorney and when it may be advisable to begin assuming simple tasks on their behalf such as the payment of regular expenses and investment decisions.

## THINGS TO CONSIDER IN DECIDING WHAT IS BEST

As caregiver and care recipient explore options, how does one decide what is best? Begin by considering, first of all, what is the kind of care that is needed and which options will best allow the senior to live with the most independence possible. Some people choose to use a combination of home and community support services to stay in their own home for as long as possible. Others choose to move to a place that offers specific care services and social supports that come with accommodations designated as catering to seniors living. Finding what is right will depend on each person's personal situation, but the following are some factors that should be considered.

## What Does The Person Value?

Each care option has advantages and disadvantages. What one person considers an advantage another might consider a disadvantage. Understanding the senior's personal preferences is a key part of the decision-making process.

## What Help Can I Provide to This Person?

For many people, there may be a broader network of family and friends to offer support. Depending on the circumstances, this may be all the support the senior needs in the beginning. On the other hand, you may be one of the many people acting as a distance caregiver providing care to an aging parent who lives in a different city, province or country. Or you may be employed full time and have a family of your own to also care for. These are important factors that must be taken into consideration.

## What Services are They Eligible For?

As some services require approval in order to be eligible for participation, this may narrow your options. There is no charge to have an assessment completed but the person being considered for eldercare must be in agreement.

## What Services Are Available in the Local Community?

There may be less selection in smaller communities, such as the availability of Supportive Housing initiatives with rent geared to income. Another aspect of availability is the length of waiting list. If there are long waiting times, the service or setting may be less of an option, depending on your urgency of need.

## What Can the Person Afford?

For most people, their financial situation is an important factor. There are a number of ways to make the costs more affordable. Cost sharing with other individuals may be an option. Government subsidies, personal insurance and retiree benefits are other possible options.

## How Urgent is the Need?

Timing also impacts what the options will be. When decisions do not have to be made for many months, there is more time to research and to plan ahead. When the need arises quickly with only a few weeks to prepare, options will be more limited. This underscores the importance of considering well in advance of need and researching availability of support in the elder's area. Have discussions with the elder to understand their preferences and then investigate to learn about what options exist.

# USING FORMAL CARE

The first point of contact in obtaining health care services is through a trained specialist such as a doctor, a nurse, a physiotherapist, or other health care professional. This point of entry is referred to as primary care and is the gateway to a host of other specialists that may be able to provide valuable formal health care assistance. Formal care is provided by trained and paid caregivers, some of which are *licensed specialists* while others are unlicensed workers with special training to work in senior care.

Licensed specialists must follow a code of conduct established by their governing body. Sanctions for misconduct include temporary or permanent license suspension. They may be required to provide therapy following a stroke, a fall, surgery, or simply to help improve ambulation. Unlicensed workers may be required to assist with activities of daily living or instrumental activities. As they do not require a license to perform their services, there is no governing body where one may register a complaint against the worker. As the need for care increases over time, the elder will require more hours of support and different types of care. Their needs will evolve from primarily needing informal support to needing significant formal support. Eventually it will cease to be cost effective to provide this care in the home and relocation to residential facilities will be necessary. This transition occurs simultaneous with the change from part-time support to the need for full-time support. Through this change, the informal caregiver becomes increasingly at risk for stress and burnout.

## Formal Caregivers

While there are many fields of formal caregiving, the following are the most likely specialists to be involved in eldercare.

### Audiologists

An audiologist works with people who have hearing, balance and ear problems. To test for the nature and extent of the problem they use various tools and instruments such as audiometers, computers, and other devices. They evaluate the person's ability to distinguish between sounds, the loudness at which they can hear sounds, and the degree to which their loss impacts daily life. Hearing aids may be prescribed, but in some instances other treatments may be required such as cleaning the ear canal or adjusting medications the senior takes which may be the source of their problem.

### Dietitians

A dietitian is a person who has a bachelor's degree specializing in food and nutrition. In Canada only a person who has achieved this level of education is entitled by law to be called a dietitian or registered dietitian. A person who calls himself or herself a nutritionist may not be a registered dietitian as this term is not regulated in all provinces. A physician may refer someone to a dietitian for assistance in developing a specialized menu required to address an underlying condition such as diabetes, high cholesterol, or if the person exhibits signs of malnutrition.

### Nurses

Registered Nurses (RN's) and Licensed Practical Nurses (LPN's) may provide home health care assistance. An RN may be involved in creating a plan of care for the senior, administering IV's, or supervising a team of LPN's. An LPN may change dressings, check blood pressure, and vital signs and report them to the Case Manager who may be an RN. Both professions are licensed disciplines.

### Occupational Therapists

Occupational therapy can help older adults to remain healthy and to live independently by teaching them skills associated with activities of daily living. It may be an injury or illness that first triggers the need, or a gradual reduction in quality of life. Therapy will help the senior to overcome barriers in their lives including physical, psycho-social, and environmental factors that may be impacting their functional abilities.

### Personal Support Workers

Personal Support Workers assist individuals with a variety of tasks including household management, family responsibilities, and personal care related to daily living. They study anatomy, physics and geriatrics amongst other things to learn proper techniques in providing care to seniors. Older adults may be at risk of fracture from thin bones. Seniors who are diabetics face increased risk when they receive skin wounds that do not heal because of their underlying condition. For these reasons the training given to personal support workers is important. In most provinces this is a non-licensed profession. Some provinces are reconsidering this issue as a means of ensuring adequate training for seniors' safety.

### Physical Therapists

This health care specialist is concerned with prevention, treatment and management of movement disorders that may be due to injury, surgery or disease such as arthritis. The goal is to lessen pain and improve mobility and functionality so the senior can continue to live independently with good quality of life.

### Respiratory Therapists

Breathing is something most of us take for granted. But some conditions can impact breathing such as asthma, chronic bronchitis and emphysema. Respiratory therapists may be consulted to help with these and other lung conditions. They are an essential part of the medical team and are leaders in the use of life support equipment. They are called in to help with conditions such as pneumonia, stroke, and heart failure.

### Social Workers

Social workers play a key role in prevention of medical needs, protection from potential health risks through early identification of warning signs, and planning assistance on obtaining community health and social support services. They can help seniors to find transportation to doctor's appointments, meal programs, and other essential services that improve their quality of living.

### Speech Therapists

A speech therapist or speech-language pathologist works with people who have difficulty speaking or swallowing. They may be brought in to help following a stroke, or for someone who has difficulty swallowing as may happen with Multiple Sclerosis, Alzheimer's or Parkinson's disease.

## WORKING WITH THE ELDER'S FAMILY PHYSICIAN

It is becoming increasingly difficult to get access to family physicians. In some cities there is a shortage. The Ontario Medical Association estimates that 1 million Ontario residents do not have a family physician and this number is increasing. When this happens the priority must shift to finding a new physician before an illness or emergency occurs. This is important because the family physician is the gateway to referrals for everything else. The best place to begin is by asking other relatives or friends for the name of their physician. Often, a physician who is not taking new patients from the general public, will accept a new client if they are referred by one of their existing clients, particularly if that person asks personally during their own visit. When this is not an option, and if the retiring physician has not arranged for a replacement or referral, then another alternative is to do a search through the College of Physicians & Surgeons website which may contain a search tool for locating a family physician in the community. In Ontario the best time to do this is when the new graduates come out of residence in July, as they may be setting up practice and open to new patients. However, it may be necessary to widen the search to a neighbouring community if no one locally is accepting new clients.

Some physicians offer evening hours and weekend hours such as Saturday mornings. This can be very helpful for a caregiver who works full-time and plans to help by accompanying the senior to their doctor's appointments. It may also come as a surprise to discover many physicians require an application to be completed with details of personal medical history after which they will decide whether to take on the person as a client. This is a method of balancing their workload by limiting the number of chronic care patients they take on.

### Getting the Best Results from Your Visit

Preparing in advance for the visit to the physician can help to ensure the best results are obtained. While it may seem impolite to pass on pleasantries and dive right into the issue, most physicians plan 10 minutes per appointment. This is how they are funded by provincial health plans. To get the most from the visit, the best communication is to tell the physician four things:

1. Where it hurts.

2. How long it has been hurting. (Date of first occurrence and subsequent occurrences. Whether the pain is daily, hourly, or intermittent.)

3. How intense the pain is. (Using a scale of 1 to 10 helps to communicate this.)

4. The nature of the pain. (Pulsating, sharp, etc.)

When there are several issues, begin with the most important first, and be prepared to book an additional appointment for secondary issues.

## FUNDING VALUABLE SERVICES

There are many different programs that offer financial assistance to help older adults with care-related expenses.

### Employee Benefit Plans

Some companies continue benefits to employees following their retirement. These retiree benefits often include provision for the cost of hearing aids, durable medical equipment, semi-private/private hospitalization, extended health care, adaptive devices, vision care, home care nursing, ambulance, prosthetic appliances, bandages and dressings, equipment rental such as wheelchairs, registered specialists such as physiotherapists, speech therapists, psychologists, social workers, massage therapist, plus more. Reimbursement is based on expenses not covered by government plans and up to the limits stipulated in the benefits contract. This can be a valuable source of dollars to help with the costs of care.

### Provincial Drug Programs

The provincial and territory governments each provide some form of assistance for the purchase of prescription drugs for seniors and other low-income groups. Residency requirements must be met and the drug being purchased must be one listed on the drug formulary. A small deductible is normally payable which may be related to the senior's annual income. Drugs not on the formulary may still be covered with special permission in some provinces.

## Financial Assistance for Home Adaptations

There are a number of programs to help older adults maintain a safe, comfortable and energy-efficient environment in the home. This can help them to remain longer living at home safely.

## Adaptations Home for Seniors' Independence Program (HASI)

This program helps homeowners and landlords pay for home adaptations. To be eligible, the senior's annual income must fall below a stipulated level. Other conditions must also be met. They must be over age 65 and having difficulty with activities of daily living due to aging and the dwelling must be a permanent residence. The financial assistance available is in the form of a forgivable loan of up to $3,500, and is for installing permanent handrails, grab bars, lever handles or easy-reach kitchen adjustments. The full loan is forgiven if the senior remains living there for six months or more following receipt of the loan.

## Residential Rehabilitation Assistance Program

The Canadian Mortgage and Housing Corporation (CMHC) offers an assistance program also as a forgivable loan based on income and home value. It deals with the need for extensive modifications such as installing wheel chair ramps, widening doors, electrical, plumbing and heating changes, or other structural changes.

## Emergency Repair Program

This program is also available through The Canadian Mortgage and Housing Corporation and is for low-income homeowners in rural areas so they can make emergency repairs to their homes. It covers repairs for the chimney, doors and windows, the electrical system, the foundation, the heating and ventilation systems, the plumbing, the roof, walls, floors and ceilings. Income criteria must be met and the house must be the primary residence.

## Financial Assistance for Veterans

Veterans Affairs Canada (VAC) offers many services and benefits to qualified veterans.

## Health Care Benefits

These benefits include medical, surgical and dental care, prosthetic devices, home adaptations, supplementary benefits such as travel costs for examinations or treatment and other community health care services and benefits.

## Drug Benefits

Disability pensioners are provided with treatment benefits such as prescription drugs directly related to their pensioned conditions.

## Veterans Independence Program Benefits

The Veterans Independence Program is a national home care program established in 1981 to help veterans remain living independently in the community. For those who qualify, they may receive any or all of the following services:

- **Grounds maintenance**, including grass cutting and snow removal;

- **Housekeeping**, including help with routine tasks such as doing the laundry, cleaning the home, or preparing meals;

- **Personal care services** to assist with personal needs such as bathing, dressing, and eating;

- **Access to nutrition services** such as Meals-on-Wheels and Wheels-to-Meals; and

- **Health and support services** provided by health professionals.

# ACCOMMODATION AND CARE ALTERNATIVES

There are a variety of services that can be provided over an extended period of time. Some services can be provided in the elder's home, or within the community. Other services involve care provided in a residential setting such as a long-term care centre, nursing home, retirement home or a supportive housing building. The elder's need for care will change over time. Change may be gradual, or sudden. Finding the right mix of home and community support can take time. Being well informed of options in advance of need can help.

The following are options a caregiver and elder can consider. The elder should be involved in the decision to the extent possible.

## Independent Living

The elder may remain in their own home or apartment, with the caregiver providing some guidance and assistance as necessary.

## Home Care

Care for the elder may be provided by either a paid or unpaid caregiver with whom they live. The caregiver is available to provide 24-hour assistance.

## Respite Care

Respite care offers relief for the caregiver so they can take a break from the demands, stresses and pressures of providing continuous care. Sources include adult day support centres and home care services as well as overnight stays in long-term care facilities that have beds set aside for this purpose. This may enable the elder to remain for a longer period of time under home care by providing periodic relief to the caregiver. It can also reduce the physical and emotional stress experienced by the caregiver.

## Hospice Care

Hospice care provides special services and therapies to individuals who are terminally ill so they can remain at home. It improves the quality of life by controlling the symptoms of the illness so the individual can maintain their dignity. Assistance includes medical and nursing care, social services, dietary consultation, and emotional support to both the elder and the caregiver.

## Adult Day Support Centres

This is a community-based group program that provides day support in a group setting. A structured comprehensive program is provided for the elder to participate in. This program offers a protective setting for elder care while the caregiver is at work. It is intended for elders who require minimal assistance, not extensive assistance. Some centres specialize in handling adults with dementia.

## Retirement Residences

The elder may live independently or semi-independently in a facility known as a retirement residence. There are two types of facilities: Independent Living, and Supportive or Assisted Living. Some residences may provide both types of accommodations within the same facility. Independent Living offers "apartment-like" suites with optional support available usually at an additional cost. Supportive or Assisted Living provides a greater level of support to those who need it. The support may be in the form of housekeeping, meal preparation, or medication dispensing. Both types of facilities are intended for elders who require light assistance only. While the facility may have nursing staff on a 24-hour basis, the level of nursing care provided is less than that offered in a long-term care facility.

## Long-Term Care Facility

This is a place where the elder lives and receives services such as nursing and personal assistance, and is intended for those who have a continuous need for professional care at some level. Most provinces operate on a similar basis. For instance, in Ontario, historically there has been three types of long-term care facilities: nursing homes, municipal homes for the aged, and charitable homes for the aged, each with separate legislation. However, the *Long-Term Care Homes Act, 2006* will bring these separate pieces of legislation together as one single piece of legislation to ensure uniform standards and accountability. The Bill of Rights for residents of Ontario nursing homes was originally enacted in 1987 and later adopted by municipal and charitable homes to ensure that long-term care facilities provide appropriate conditions that recognize these facilities as homes for the elders that reside within them. It deals with issues of rights of the elderly such as the rights to privacy, respect, information, refuse medication, leave, have medical records kept confidential, refuse the use of restraints, have visitors, speak freely, and form friendships and relationships with others.

Access to these facilities is government controlled, with priority being given to those in greatest need for medical care. The decision to use a long-term care facility may be based both upon medical need and financial ability.

## CAREGIVING ACROSS THE GENERATION GAP

Adult children eventually find themselves in the role of caregiver to aging parents and may be at a loss at times to understand why their parents are so reluctant to accept help being offered to them, or to ask for assistance when needed. To be a better communicator with parents, it helps to start by understanding who they were, who they are today, and who they will be in the near future.

### Who They Were

People born between 1909 and 1945 are often referred to as *The Mature Segment*. Historical events and social institutions around them have shaped their value systems. Some of the more significant historical influencers included the world wars and the Great Depression. How they think and behave today is largely related to these past experiences. Adults born in the Baby Boom generation see the world quite differently. Their conspicuous consumption patterns are evidence that they have never learned to distinguish between "need" versus "want"; preferring to pay more for sporting the "right brand". This is a generation better educated than their parents and they are more inclined to conduct their own research prior to making a purchasing decision. Questioning comes naturally to boomers, whereas their parents were taught respect for authority without question.

### Who They Are Today

This contrast in value systems prevents boomers at times from understanding why their parents are so reluctant to accept help from others — help with cutting the grass, or cleaning the home. Paying for services they can do for themselves is incongruent with Mature value systems (the Great Depression taught the lesson of not paying for services that they can do for themselves). It is also at work when they visit their physician. The doctor's advice is to be accepted without question. This translates into situations where they may not know what the medication they are taking has been prescribed for; or what various alternatives exist concerning treatment for diagnosed conditions. Today, many medications are prescribed for a totally different condition than they were originally developed to treat. This could lead to incorrect assumptions about what underlying condition a person has simply based on looking at their medication on hand. For instance, Gabapentin is primarily used to treat and prevent seizures in certain types of epilepsy. However, it may also be used to treat migraine headaches or to reduce extreme changes in moods for people with bipolar disorder or anxiety. This may lead to incorrect protocols during an emergency by incorrectly assuming the wrong underlying condition.

### Who They Will Be

The aging process brings with it several changes. The most notable of these are changes in cognition, sensory changes, and mobility. Chronological age is a less relevant measure than is cognitive (self-perceived) age and physiological age. Self-perceived age, the age one thinks of themselves as being, can be as much as 10 years younger, while physiological age (physical well-being) may be significantly older if one's health is not good. Edgar A. Guest sums this up quite succinctly in his poem *Old Age*:

> *I used to think that growing old was reckoned just in years,*
> *But who can name the very date when weariness appears?*
> *I find no stated time when man, obedient to a law,*
> *Must settle in an easy chair and from the world withdraw.*
> *Old Age is rather curious, or so it seems to me.*
> *I know old men at forty and young men at seventy-three.*
>
> *I'm done with counting life by years or temples turning gray.*
> *No man is old who wakes with joy to greet another day.*
> *What if the body cannot dance with youth's elastic spring?*
> *There's many a vibrant interest to which the mind can cling.*
> *'Tis in the spirit Age must dwell, or this would never be:*
> *I know old men at forty and young men at seventy-three.*

## ADULT CHILDREN AS CAREGIVERS TO PARENTS

There is a misconception that exists regarding the role adult children should assume in helping or caring for their parent. This has led to the erroneous term, "parenting" your parent. Caregivers should never try to be a "parent" to their parent; this lack of respect for their rightful role can lead to ineffective communications and patterns of behaviour that impact the older adult's sense of dignity, independence and the relationship between caregiver and adult. Verbal communications, particularly face to face, are at the centre of human social relationships. Your relationship will be more effective if you can create a safe and mutually respectful environment. Communication patterns in families are complex and old patterns may be difficult to break; but improved communication patterns will make it easier to deal with things in the future.

A Montreal-born psychoanalyst, Eric Berne, identified interpersonal relationships as being associated with three ego-states of the individuals involved: the Parent, the Adult, and the Child state. He referred to these interactions as "transactions". When the adult child adopts the parent-state, the transaction becomes hierarchical with the true parent being subordinated. How we initiate a transaction with a parent acts as a stimulus; and the response may be either favourable or unfavourable. The goal should be transactions that are adult to adult. This allows the parent to retain a feeling of control, dignity, and self-esteem and the outcome will be much more favourable for everyone concerned. Some clues that communications are coming from the parent state are phrases such as "you should", "don't forget", "how to", "under no circumstances" and "always". It is the ingrained voice of authority. Communicating from the parent state is likely to elicit a response from the receiver's child state. The child state responds with internal feelings. When a person's internal reaction is anger or despair, the inner child is in control. There should be no surprise when communications break down when communicating from the parent state. Accepting help is difficult for almost everyone, even when it is offered on an adult to adult basis. Our adult state is our ability to think and determine actions for ourselves based on data we receive. Providing assistance is possible even to someone who is quite dependent physically and mentally while still maintaining respect for him or her as an adult. Some clues that communications are coming from the adult state are reasoned statements and words such as "probably", "possibly", "I think", "I realize", "I see", "I believe", and "in my opinion".

Look for solutions that are congruent with the older adult's value system, communicate from an adult state, and ask their opinions, honour their wishes, and respect their right to make their own decisions.

# Chapter 7

# End-of-Life Issues

## PLANNING FOR END-OF-LIFE

People who have been caregivers to their parents during their final years comment how grateful they are when their parents have made advance directives, planned their estate, considered their final wishes, and provided adequate financial resources to support their end-of-life care issues. For the majority however, the final days come with too little advance preparation. Sometimes the problem lies with the caregiver who is not comfortable talking about these issues with the parents. Having faced good times and bad throughout their lives, parents are generally under no illusion they will live forever and would welcome the assistance and advice on such planning issues. Helping them put their affairs in order will help reduce stress during a time of grieving. It will also help parents to feel peace of mind and have some sense of closure.

## Where to Begin

Having the right information on hand will save caregivers a lot of stress down the road, so the best place to begin is by gathering the following information:

- Bank account details including names and locations of banks and pass book location

- Insurance policies — summary of coverage, insurers, location of policies

- Investment information — itemized list of holdings and location of documents

- Safety deposit box details — location of box and location of keys

- Pension and retirement benefits details

- Location of important documents including birth, marriage certificates, social insurance numbers, divorce decrees, wills

- Name of lawyer and executor

- Names and contact details of other professional advisors: financial consultant, accountant, benefits advisor

## ADVANCE CARE DIRECTIVES

Derek and his sister Samantha had been secondary caregivers to their father through his end-of-life journey recently. Now aware of the issues they would once again inevitably face with their mother, Derek and Samantha had a heart-felt discussion with their mom about what might happen should end-of-life be near for her. They began by asking her that should there come a time when she could no longer communicate, enjoy food or many of the simple daily pleasures such as listening to a radio or reading a newspaper, what would she like them to do. These were the things Derek and Samantha knew indicated quality of life to their mom. The answer they received was "don't do anything heroic — just let me go in peace". This gave them the information they needed and the confidence that they knew what their mother would want if end-of-life were near.

Knowing one's wishes when it comes time to make health care decisions on their behalf can seem like an overwhelming task. An Advance Care Directive or a Power of Attorney for Personal Care (sometimes called a "living will") can help by documenting one's personal wishes about medical options that could prolong life. Different provinces have slightly different names for a living will document but the intent is the same, namely to help fulfill the wishes of the ill person. The most important aspect of a living will is thinking ahead about what treatments are not wanted in the event of a health emergency. Telling the family to "just pull the plug" is not helpful!

## Medical Actions to Prolong Life

Medical staff may use medications, equipment, or medical actions to continue life when the person is near the end of life. Such procedures become a "heroic measure" when introduced near the end of life. The following can all be considered a heroic measure when cure is no longer a possibility: a feeding tube that provides nutrition, antibiotics that fight infection, a kidney machine that filters blood, a respirator to assist with breathing or cardiopulmonary resuscitation to keep the lungs and heart working.

## Giving a DNR Directive

A Do Not Resuscitate or DNR directive tells medical staff that the patient does not want to be resuscitated if the heart or lungs stop working. if this instruction is not given ahead of time, medical staff must by law perform CPR.

## Substitute Decision Maker, Proxy and Power of Attorney for Personal Care

Sometimes adult children have a clear idea about what their parents may want in terms of medical intervention while at other times they may be just guessing. When parents have given clear directives in advance, feelings of tension and guilt can be considerably reduced, or even avoided altogether. It is wise to appoint a substitute decision maker or proxy to make medical decisions when you cannot do so yourself. This may be a spouse, an adult child, or another trusted family member. It is ideal to have one's wishes written down, but equally important is to have a conversation about these issues so the proxy will understand what is wanted. The proxy's role is to make decisions that are consistent with the ill person's wishes, and not what the proxy would personally want in these circumstances.

## Creating a Living Will

### Medical Advice

One's family physician is an ideal person from whom to seek advice about medical methods that might be used at a critical time. The doctor can discuss pros and cons of CPR and other interventions. The person will have a clearer idea of what might fit in with their beliefs and values about death and dying. When one cannot speak for oneself, the living will or advance directive is the document the proxy will use for guidance and authority when making health decisions for another. Consequently the proxy should have a copy of it, and a good understanding of how the person thinks of such issues.

**Legal Advice**

Having a discussion with the proxy is an excellent place to begin communicating one's wishes regarding heroic measures. Ideally these need to be documented in an Advance Care Directive or a Power of Attorney for Personal Care. Engaging a lawyer who specializes in this area best protects them. While it is possible in many provinces to secure templates for self-completion, the value of going through a lawyer goes beyond having someone prepare the forms; the legal advice surrounding end-of-life issues is just as important. The provincial law society can recommend a lawyer and if need be, provincial legal aid is available for financial assistance. Laws vary from province to province, therefore if the person plans to travel outside their home province, it is important to consider the validity of such documents in the province or country they plan to spend time in.

**Estate Planning**

"Leaving a legacy", "legacy planning", and "estate planning" are all terms being used more often today. Many older adults have been through war and depression. They place great value in what they have been able to save, their home and special mementos. Leaving something behind that would help their adult children have a "good life" or their grandchildren to obtain higher education is often of great importance to seniors of modest income levels, not just amongst the wealthy. In practical terms estate planning is about building, preserving, and transferring wealth and property. Most importantly estate planning is about creating lasting bonds within families.

Proper planning can help ensure that the needs of heirs are met and that funding mechanisms such as life insurance are considered and implemented where possible. It involves professional advice on tax planning strategies that can minimize taxation. It also involves drawing up important legal directives such as a last will and testament, durable power of attorney for property, and a power of attorney for personal care ("living will"). These directives can play a big part in helping older adults to ensure their wishes are carried out, even if their health fails. Children who will one day be caregivers to their aging parents should ask them which of these steps they have taken in these important areas of planning. Dying intestate will mean assets are not likely to be distributed according to one's wishes and the outcome may be a higher tax bill and less money left over for the family. Some seniors may have taken steps many years ago but have never reviewed their documents since that time with a lawyer to consider the impact of changes in laws in the meantime. Or perhaps they have moved to be closer to their adult children and original documents were drawn up in a different province, and validity could be an issue.

**Executor**

Provinces vary as to the formal title given to the person who performs the role of executor. Regardless, the fundamentals are the same — namely, this individual is in a position of great trust and needs to be selected carefully. Choosing more than one person to be executor such as "all the children" can lead to dissension in the family and is often not the best alternative. The role of the executor is to maintain and protect the estate before distributing the assets to the beneficiaries. Responsibilities could include ensuring valuables are safely stored, key assets such as a house are insured and maintained, and that investments continue to earn income and are not at risk.

### Continuing Power of Attorney for Property

A serious physical or mental illness could leave a person in need of another to take on tasks such as paying bills and making larger decisions about such things as investments and taxes. If no one has been appointed then the court will do so. Consequently, another essential issue of end-of-life planning is to have a continuing power of attorney for personal property prepared, which will allow a named family member or trusted friend to manage affairs if unable to personally do so. Expert legal advice is important and can bring peace of mind.

### Storing Documents

Documents need to be accessible and not locked in a safety deposit box which could render them inaccessible. Relevant documents should be provided to the executor, the power of attorney for personal care, the power of attorney for property and the financial manager if one has been employed.

### Summing Up

End-of-Life planning is really about allowing a person to be remembered the way he or she wants to be remembered. Creating the various legal documents and other recommended steps are merely tools that ensure a person's wishes are indeed carried out!

# HOSPICE AND PALLIATIVE CARE

People are living longer and expectations about quality of life throughout the full life span are also changing. Modern medicine and other improvements have successfully pushed out life expectancy but unfortunately death itself is not preventable and most people eventually die as a result of chronic disease. Studies have shown that many people dying with cancer and other chronic disease suffer unrelieved symptoms in their final days perhaps as high as 50%. There is a growing recognition that end-of-life care is an important societal health issue. While death itself is not preventable, much of the suffering that accompanies terminal illness for the person as well as their loved ones who support them through their final journey can be addressed more effectively with improved access to hospice care by a greater number of terminally ill people. Some people may simply not be aware of their options, others may have different beliefs regarding end of life, but for many it is often a case of lack of access to hospice and palliative care that is the issue.

Quality of life remains important even when illness cure is no longer possible. The dying need help to derive joy and minimize pain each and every day.

## What is Hospice and Palliative Care?

Hospice, in the earliest days, was a concept rooted in the centuries-old idea of offering a place of shelter and rest, or "hospitality" to weary and sick travelers on a long journey. Today, hospice care provides humane and compassionate care for people in the last phases of incurable disease so they may live as fully and comfortably as possible.

Hospice is not a place, but a concept of care. It is about caring when curing is not possible. Hospice is about the quality of life during the last stages of life. Death is recognized as the final stage of life and hospice care seeks to enable patients to continue an alert, pain-free life and to manage other symptoms so their last days may be spent with dignity and quality, surrounded by their loved ones. It does not attempt to hasten or to postpone death, and treatment is focused on the person rather than the disease. It provides family-centred care involving the patient and the family in making decisions. Care is provided 24 hours a day, seven days a week, generally for people whose life expectancy is less than six months.

Hospice and palliative care both focus on "palliation", that is, comfort. For this reason, hospice care is often referred to as palliative care, though some people sometimes use the term palliative care to distinguish care received in a hospital setting. Others say the difference is that palliative care is care that still aims to cure or slow down progression of a terminal illness, while hospice care is elected by the patient who is no longer pursuing a cure for a terminal illness, but to spend their final days managing their symptoms and in the presence of their family. Generally in Canada, the two terms are used to refer to the same thing.

## Providing Care

An interdisciplinary team of professionals and volunteers including doctors, nurses, therapists, clergy, homemakers and other counselors and caregivers usually provides care. There are some individuals who prefer to be in hospital for their final days while others will prefer to die at home. Regardless, the goal of the team is to ensure emotional, spiritual, physical and practical needs of both the person and their family are met. A palliative care or hospice program may provide some or all of the following: emotional support, collaboration and coordination with other agencies, personal care, respite care, spiritual support, financial and legal planning, family support and bereavement support. Medical staff such as registered nurses may be provided for a finite number of hours and are arranged through Community Care Access Centres and Regional Health Authorities.

These centres provide a single point of access to health and personal support services. There are also some palliative and hospice care providers that are charitable, not-for-profit groups that may provide volunteer services at no cost to the person.

## Making the Most of the Last Days

Whether we lose a loved one suddenly or through a long illness there are always losses and pain. While time never heals the pain completely, it does help. Time can be a gift in other ways as well. Knowing in advance that a loved one is dying can allow an individual to make the most of the time left. Now is the time for seeking answers to questions unasked, and communicating thoughts previously left unspoken — forgiveness, love, and other messages that will make the grief and loss easier to bear.

When there is less time ahead of us than behind us it is natural to reminisce. Recalling and sharing these memories of special family events can bring moments of joy. Inviting tips and wisdom about their areas of expertise like gardening can be part of the legacy they leave you! Adding special things to enhance the surroundings such as favourite artwork, family photos or drawings prepared by grandchildren can bring warm feelings and comfort. Just being present, offering hugs, a smile or laugh can be enriching.

## PERSONAL ADJUSTMENT UPON LOSING A LOVED ONE

Losing a loved one such as a parent brings profound hurt. No one has known us longer than our parent and they hold memories of us from a time before we can remember ourselves. According to authors Lewis, Armini and Lannon in their book "A General Theory of Love"[1], an infant remembers his mother's voice and face within thirty-six hours of birth and begins laying down autobiographical memories at around the age of two. Is it any wonder that the parent-child connection is so strong and the loss of a parent is so significant no matter what our age?

While as individuals we manage adjustment to loss differently, there is a common pattern to the grieving process that indicates where we are and points the way to healing. It was Dr. Elizabeth Kubler Ross that first identified the process of loss and grief.

The following is an example of "healthy grieving":

Mary's mother developed terminal Non-Hodgkin's Lymphoma. She just couldn't believe it! At first she did not want to believe it was true, and she avoided any discussion about it. After her mother passed away, she wondered whether there was something else she could have done that would have made a difference to change the outcome. She had left the hospital one afternoon for a much-needed break and it was during that time her mother

---

[1] Lewis, Thomas; Armini, Fari; and Richard Lannon. 2000, *A General Theory of Love*, New York: Vintage Books.

passed on. She couldn't help but think if she had only stayed, this would not have happened. After a while of living with the loss she began to accept that this experience was real and her mother was not coming back. The word that best describes this feeling is *bereft*. Mary could not eat or sleep and despite the fact there were people all around her, she felt so alone. Being left behind can lead to feelings of anger and a belief the world is unjust. Given time and allowing ourselves to feel the feelings of loss, we begin to accept and live with the loss. As much as we wish not to have to live with this "hole in our heart" we do begin to heal and move on in our life.

Given that we are individuals, our grieving process is also unique. Some people pass through stages such as the *anger stage* quickly while others linger or revisit it. Picture this process not as a straight line from denial to acceptance but rather a spiral of up and down. We may occasionally feel we take one step forward and two steps back. The problem arises when we get "stuck" in one stage or another of the grieving process. There can be circumstances that interfere with healthy grieving. After the loss we may have new and increased responsibilities that we begin to focus on and put our feelings of loss "on hold". If we are worried about a surviving parent after one has passed away for example, all our attention and energy may be directed to this parent with no room to express our own pain and loss. It may happen that the next loss triggers all the unprocessed grief from past losses. The depths of our feelings may surprise us. We may also unconsciously think that a measure of our love is reflected in the depth of our pain. Unresolved and ongoing grief can disable us and prevent us from moving on. Unprocessed grief may manifest itself in other symptoms such as chest pain or anxiety disorders.

Self-care is very important when you have suffered a loss and it is important to allow yourself to acknowledge your feelings, and to seek professional help if you find yourself unable to pass through the grieving stages because it will not otherwise simply "go away".

Also remember that no one, even our parents are perfect. In the early days of loss it may be easy to focus on what more we might have done or their shortcomings during our lives. After a while the good memories of our parents begin to resurface and you will find joy in recalling memories of funny stories and celebrations. This is part of the legacy they have left with us.

# Chapter 8

# Provincial Programs — The Continuing Care System

## THE CONTINUING CARE SYSTEM

Care follows a continuum of needs that change over time from light assistance through to 24-hour nursing care. It is comprised of a combination of health care services and social services. Some services may be provided through a plan of home care delivered in the person's home or in a seniors' retirement residence. When there is a need for 24-hour nursing care, then services are provided in a long-term care facility, also known as a nursing home.

The provinces are responsible for design and delivery of home care programs through their respective ministries of health. Some provinces combine health services and social services (also known in some provinces as community services) through one ministry, thereby allowing for better integration of services. All provinces have basic requirements that must be met to qualify for services. For instance, the intended recipient must be covered by the provincial government health insurance plan, they must have resided in the province for a specified minimum time, they must agree to a needs assessment, the home environment must meet certain safety requirements, and the intended recipient must be willing to accept the services.

A single entry point to services is in place in all provinces thereby enhancing ease of access and co-ordination. Names for the single entry point vary; some of them are Regional Health Authority, District Health Authority, Community Care Access Centre, or Single Entry Access (SEA). Regardless of name, services are coordinated for needs assessment, case management, and access to nursing homes and respite stay, through one central contact. The most comprehensive single entry access is in place in British Columbia, Alberta, Saskatchewan, and Manitoba. These provinces provide coordination of additional services including adult day support centres, Meals-on-Wheels programs, and supportive living retirement homes. Assessment tools and information management systems are standardized for home care. Only British Columbia has implemented one central data bank to manage both home care and institutional care using the same functional classification system. All provinces provide some level of home nursing care at no charge, but home support services may require fees in some provinces.

Most provinces moved to regionalization almost a decade ago, for service planning and delivery, to bring the control of programs closer to the area where services are delivered. Ontario was first to move away from this model. They introduced Local Health Integration Networks designed to eliminate funding "smoke stacks" across the health care delivery system and to achieve better integration in service funding and delivery. In May 2008, Alberta Health and Wellness announced that it was moving to one provincial governance board called the Alberta Health Services Board from the previous nine. The purpose of the change was to ensure the system is patient-focused and provides equitable access to all residents of Alberta. The new board will report to the Minister of Health and Wellness. New Brunswick has unveiled its health plan for 2008–2012, which provides for revamping its former system of eight Regional Health Authorities (RHAs) into two by September 2008. The old system was believed to hinder the development of an integrated and uniform health care system for the province. A Board of Directors comprised of members selected on the basis of required skills and competencies will govern the two new RHAs. The new RHA boards will report to the Minister of Health and the chief executive officers will report directly to the RHA chairs.

Provinces differ in their approach to home support services, which consist of personal care and homemaking. Fees are assessed in some provinces based on income and asset testing with priority given to low-income clients, others charge a flat rate per hour after applying any personal medical insurance the individual has that covers the required service. The range of services covered also varies from one province to another.

In Saskatchewan, home care workers providing the covered services are public employees, whereas in Ontario there is a combination of private and public employees as for-profit enterprises are encouraged to bid on contracts for service delivery. This approach is intended to create cost efficiency through a competitive bidding process.

Perhaps the greatest difference from one province to another is the per capita funding for home care, which ranges from a low of $24 to a high of $124 per capita. This is no doubt a key driver behind differences in copayments, access to services, and breadth of services.

These programs play a major role in the health care delivery system. Fewer people are being admitted to hospitals and more people are receiving care at home. The average stay in a hospital has reduced. More surgeries are being performed on a day-surgery basis. Better techniques such as the ability to use lasers in surgery, cuts down recover times because smaller incisions heal faster and this means less time spent in the hospital. Care is being pushed out into the community with the support of home care and community assistance. As Canada's population continues to age, the Continuing Care System will play an increasingly vital role in delivering health care services to the elderly population with even more emphasis being placed on programs that support the aging at home.

## WHAT IS CONTINUING CARE?

Continuing Care is a system of service delivery. It provides people who have chronic conditions with access to services that enable them to maintain their independence, or to prevent further deterioration, and to have quality living. It is comprised of a wide range of services such as therapeutic services, personal care services, and a broad array of other services. It is multi-disciplined and combines both health services such as registered nursing care and physiotherapy as well as social services such as Meals-on-Wheels and housekeeping services. They may be provided over a short period or a long term. They may be delivered in the community such as in one's own home or a supportive living residence, or in a long-term care facility.

## THREE STREAMS

The three streams where services may be delivered are:

### Home Living

The preferred choice by all is to maintain the recipient's independence in their own home by providing supports that enable them to do so. This option is most appropriate for individuals whose needs are minimal or temporary. Home care services may be provided by the local health authority (single entry point) or purchased privately through a home care service provider.

### Supportive Living

At some point, the recipient's need for assistance with instrumental activities of daily living (grocery shopping, meal preparation, laundry, home maintenance, and so on) may be greater than can be provided to them. At this point, they may move to a group residence with supportive living. Supportive living is both a philosophy and an approach for providing services. Services are provided in a residential setting where people continue to enjoy independence while receiving support services. The numbers of residents vary depending on the setting but may range from five or six people in a personal care home to 250 or more residents in a supportive housing or assisted living retirement home. Group homes may be just that — homes in residential neighbourhoods housing five or six people. Retirement homes with supportive or assisted living are apartment-like towers consisting of small two-room suites or single bedrooms with community meals and activities in the building. Some provinces have integrated supportive living residences into their single entry point system while others refer intended recipients to public providers.

More provinces are recognizing there is a gap in the care continuum between home care and long-term care. For instance, in some regions of Ontario, increasing emphasis is being placed on Supportive Housing, or what is now referred to as Supports for Daily Living. In this setting, seniors can receive 24-hour practical assistance with the essential activities of daily living. This program is designed to be delivered in a setting where groups of seniors reside in a designated building or a designated neighbourhood. The level of care provided is appropriate for someone who does not require 24-hour medical assistance or supervision, but who is able to maintain independence with the 24-hour practical supports provided. An assessment determines their eligibility.

## Facility Living

Long-term care facilities, homes for the aged, or nursing homes provide 24-hour nursing service with the supervision of a medical doctor. Other personal services usually include on-site physiotherapy, occupational therapy, bathing, hair dressing, and laundry service. Life enrichment programs include religious services (usually non-denominational or rotational), games, entertainment, and exercise. These facilities are restricted to residents with a chronic condition who cannot manage with a lower level of care and need the availability of 24-hour nursing service. The need may be temporary such as following surgery, or long-term. It serves to maintain a standard of living and to prevent further deterioration and is therefore sometimes referred to as Maintenance Care or Chronic Care. This is different from Acute Care, which is delivered in a hospital setting.

## Determining the Appropriate Stream

In determining which stream is the right level of care for the intended recipient, the evaluation process looks at whether the necessary level of support required can be provided through scheduled activities, where appointments can be set, such as assistance with bathing. Some services may be required on demand and only provided in an environment that offers 24-hour nursing care such as assistance with eating, bathing, toileting, transferring (getting in and out of bed), and dressing. These activities are referred to as activities of daily living (ADLs). Studies show the loss of ability to perform these skills tends to occur in the reverse order to which people learned them as infants due to the mental complexity associated with performing the task. A sixth ADL, which is incontinence (the ability to maintain bladder control), is sometimes measured. The loss of this latter ability tends to occur in no particular order but generally is accompanied by the loss of one of the primary five ADLs. The assistance required might be either skilled nursing assistance or personal care assistance. Skilled nursing assistance is provided by a registered nurse (RN) or a Licensed Practical Nurse (LPN), while personal care assistance is often provided by a Personal Care Worker, also known as a Support Worker.

# THE CARE CONTINUUM

Throughout the years, there may be intermittent periods requiring hospitalization or visits to the Emergency Department. The treatment in a hospital setting deals with the need for Acute Care. This type of care is short-term in nature and deals with a specific symptom with the goal of relief or cure. This may be followed by a plan of home care. When the recipients need for care increases, the next step is often Supportive Living, then eventually Long-term Facility Care. Sometimes the need for support is short-term for the purpose of providing relief to an informal caregiver. This is referred to as Respite Care. Long-term care facilities allocate a certain number of beds for the purpose of short-term stays as respite relief. The single entry point assigns these beds and limits the use of these services to an annual maximum normally in the range of two or three weeks per year. Eventually, when end-of-life is near, Palliative Care may be necessary. The need for support again changes and now the focus is on providing comfort and support to the person and the family. Palliative care neither hastens nor delays death; the goal is to ease pain and other symptoms and to support the person and the family through the journey. It is also known as Hospice Care.

The system always looks for the least intrusive and most cost-effective method of support for the intended recipient. When improvement in quality of life is not possible, the objectives are to maintain or prevent further deterioration. When that is not possible, then the aim is to provide comfort and relief from pain.

## FACTORS THAT INFLUENCE CARE OPTIONS

When evaluating care options, the intended recipient should be involved in the decision process. A social worker or community care worker will assist in the process of discussing care options with the elder and the family. Some of the factors that influence the decision regarding the best care option are:

- Are they unable to live alone due to either a medical or physical limitation?

- Is there no informal caregiver available to help?

- Do they require assistance in taking medication that cannot be provided on a home care basis?

- Is the need for assistance only available on demand and cannot be met on a scheduled basis?

- Do they need 24-hour care and supervision? Is it nursing care or personal support care?

- Are they chronically ill but not enough to need to be hospitalized?

- Do they need help with one or more ADLs?

If the answers to these questions are no, then the elder may benefit from a program of home care with supports from community-based services. This enables the person to live at home but to receive assistance on a daily basis with light housekeeping, meal preparation, yard work, and limited assistance with medication such as preparation of dosette boxes. If the answer to one or more of these questions is yes, then the care recipient may need to move to a residence or facility with 24-hour assistance.

# OBTAINING SUPPORT

## Single Entry Point

Centralized access to the care continuum enables prioritization on a "most needed" basis. It also ensures that the most economical means of providing health care assistance is employed. Navigating the health care system can be a challenge and single entry point systems make it easier to locate and arrange valuable services. The need may be triggered following hospitalization, and upon release. Discharge planning in hospitals has changed as provinces try to balance their health care budgets. In some provinces, the need for home care services is determined during discharge planning. Conversely, Ontario for instance, removed Community Care Access staff from hospitals as part of a cost reduction measure. The revised strategy called for the Discharge Planner to contact the Community Care Access Centre (CCAC) upon release of a patient in need of home care. The CCAC office would then be responsible for calling the intended recipient to arrange for an in-home assessment following hospital release. Gaps of time occurred leaving newly released patients at risk and the result was increased relapses, calls to 911 for emergency responders, and more visits to Emergency Departments. The Ontario Government has since reallocated dollars to rectify this problem.

## Roles and Responsibilities of Single Entry Point

Each province may have slightly different roles and responsibilities assigned to their single entry point, just as they have slightly different names (Regional Health Authority, District Health Authority, Community Care Access Centre, Single Entry Access — to name a few). Below are the most common functions performed:

- Accepting referrals and determining eligibility for covered services

- Developing a plan of care which takes into account the needs of the intended recipient, their family, and available resources in the community

- Determining the amount and type of services for in-home care

- Securing, scheduling, and supervising the resources utilized in care delivery

- Developing and maintaining a pool of service providers, including negotiating contracts with intended vendors as service providers

- Establishing quality assurance processes such as documentation of policies and procedures

- Monitoring ongoing effectiveness of the care plan and conducting periodic reassessments

- Managing the waiting list, placement process, and assignment to long-term care facilities

- Approving subsidies for individuals based upon needs and financial assessment

## CASE MANAGERS

During the initial contact, there is a screening process that is used to determine whether an assessment should take place. A case manager or coordinator is then assigned and an initial visit is scheduled. In some provinces the initial assessment is conducted jointly by both a social worker and a health care professional. It is the social worker that ultimately assumes the role of case coordinator. There is no charge for this assessment. However, to be eligible for access to provincial programs, the individual must have a valid provincial health card and meet certain residency requirements.

If it is determined during the initial visit that the intended recipient is either not eligible for care or does not wish to receive the recommended care, referrals are made to other organizations that may be helpful such as support groups, or literature may be provided. A person who has not been approved may appeal a decision by going to their provincial health services Board.

The assessment usually takes place in the intended recipient's place of residence. This provides valuable first-hand information to the case manager regarding supports in the environment and how well the individual is coping in their environment. The assessment determines the elder's needs, identifies what support is available from family and the community, and decides what personal services could be provided on an in-home basis. Based on the assessment, a Classification Panel or Review Board classifies the individual according to the level of care required and places the individual into the most appropriate stream of care. A panel review of all admissions ensures fairness and uniformity in assessment and that the decision has not been made solely on the basis of one person's viewpoint. Use of assessment tools ensures objective rather than subjective decision-making.

The case manager develops a plan of care by working with the family and negotiates with other agencies to put the plan of care into action. The efficacy of the treatment plan is monitored on an ongoing basis and adjusted as the recipient's condition changes.

## ASSESSMENT TOOLS

Specific assessment tools are used to make evidence-based clinical practice and policy decisions. The standard tools used in most provinces are interRAI, and consist of a family of assessment tools designed for specific populations (home care versus long-term care). Only some provinces use standardized assessment across care options. Using standardized assessment tools across populations enables a common language and methodology for assessment. Case managers in different care settings can then use the results to provide continuity in care for the recipient. Someone with a chronic condition will depend on a variety of clinical and support services over time, which will occur across multiple care settings. For instance, a patient may transfer from hospital to home care, then to supportive living, and eventually to a long-term care centre. Using standardized assessment tools that share a common language enables case managers to develop a plan of care that follows through the care continuum to ensure the right care is being provided at the right time in the right setting. Meaningful dialogue can be held about the recipient's needs and abilities such as whether the level of care is sufficient, or if there is a need for a higher level of care that requires progression to the next service supports. Different specific assessments are used based on the care option. Assessments are specific for initial screening, home care assessment, supportive living, long-term care assessment, palliative care, acute care, and post-acute care. Using standardized testing across the provinces can allow for meaningful comparisons by policymakers, which are helpful in developing policy. To date, this is only occurring in the area of home care.

Assessments identify "triggers", or signs that indicate a person may be at risk for a specific problem. For instance, an elder who may be at risk for falls, will be assessed for an unsteady gait, dizziness, or a history of falls. The assessment generates a score which determines whether the person is at high risk, or minimal and therefore, not eligible for services.

## MAKING A REFERRAL

While normally the family physician will be involved in making a referral, anyone can make a referral by calling the intake line. However, the intended recipient must be in agreement with the referral and consent to the in-home assessment. Otherwise, if an elder is in need of assistance and does not consent, and there is concern for their safety, the area responsible in most provinces is the Adult Protection Services. Seniors have the right to live at risk, but a person who is mentally not capable of discerning risk may need intervention assistance.

## APPROVING ACCESS TO LONG-TERM CARE FACILITIES

### Waiting List Assignments

One of the objectives of the Single Entry Point is to maintain the waiting lists and determine prioritization of candidates awaiting access. An individual may indicate their preference for a facility; however, if they have been designated as "priority-1" and refuse the first bed that becomes available, they will no longer be considered a priority case. An elder who accepts this first assignment, may at their discretion, continue to be "wait listed" for the facility of their choice and transfer when their name rises to the top.

Assignment of beds is done within a region and not across regions unless the elder and their family authorize this. For instance, a resident of Peel Region in Ontario would be required to accept the first available bed in Brampton or Mississauga, but not a bed in Oakville, Toronto or Kitchener as this would be outside their region. Should they wish, however, they may add other regions that they consider acceptable to their list. This could result in receiving a bed sooner.

Once an individual becomes a resident in a long-term care centre, they are assessed once per year by assessors who are external to the facility.

In order for the individual's name to be placed on the waiting list for admission to a long-term care facility, the individual or their representative who holds a Power of Attorney must sign a consent form.

## Sample Consent Form

### Consent for Placement Service

*I hereby apply for eligibility determination and admission to a long-term care facility and request that (name of community centre) collect all personal and medical information necessary to determine eligibility for admission. I authorize release of this information to the long-term care facilities of my choice. I acknowledge that I have been informed of the reasons why this information is needed and I understand them. I understand this information will also be shared with referring agents and the chosen facilities. In the event I choose admission to facilities outside my region's area, I consent to release of this information to the placement service for those facilities that I have selected. This authorization is valid for a period of one year but may be withdrawn by me at any time by written notification to you.*

## Facilities Selection Form

The family is provided with a listing of the facilities to indicate their preferences. If they wish to wait until the elder's name comes to the top of the list, they may do so. This list contains names of all facilities that receive government subsidization including both privately-owned and municipal-owned facilities. It does not include names of facilities that are privately-run and that do not receive government assistance. An individual who refuses a bed in the long-term care facility of their choice, may have their name removed from the waiting list.

## Power of Attorney

When a family member is acting for the elder, they must provide a copy of a Power of Attorney to show that they are authorized to transact for the elder. However, the intended care recipient should always be included in the decision to move to a long-term care facility.

## AWAITING PLACEMENT WHILE IN HOSPITAL

Most provinces have a No Preference admission policy also known as the First Available Bed policy. It deals with the critical need for acute care beds in hospitals. A person who is hospitalized and awaiting placement in a long-term care facility must take the first available bed regardless of whether it is in the facility of their choice or not. They can remain wait-listed for a later transfer, but if they refuse the first location to become available then they will be charged $200 per day for the cost of the hospital room and board for each day they occupy it following medical discharge. However, if the person accepts the first available bed within a designated distance and is only waiting for the completion of their papers, the rate will be dropped to $50 per day from the day they are medically discharged but continue to occupy the hospital bed while awaiting placement. The designated distance is usually about 100 kilometres from one's residential community. The hospital charges begin once the physician has advised the person their condition no longer requires hospitalization. The $50 per day charge is in the range of the daily room charge in a nursing home.

A person who does not accept the first available bed will also have their name removed from the waiting list as they will be considered not available for placement. If they do accept it, they can continue to remain wait-listed for the long-term care facility of their choice. Consequently, it is advisable to accept the first available bed and transfer later.

## COMPLEX CONTINUING CARE

In 2007, Ontario introduced Complex Continuing Care (CCC) in hospitals. This refers to treatment for chronic care received in a hospital setting. The nature of chronic care is long-term and requires skilled, technology-based care not available at home or in a long-term care centre. There is a co-payment associated with this treatment similar to the cost of the daily basic rate for a bed in a long-term care centre (roughly $50). While the charge is somewhat controversial, the money received is used to support the services provided. Low-income families may be eligible for a lower co-payment or for the co-payment to be waived.

## FINDING NEW APPROACHES

Balancing the health care resources continues to be a challenge facing provincial governments. In their attempt to balance hospital budgets, many have closed beds and downloaded the responsibility for chronic care to home care and long-term care facilities. This has brought about its own set of challenges and task force teams are trying out-of-the-box thinking to create new approaches such as the following:

## Wait at Home Program

The Wait at Home Program was a pilot project created in January 2008 in one region of Ontario for the purpose of alleviating pressures on hospitals where patients in acute care beds and in Emergency Departments await placement in long-term care beds after they cease to need acute care. The goal is to place these individuals in the most appropriate care setting to meet their needs while they wait for availability of a long-term care bed. The program utilizes an enhanced package of in-home and community support services to support the individual. It is intended to bridge a 30-day period.

## Short-Stay Restorative Program

The Short-Stay Restorative Program is another example of a pilot project dealing with the issue of seniors' care. This program is aimed at early identification of patients at high risk for long-term care placement with the goal of helping individuals to avert the need through early intervention care and alternate supports.

## Pre-Habilitation Programs

Surgery candidates that may have higher risk during recovery due to their pre-surgery health status may have their surgery postponed until completion of certain programs in advance of surgery that will improve their condition going into it. These programs may focus on weight reduction, lowering blood pressure, or stabilizing other conditions that place them at higher risk.

# Chapter 9

# Housing Options: Remaining At Home

Over the next 15 years, close to six million Canadians over age 65 will be living alone. Roughly 20% of these seniors will have some limitations and require assistance at least part-time. Many community services and for-profit businesses are surfacing to help seniors who need elder care. Home care is the fastest growing segment of health care due in large part to public spending. A number of developments have pushed this industry forward such as advancements in technology, less intrusive surgical techniques, new drugs, and changing attitudes towards institutionalization. But the greatest driver behind increasing public expenditure has been cost containment by governments. Some seniors may have adult children assisting as informal caregivers, but for most, the reality will be their children are employed full-time, raising families of their own, often at a distance.

This chapter will explore why seniors want to remain home and how they can by addressing their needs for safety and health care and the use of community services.

## HOME SWEET HOME

Seniors have unique needs in housing related to changes that occur with age. Some of these changes may be a normal part of healthy aging, while others may be related to unhealthy aging. Chronic conditions and physical limitations can impact their safety in the home and their need for assistance. The design of older homes may not support aging at home. For instance, consider how popular split-level architecture was in home design in the 1960s. The arthritic senior will find the numerous levels of stairs to be a barrier to aging-in-place. Their housing must take into consideration their need for safety, health care, physical activity, and social interaction. These needs will change with time.

Most seniors still prefer to remain at home for as long as possible. It offers familiarity, comfort, a feeling of peace, and fond memories. Often, it is the connection to years gone by of birthday celebrations, anniversaries, the centre of family traditions, and the last connection to a spouse who has passed away. Moving can mean a series of losses — the loss of independence, of privacy, and the need to live by someone else's routine. There is a stigma attached to moving to the "old folks home", and a loss of self-identity. Women may feel they have lost their role as the family matriarch, and men also feel a loss of self-worth once they are no longer viewed as the breadwinner.

A study was undertaken in the late 1990s by the construction industry to learn about the reasons why seniors move and what they wanted in housing. They discovered the reasons why seniors move could be grouped by age:

**Ages 55 to 64 — "pre-seniors"** were empty-nesters. Having satisfied their desire to have the large home during their child-rearing years, they were downsizing to smaller bungalows, not quite ready yet to give up home ownership.

**Ages 65 to 80** — "middle-aged seniors" were seeking homes with no maintenance and no stairs. Now on a fixed income, they wanted to travel, enjoy life, and focus on themselves. Some were moving for financial reasons as they no longer could do home maintenance personally and the cost of hiring it done was a strain on their fixed incomes.

**Ages 81 and up** — "senior-seniors" were seeking personal assistance or even health care assistance provided in an institutional setting. Their move often involved relocating closer to family in a different city or province.

When seniors move, it is a traumatic life event and the adjustment can take many months. It often takes a great toll on their health physically and emotionally and this must be considered prior to making the decision to move.

# REMAIN SAFELY AT HOME

There are many precautions that can be taken to help a senior remain safely at home. While it may seem like the safest place in the world, most injuries occur at home, many of which are preventable. The best way to reduce the risk is by identifying hazards that may lead to injuries. Taking a few safety precautions can make a big difference. Living at home safely involves adapting the environment, one's behaviour and lifestyle, in accordance with the changes that aging brings about.

## Some Simple Facts[1]

Falls cause injuries and death. More than half of all injuries that happen to people over age 65 are due to falls. Roughly one-third of seniors who live in the community fall at least once each year and half of those will fall more than once. The chance of dying from a fall-related injury increases with age. As much as 20% of deaths due to injury can be traced back to a fall. Fractured hips can ultimately lead to death because of immobility; lack of circulation can affect major organs, the muscles atrophy and joints stiffen.

Forty percent of falls that happen to seniors result in hip fractures and half of them never walk unassisted again. Also, 40% of nursing home admissions are the result of a senior falling.

Fifteen percent of falls that occur at home happen in the bathroom and on the stairs. Seniors who fall are more fearful of falling again and this also leads to more falls.

These simple facts highlight the importance of conducting a home safety audit and investing in safety improvements for seniors who plan to remain living at home.

---

[1] *The Safe Living Guide*, Division of Aging and Seniors, Cat. No. H88-3/18-2005E, ISBN 0-662-33407-8.

## Causes of Injury

Aging brings changes that increase the risk of injury. Changes in vision occur that make the eyes take longer to adjust from dark to light and colours are more difficult to discern. Seniors need adequate lighting in the home, particularly on stairs to reduce the risk of falls. Carpeting on stairs should always be light to improve the ability to see each step. Dark carpeting casts shadows increasing the risk of falling. Sensory changes occur — touch, smell, and hearing are less sensitive. Seniors are at a greater risk of burns from hot water and their sensitive skin means a burn can occur quickly. A reduced sense of smell makes it more difficult to identify spoiled food and detect smoke or gas leaks. Reduced hearing makes it more difficult to hear doorbells and fire alarms or other warnings of danger.

Bones lose density and are easier to break and harder to mend. Changes in gait occur with age. Many things can affect balance because it is a complex function involving eyes, inner ear, muscle strength and joint flexibility. A change to any one of these can affect balance and increase the risk of falling.

Memory is less efficient and it is easier to forget to turn off appliances or to forget where something was put. Last minute rushing to find misplaced keys and other items can result in falls.

Changes in medication can cause blood pressure to drop suddenly and dizziness can lead to falls. Medication for heart problems, dementia, and antidepressants are a few examples of medications that are likely to cause this to happen.

There are also risks in the environment such as loose scatter rugs, dim lighting, missing rails on stairways, slippery floor surfaces, and uneven thresholds in doorways. Safety risks may exist outside the home as well. Poor exterior door lighting, wet grass, snow or ice on walkways in the winter, and overgrown bushes that block visibility are just a few example of why it is just as important to survey the outer surroundings of the home as it is to assess safety within the home.

## Safety Solutions

There are many ways the home environment can be made safer, and together with some modest behaviour or lifestyle changes safety can be improved. The following are some examples:

- Now is the time to become familiar with how to use a microwave if you have resisted doing so. Programs such as Meals-on-Wheels can help seniors remain living longer in the community by providing nutritious meals delivered to their home. However, most programs operate Monday to Friday and deliver frozen meals to use through the weekend.

- Using appliances that have automatic shut-offs is also wise, such as tea kettles, coffee machines, and irons.

- Assign a specific place for eye wear, keys, remote controls, or other items that tend to get misplaced and make a habit of only ever setting them down in the allocated place. This will avoid last-minute rushing around to locate items, which often leads to accidents.

- Dial down the temperature on the hot water tank to reduce the likelihood of burns. The recommended temperature is 49°C or 120°F.

- Install lever-type faucets, grab bars around toilet and bathtubs and raised toilet seats. Ensure floor surfaces have non-slip surfaces. This will make the bathroom a safer place.

- Reorganize kitchen cupboards to improve accessibility to pots, pans, canned goods and other frequently used items. These should be stored between knee and shoulder height so stooping is avoided.

- Check for working smoke detectors, fire extinguishers, and carbon monoxide detectors. Create and practice an escape route in case of fire. "Top up" your first aid kit and ensure that the contents have not passed the expiry date. Tie this routine to the clock time change for checking batteries, refreshing the first aid kit, and practicing emergency plans twice a year in spring and fall.

- Introduce seniors with dementia to changes early while they can still learn to use new devices such as microwaves, coffee makers, and walkers with wheels and hand-breaks. They will have difficulty mastering new tasks as time goes by.

- Keep a working flashlight on the night table beside the bed. If the hydro goes off, or when getting up in the night, it can provide light.

- Encourage seniors to wear proper footwear (rubber soles) to grip floors. Eliminate shoelaces that require bending to tie and can come undone causing falls. Keep a chair or bench near the entrance door to encourage sitting while removing or putting on footwear.

- Encourage seniors to exercise and improve balance through programs like tai chi and yoga. This will help to reduce the chance of falling and improve their ability to make a quick recovery when they begin to stumble.

- Convert a main floor room to a bedroom (if one does not exist) and similarly install a main floor bathroom. Eliminating frequent use of stairs reduces the risk of falls. Seniors who are ill are particularly vulnerable to falls when trying to get from the bedroom to the bathroom. This often occurs in the middle of the night when lighting is low.

Someone who may be considering changes to the home to accommodate aging-in-home can explore government programs to assist with funding for low-income seniors by visiting the website for the Canada Mortgage and Housing Corporation at: www.cmhc-schl.gc.ca. For printable checklists on conducting a home audit go to: www.forseniors.ca.

## Transgenerational Design

You may be considering remodeling or building a home where you can age in place. The concept of Transgenerational Design can help people to remain in their homes longer by creating a friendlier environment. Also known as Universal Design, it is a framework for designing places, things, and information to be usable by the widest range of people operating in the widest range of situations. It is not about building based on a person's age; the focus is on creating usefulness as an integrated feature of home design. Although seniors have some unique usability constraints, studies show that when usability and safety are improved for older adults, they improve for younger adults and children too.

Some of the design features include the following:

- Raising the height of electrical outlets higher so one does not have to bend down (this has the added benefit of also improving child safety).

- Installing a pass-through from entrance halls to the kitchen to assist with passing groceries when unloading the car.

- Kitchens designed with pull-out drawers to eliminate bending and squatting.

- Doorbells with redundant cuing — a ring sounds *and* a light flashes so those with hearing impairment can detect someone is at the door.

- Reinforced walls for eventual grab bar installation in bathrooms.

- Closets stacked above each other in two-story homes for later conversion to an elevator shaft.

- Additional lighting to accommodate loss of vision.

- Keyless entries to eliminate fumbling with keys.

There are many more design features used in transgenerational design, all of which are intended to improve functionality across generations. More information is available at: www.forseniors.ca.

## HOME CARE AND COMMUNITY SUPPORT

When illness or injury occurs, home care and community support will be required. A person may be a candidate for home care and community support if they are having difficulties with activities of daily living and can benefit from a combination of skilled care and personal support.

Home care may serve to accomplish one of three objectives. First, it may maintain a person's ability to live independently and aid in preventing further health deterioration. Second, it may act as a substitution for long-term care in an institutional setting. Third, it may be a short-term alternative for delivering acute care. Approximately 78% of families are made up of dual-earner couples.[2] The increasing presence of women in the workforce means that fewer women are home to be full time caregivers to an aging parent. Despite this, many people are opting for caring for an elder in their home. This may be a viable option of choice for some people through the use of local community support. In 1996, roughly 130,000 Canadians moved in with the person they were helping or the person who was helping them.[3]

Regional community support services are available to assist people to live in their own homes and in the communities. The goal is to help seniors function as independently as possible and with quality of life. Not surprisingly, most seniors want to remain in their own homes. However, the reality is that this is not always possible without some assistance. The government provides subsidization to various programs that will assist the elderly or aid caregivers with whom an elder may be residing. The purpose of community-provided home care services is to act as a supplement to care provided by others and not as a substitute for it. Consequently, an adult child who takes on the role of informal caregiver needs to be very clear up front with the community care workers about the ways in which they can help, and the ways in which they cannot. Drawing clear boundaries up front will reduce the chances of caregiver burnout caused by increasing caregiver duties as time goes by stacked on top of family and work responsibilities. Government-funded services are obtained by contacting the Single Entry Point for local community support (Regional Health Authority, Community Care Access Centre, etc.) who will assign a case worker to evaluate the intended care recipient and determine the services they are eligible for. All provinces have a similar single entry point although the name for services varies somewhat in each province.

There are two general service categories; health care services and home support services. The latter is comprised of personal care and home-making. Health care services are provided by professionals and paraprofessionals and are medically-related services. Home support services are services that fall outside the skilled category and include such assistance as grocery purchase, meal preparation, and assistance with activities of daily living.

More specifically, the services offered include the following:

- **Nursing assistance** — miscellaneous services that require a skilled nurse to perform them such as intravenous therapy, dressings, instructional assistance to families and elders, and assistance preparing dosette boxes for taking daily medication.

---

[2] Mireille Marcil, Corporate Work/Life Services Web site (January 06, 2000).

[3] 1996 General Social Survey (GSS), Statistics Canada, *Social Trends*, Catalogue No. 11-008, Winter 1999, No. 55, p. 11.

- **Physiotherapy** — muscle, bone, and joint therapy to restore or improve use.

- **Occupational therapy** — therapy that is designed to improve or restore fine motor skills often associated with stroke victims.

- **Speech therapy** — to assist elders to improve speech following a stroke.

- **Alzheimer's Day Program** — therapeutic social and recreational group activities for people with Alzheimer's disease or other dementias that often includes meals, personal day care, transportation and health monitoring.

- **Counseling** — client counseling to deal with complex or individual needs.

- **Foot care** — for seniors who have foot ailments or are at risk of infection.

- **Friendly visiting** — routine visits by agency-supervised volunteers to isolated elders to keep them integrated into the community.

- **Transportation** — assistance in getting to appointments, shopping, seniors' activities, and seniors' centres for seniors who cannot use normal means of transportation due to physical or cognitive limitations or due to limited financial means.

- **Homemaking** — assistance with homemaking duties that cannot be easily done or safely done, such as housekeeping, laundry, food purchase and preparation, and bill payment.

- **Personal care** — assistance such as bathing, dressing, and feeding.

- **Home maintenance** — assistance with minor repairs and maintenance such as snow removal, grass cutting, etc. to ensure a safe environment.

- **Information and referral** — links to other support networks.

- **Intergenerational** — programs linking seniors with teens and children such as seniors assisting in schools and teen volunteers assisting seniors.

- **Companion care** — one of the most important aspects of in-home care is providing a strong sense of belonging and comfort. Having someone available to take an interest in their life, play a favourite board game, or go for a walk can be a valuable service.

- **Meals-on-Wheels** — a service supported by volunteers whereby meals are delivered to home bound people to ensure their nutritional needs are met.

- **Wheels-to-Meals** — a service which brings seniors to congregate dining services where they can join other seniors for nutritious meals.

- **Respite care** — a home support service to relieve the caregiver whereby assistance is provided in the home or through the use of a group facility such as a retirement home or long-term care facility.

- **Senior Day program** — a form of adult day support in a centre that provides supervised activities for elders and people with special needs, generally in the form of cognitive or physical impairment; services include activities, meals, personal care, and administration of medication.

- **Emergency response** — a program of regular contact with elders by phone or in person to ensure medication is being taken, and to ensure help is available when required.

- **Congregate dining** — a service that provides a central location for ensuring that elderly persons with social and/or physical disabilities receive nutritious meals and have an opportunity for social interaction within the community.

Most of these programs have a nominal charge, and some charges may vary based on the recipient's financial situation. The case worker assigned to assess the care requirements will make arrangements for the necessary services and will advise which services will be paid partially or fully by the government. There is an upper limit regarding the number of weekly visits and maximum hours per day for services that are funded by the government. For example, skilled nursing services and personal care are normally limited to two or three hours of care per week. Some services are not offered through the community care (Single Entry Point) and may be purchased directly from home care agencies such as Home Instead Senior Care, an international non-medical home care service provider, or We Care, a national provider of medical and non-medical home care services.

## COST OF SERVICES

The following are examples of the cost of home care services through a public for-profit service provider, though prices will vary by provider and by province.

### Skilled Nursing Care — $38 to $50 per hour

- Post-surgical care
- Changing dressings
- Administering IVs
- Arranging dosette boxes
- Instructional assistance to families
- Administering injections

### Companionship Services — $18 per hour

- Friendly visiting and conversation
- Medication reminders
- Reading and writing letters
- Playing games or cards

### Home Helper Services — $20 per hour

- Light housekeeping
- Light laundry and ironing
- Accompany to appointments, gatherings with friends, church
- Providing transportation or running errands
- Shopping with the client or for the client
- Gardening
- Plan, prepare and cleanup for meals

### Personal Care Services — $24 per hour

- Feeding
- Assistance with bathing
- Assistance with incontinences care
- Assistance using the restroom

### Overnight Stay — $170/10 hour shift

- Useful for caregiver respite relief

Services that are purchased through a home care agency are taxable for GST and normally increase during statutory holidays by 50%.

### Foot Care — $25

Many communities run local clinics for seniors for foot care. These services are normally in the range of $25. The senior may be required to bring their own towel. A trained foot care specialist (usually a nurse), will inspect the senior's feet for visible signs of infection or other foot conditions and to trim the nails. This is a valuable service for seniors because with age it becomes more difficult to tend to this aspect of personal grooming as dexterity and flexibility are reduced.

## SERVICE PLANNER CHECKLIST

The following checklist will assist as a service planner in determining which services may help the intended care recipient to remain living at home. The informal caregiver and family can determine which they can take on, and which tasks should be outsourced to a local agency.

❏ Arrange appointments

❏ Assist with walking

❏ Assist with writing and correspondence and reading

❏ Meal planning

❏ Prepare, sort, read, process mail

❏ Stabilize while bathing

❏ Light housekeeping

❏ Wash dishes

❏ Take out garbage

❏ Change linens and make bed

❏ Vacuum

❏ Drop off and pick up cleaning

❏ Pick up prescriptions

❏ Dust and polish furnishings

❏ Organize and clean closets

❏ Participate in board games, crafts, cards, sewing for mind stimulation and entertainment

❏ Reminisce about past

❏ Answer telephone/door — monitor nature of contacts for protection

❏ Apparel selection

❏ Care for house plants

❏ Appointment reminders

❏ Assist in decision making

❏ Monitor diet and eating habits

❏ Record and arrange recipes

❏ Oversee home deliveries

❏ Coordinate lawn care

❏ Buy newspapers, magazines, books

❏ Rent and view videos

❏ Plan and participate in trips, excursions, visits to friends, concerts, receptions

❏ Participate in religious celebrations

❏ Birthday and anniversary planning and celebration

❏ Maintain calendar of events and appointments

❏ Record family history

❏ Medication reminders

❏ Pantry cleaning, fridge and stove cleaning

❏ General grocery shopping

❏ Travel planning assistance and airline departure and arrival arrangements

❏ Assistance purchasing travel insurance

❏ Assistance to coordinate snow removal

❏ Assistance to arrange home maintenance and improvements

❏ Grocery list coupon clipping

❏ Listen and alert to weather changes

❏ Assist with pet care

❏ Monitor food freshness, expiry dates on staples and canned goods

❏ Assistance with bill payment, monitor for expirations

## CAREGIVERS DEALING WITH CHRONIC ILLNESS

A caregiver that decides to provide home care may find it necessary to make physical changes in the home to accommodate the care recipient. These may include changes such as the addition of railings in the bathroom, marking paths and labeling doors with pictures, or possibly the need for remodeling the home to accommodate a main-floor bedroom, thereby eliminating stairs. Caregivers to persons with Alzheimer's disease and other forms of dementia face some special issues.

### Assistance with Dressing

The caregiver may need to change the type of clothing worn by the elder to make it easier for the elder to dress independently or with assistance. This includes eliminating zippers, belts, and pullover sweaters in favour of track pants, cardigans, and velcro attachments. The goal is to help the person retain their independence for as long as possible.

### Assistance with Eating

Difficulties arise when the care recipient loses skills needed for eating and becomes less aware of acceptable social behaviours. The caregiver may need to change the type of food offered and must ensure the person is getting enough to eat and drink for proper nourishment. The care recipient may be easily confused by too many pieces of cutlery at their place setting, or by the use of separate plates for salads and entrees. As dexterity diminishes, they may need assistance with cutting meat. Eventually, foods may need to be pureed.

Elders who have Alzheimer's disease may eventually require extensive encouragement to eat and to maintain sufficient fluids to prevent dehydration. The caregiver should watch for signs such as dryness of skin which show that the person is not drinking sufficient fluids .

### Physical Fitness

Exercise is an important part of the daily regimen. The caregiver must ensure the care recipient is getting adequate use of their muscles every day. Muscle atrophy can occur rather quickly and this significantly reduces quality of life.

### Assistance from Community Services

Many caregivers receive additional assistance from community programs. Some of these programs include:

- homemaking services

- nursing services from staff of community agencies

- meals-on-wheels

- transportation to and from adult day care facilities

## RESPITE CARE

Being a primary caregiver for an elder can be rewarding, but at the same time stressful and tiring. The responsibility demands 24-hour assistance, seven days a week. Illnesses such as Parkinson's and Alzheimer's disease can cause an elder to behave in difficult and demanding ways, regardless of how patient and loving the caregiver is. Respite care is intended to provide relief to caregivers by relieving them of their responsibilities in order for them to care for their own physical and mental health.

Respite care can be either formal or informal. Informal arrangements arise when family or friends take over care giving responsibilities for a few hours or a few days. Formal arrangements include the use of Adult Day Care, Skilled Nursing Facilities, or Seniors Centres. Some facilities such as Adult Day Centres may even provide transportation for the elder to and from the centre for a small fee if transportation is not otherwise available.

Regional community support services that offer assistance for independent living, can also provide help by assigning a homemaker or health aide or by making arrangements through one of the long-term care centres, as many of these reserve a limited number of beds for respite care.

## The Importance of Respite Care

A debilitating illness can last many years and without personal relief for the caregiver, burnout and exhaustion can occur. This necessitates that the caregiver set aside personal time for engaging in hobbies, recreation, social activities and personal relationships. Without this relief, the caregiver will be unable to provide quality care to the elder.

## Warning Signals to the Caregiver

Some signs that the caregiver is in need of a break and should arrange for respite care are:

- difficulty sleeping

- increased irritability

- anxious behaviour

- exhaustion

- feelings of anger or resentment towards the elder in their care

- shortness with family, co-workers and friends

# ADULT DAY CENTRES

Adult Day Centres include centres where elders can spend the day in a supervised group setting away from home. The services and activities vary from facility to facility. There are two types of facilities: social centres and day support centres. The concept of adult day support began in the 1920s in Europe and the Soviet Union. It later spread to the United States where the number of care centres has grown from a dozen in the early 1970s to over 2,000 today.[4]

## Social Centres

Social day centres are outside of the medical model, and function as social and recreation "clubs" for seniors to go to daily or occasionally. There is often an annual membership charge to belong around $20 or $25 per year. A separate fee may apply in addition to the membership rate for participation in various activities offered by the centre. They cater to healthy seniors as opposed to those with failing health that require assistance.

---

[4] The Ohio State University Website (January 7, 2000), Article Entitled *Getting A Break — Adult Day Care Helps Caregivers.*

Services generally include:

• Exercise

• Social activities such as bridge, bingo, carpet bowling, billiards, etc.

Social centres provide an outlet for seniors to be with other seniors in the community and to remain active and involved both mentally and physically. Social centres do not provide medical assistance or day care to elders.

## Medical-Assisted Day Support Centres

A Day Support Centre is one for elders with physical or mental limitations to spend the day in a supervised group setting away from home. Unlike long-term care homes where application is made through a single point entry, a caregiver may contact the care centre directly to make arrangements for the elder to be evaluated by the individual centre for acceptance into their day program.

Day Support Centres provide valuable assistance to caregivers in the form of respite and to older adults by enabling them to remain in the community outside of institutions for a longer period of time. Many attendees at the centres are seniors who are currently on waiting lists for admission to a long-term care facility.

Most facilities in Canada are for seniors with dementia, although some also accept people who have physical disabilities. Facilities receive government financial subsidization, and this keeps the cost to the caregiver down substantially. The average fee paid by the caregiver is about $16 per day for services that in total cost in the range of $100 per day, with the difference being subsidized by the government. Transportation is often available through services such as the Red Cross for an additional fee of $5.00. Most facilities have a sliding scale whereby those who cannot afford to pay may qualify for additional subsidization.

Some facilities operate from 7:00 a.m. to 7:00 p.m., while others limit hours of service from 10:00 a.m. to 3:00 p.m. There may be stipulations that require the individual to attend five days per week to remain in the program, while others offer more flexible arrangements to suit the caregiver's needs with a minimum weekly participation requirement of two days weekly.

Alberta is one of the few provinces to offer evening hours, which can accommodate a caregiver who works nights, and is caring for a parent.

The following services are provided:

• Light breakfast, snack, and hot lunch

• Recreational activities

• Exercise

• Discussion and conversation

• Some assistance with activities of daily living (ADL) as necessary

Some facilities accept participants who have ADL limitations such as incontinence, feeding, etc. Many facilities have waiting lists for admission, due to their size. An average range is 10 to 25 participants per day.

Some long-term care centres also accept a limited number of day attendees. A list of facilities can be obtained by contacting the local Community Care Access Centre or the Ministry of Health.

## EVALUATING ADULT DAY SUPPORT CENTRES AS AN OPTION

The caregiver should consider the following three questions to determine whether a day support centre is a viable option:

1. Has the elder been diagnosed with a debilitating condition such as Alzheimer's or Parkinson's disease?

2. Does the caregiver feel they can no longer provide the level of care required without additional assistance?

3. Is there a desire to keep the elder outside of long-term care facilities as long as possible?

If the answer is yes to these questions, then the caregiver should consider the use of a day support centre. A list of local centres is generally available by contacting the regional community care centre. The caregiver can then visit several facilities to determine the one most suitable to their needs, and arrange for an evaluation of the elder by the centre who will determine their eligibility to attend. Adult day support can delay the need for placement in a long-term care home by an average of 18 to 22 months. The cost is considerably less, averaging $300 to $400 per month compared with residence in a retirement home or long-term care centre being in the range of $1,600 to as much as $4,000 per month.

## CHECKLIST FOR SELECTING A DAY SUPPORT CENTRE

The following are important things to consider when selecting a centre:

❏ What are the needs of the elder and does the centre have adequate skilled staff and equipment to accommodate the needs?

❏ Is the environment one that is conducive to ensuring the elder can remain at their maximum functional capacity and ability of independence?

❏ Is the atmosphere pleasant, and do other participants appear to enjoy being there?

❏ Are the programs structured to the interests and needs of elders?

❏ Are participants treated with dignity and patience?

❏ Is the centre clean and free of odor?

❑ Do staff members sufficiently interact with participants and in a friendly, inviting way?

❑ Are participants sitting alone or sleeping?

❑ Does the centre provide assistance with activities of daily living?

❑ Are hot meals served or cold snacks only?

❑ Do the hours coincide with the needs of the caregiver's schedule?

❑ Is there a written policy on fees and emergency procedures?

❑ Does the centre document a written plan of care for each participant?

❑ Do they have the ability to adjust meals to special dietary needs?

❑ What communication and feedback do they provide daily to the caregiver?

❑ Are staff members trained in CPR and first aid?

For working adults caring for a semi-independent parent at home, adult support is worth exploring. It offers supervised care for elders in a supportive group atmosphere. It offers a safer setting for those suffering from severe memory loss, disorientation, or a medical condition that requires frequent monitoring. It delivers comfort in knowing that the family member has companionship and support throughout the day.

## HIRING A CARE MANAGER

Sometimes it is not possible to spend the time required to do the research, make arrangements, and personally oversee care arrangements for the intended recipient. This may particularly apply to distance caregivers who are dealing with planning from a different city. A care manager can be hired to fulfill this role and report to the informal caregiver on progress. A care manager is a professional who specializes in assisting caregivers in meeting the long-term arrangements required for the intended care recipient. They can be the local eyes and ears and be available for crisis intervention. A caregiver might begin with using the services of a care manager to conduct a care planning assessment independent of the government agency's Regional Health Authority (Community Care Access Centre). The planning process will entail:

- Identifying the problems the elder is having.

- Determine their eligibility for government assistance by interacting with the government agency.

- Arrange for supplementary services the family wants, provided that the agency is not able or willing to support.

When the time comes for the elder to move to the next phase of care, the care manager can also assist with selection of the centre, and the eventual move. These services are outside of government-funded assistance and available through public home care agencies.

*Chapter 10*

# Housing Options: Residential Care

## RESIDENTIAL FACILITY OPTIONS

As people age, their needs and capabilities change. They may no longer be able to carry the responsibilities of maintaining a home, and simultaneously deal with their own changing health needs. At some point, they may need to consider whether relocation to new living quarters is desirable. There are many different options in this respect, ranging from retirement residences that offer independent living free from home maintenance responsibilities, to long-term care centres that provide 24-hour professional care and assistance with activities of daily living.

Care is a continuum of needs that will change over time so it is best to try and anticipate in advance what these evolving needs may be, and over what time frame they might occur. Moving is stressful for anyone, but for older adults it is even more difficult and can take a great toll on their health. It can take as long as six months to settle in following a change. Trying to anticipate the timeline and expected changes that are likely to occur may mean less possibility of having to go through a second move shortly after the relocation if the elder's condition suddenly deteriorates.

Moving a loved one from home to a residential facility involves four phases:

- Communicating the need and preparing the person for the move.

- Sourcing, evaluating and selecting the new residence.

- Moving in day.

- Easing the change by helping the person to settle in after the move has taken place.

Recognize in advance that it will take time following the change for the person to feel comfortable and at home. There may be times when things do not go as smoothly as hoped, either due to the person's difficulty in adjusting to the change, or due to staff or facilities-related issues. It pays to learn in advance what your remedies are should an issue arise.

## COMMUNICATING THE NEED AND PREPARING FOR CHANGE

### Having the Discussion

An adult child may be in the role of caregiver to an aging parent who is approaching the need to evaluate alternative accommodation options. Communication can be challenging in the best of times, but when the issue for resolution involves something as personal as leaving one's home, the caregiver's role becomes even more difficult. This may be further exacerbated if the elder suffers from dementia or confusion.

It is important, nevertheless, to involve the parent in the discussion and to avoid slipping into a role reversal. A parent who has had no say or involvement in developing a plan of action is unlikely to agree to the change. Even a person who has dementia should be included in the discussion, regardless of whether they may be likely to forget much of the information. They will remember the feelings of inclusion even if the details become confused or forgotten. They will be less likely to build barriers and resist a necessary change. The caregiver must distinguish between issues related to quality of life and those that concern risk or danger.

The following points may help the caregiver and family to have a more meaningful conversation with an aging parent who has cognitive impairment or suffers from confusion when discussing a change in residence:

- The inclusion of someone from outside the immediate family often aids in keeping the elder focused on the issue.

- Remain positive, listen to the elder's statements without interruption, and maintain eye contact.

- Hold the discussion in a quiet area that is free from distracting sounds or sights including televisions, outdoor traffic, air conditioning motors, or public areas.

- Be clear, direct, and speak in simple sentences that the elder can comprehend, without being demeaning, ambiguous, or coy.

- Pause periodically to enable the elder to absorb the point; even though they may have heard, they may not have comprehended the information.

- Be brief in the communication. An elder who is suffering from confusion or other cognitive impairment may only be able to process questions that require a "yes" or "no"; not questions that require selecting options from "a", "b" and "c".

- Check for comprehension by asking the elder to repeat the message back.

- Check to ensure that the elder is able to hear, particularly if they also suffer from a hearing impairment.

Talk openly and positively about the change and the new residence so the person will know what to expect. Offer reassurances that while the move itself may be difficult and life will be different, the support and love of family and friends will always be there. Focus on the positive such as the programs, activities and companionship available and that their health and independence may even improve because of the care provided.

Some places offer a trial period where the senior can visit temporarily for a week or two. This may help to ease the transition and to evaluate whether there is a good cultural fit.

## ASSESSING RESIDENCE REQUIREMENTS

When evaluating the various residential options, involve the person as much as possible in the process.

Two considerations must be evaluated:

1. What are the elder's needs?

2. Is there a cultural fit?

## What are the Elder's Needs?

Consider what symptoms or conditions triggered the original concern. This will assist in determining the level of care and services that should be available in the new residence. Some examples follow.

| Symptom | Possible Condition | Support Required |
|---|---|---|
| • Forgetting people, dates, commitments, addresses, phone numbers, familiar surroundings<br>• Bills not being paid on time<br>• Confusion taking medication, dosages<br>• Wandering away from home | Memory impairment | • Supervised building with security alarm system<br>• Nursing care for administering medications<br>• Eventual assistance with activities of daily living |
| • Behavioural or mood changes | Social isolation or depression | • Companion setting<br>• May require nursing care to ensure correct medication compliance |
| • Difficulty hearing<br>• Difficulty with vision | Sensory changes — increased risk of being taken advantage of by telephone callers, when shopping, or by door-to-door callers at the home | • Controlled entrances to residence<br>• Companion setting<br>• Emergency button |
| • Decreased mobility, increased incidences of accidental falls | Mobility changes | • Residence free from stairs, wider halls to accommodate a walker<br>• Maintenance-free setting<br>• Access to physiotherapy<br>• Assistance with grocery shopping and house cleaning |
| • Soiled clothes<br>• Weight loss<br>• Difficulty chewing or swallowing or using utensils | Limitations in activities of daily living (ADL) | • 24-hour para- and professional care to assist with activities<br>• Physiotherapy |
| • Difficulty with personal financial matters such as writing cheques, paying bills<br>• Difficulty with preparing meals, using a telephone | Limitations in More Complex Activities Known as Instrumental Activities of Daily Living (I.A.D.Ls) | • Companion setting<br>• Maintenance-free residential setting<br>• Facilities with common dining area, laundry services |

In summary, the care and service assistance required in the new residence may be in one or more areas related to simple or complex cognitive changes, behavioural changes, sensory changes, mobility changes, personal hygiene and daily living activities.

### Is There a Cultural Fit?

Someone who has Alzheimer's disease or other dementia and whose first language is not English, may have difficulties later with communication as their illness progresses. Many residences cater to specific cultural groups and have staff and residents who speak the same language and this can be a comfort to the person. Every cultural group has specific traditions that are unique and cherished, such as those related to special cuisine, holiday celebrations, and religious practices.

Men often have more difficulty settling in, as the percentage of women far outnumber the percentage of male residents and this can affect a male elder's ability to successfully integrate if they cannot identify with the other residents.

## MOVING IN DAY

Personalizing the room with belongings from home can help create a more familiar feel to the new surroundings. Articles such as pictures, bed covers, and a favourite chair can create warmth and a personal touch. Bring sufficient clothing and the right type of clothing. Keep in mind space is limited, and not only must one consider seasonal suitability, but function-ality too. With age, dexterity diminishes and the person may have difficulty dressing themselves. Eliminate numerous buttons and zippers in favour of slip-on tracksuits and velcro closures as this can enable someone to retain independence longer and make them feel more in control. Specialty clothing is available through stores and online businesses for someone who has difficulty dressing due to illness or physical limitations.

Discuss with staff, the preferences of the elder with respect to food, routines, hobbies, and other likes/dislikes. Introduce yourself and the elder to others, including staff and other residents.

## EASING THE CHANGE AND SETTLING IN

The elder may be feeling depressed about the change and leaving their residence behind and it will take some time, perhaps as long as six months, before they feel settled. This is the time to reassure the person and to be there often so they will feel continuity, knowing they have not been aban-doned. Residences have activity boards where events, excursions, and various activities for the week or the month are posted. Family members can usually participate in these events. Newsletters highlight stories of residents and other news. This is an excellent source for becoming more familiar with the community. Nursing homes conduct care conferences where staff meet with the family to brief them on their loved one's issues and progress. This is an excellent opportunity to participate in the design of your loved one's care plan.

## Remedies for Issues That Arise

Residential facilities are governed by regulatory legislation, which varies by province. As an example, in Ontario supportive housing initiatives are protected by the *Tenant Protection Act*, which regulates tenancy and the *Health Protection and Promotion Act*, and Public Health Departments concerning food safety and other health safety issues. Self-regulation also applies through various associations such as the Ontario Residential Care Association where complaints can be lodged against a member residence. Other provinces have similar legislation to protect residents.

All provinces have a "Bill of Rights" for home care and long-term care, which outline the care recipient's rights. Seniors have the right to freedom from abuse, the right to privacy and choice, and the right to have preferences honoured regarding religious and cultural beliefs. They also have the right to information, to participate in their care plan, and the right to refuse treatment. They are also protected under the Bill of Rights from reprisals, have the right to be advised about legal remedies at their disposal and the right to confidentiality.

When a breach occurs, the nature of remedies available depends upon the type of accommodation they are in, as different legislation may apply in a given province to supportive housing initiatives (assisted living facilities) as opposed to nursing homes.

Remedies may include any or all of the following:

• Lodging a complaint to the facility

• Suing for breach of contract

• Taking criminal issues to the police

• Contacting the particular practitioner's college or licensing body

• Taking humans rights issues to the Human Rights Commission

A senior who may not be able to afford to hire a lawyer can contact the province's legal aid and a lawyer will be appointed at no cost to the individual.

# RETIREMENT RESIDENCES WITH SUPPORTS AND NURSING HOMES

How do you choose between the two? When home care is no longer a viable option, the elder's condition will dictate whether the next step in care will be in supportive housing (also known as assisted living) or a nursing home. Unless you are considering a private nursing home that does not receive government funding, the reality is that you will not be able to opt for moving to a nursing home unless an evaluation of the elder's needs indicates this is essential for meeting their care requirements.

## Care Continuums

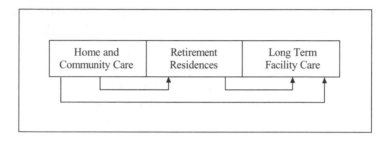

## Retirement Residences with Supports

### What Is It?

Several names have been used to refer to retirement residences that offer supports to seniors, enabling them to remain in the community such as Personal Care Homes, Lodges, Assisted Living Facilities (ALF) and Supportive Housing. More recently, they are being referred to simply as retirement residences with supports. Regardless, this category of residential care is distinct from retirement residences that cater to healthy adults who choose to live in adult-only buildings or townhouse complexes restricted to people over age 65. In some provinces, they receive government funding and are part of the continuing care system, while in other provinces they fall outside the system and are not subsidized. In this instance, an interested candidate would approach the residence directly to indicate their interest.

### Regulations

Retirement residences that are outside of the provincial continuing care system do not receive subsidization. While most of these are privately owned for-profit, charitable foundations operate a few. In most provinces they are not subject to the same regulations as nursing homes or long-term care centres. They are only subject to the *Landlord and Tenant Act*, municipal zoning and fire and public health regulations. However, most retirement residences belong to provincial associations that have minimum standards and periodic inspections. Membership of an association also offers residents and their families the benefit of providing an independent source for resolving concerns and complaints.

## Profile of Residents

Retirement residences with supports require that the intended resident be over age 65 and has difficulty managing several *instrumental activities* of daily living that place them at risk living on their own. Examples of these activities include difficulty managing medication and/or activities associated with preparing meals such as grocery shopping, and cooking or are at greater risk of falling or injuring themselves. The intended resident must be able to manage on their own with activities of daily living such as dressing, bathing, getting in and out of bed, getting to the toilet and maintaining general hygiene associated with incontinence.

They may serve as an alternative to home care for those who do not have the benefit of a family member in their local area to act as a caregiver. They may fulfill the need for greater assistance than that provided under home and community care for those who do not require 24-hour care.

## Services Offered

Retirement residences offer a variety of services including dining rooms, recreational activities, housekeeping, laundry services, beauty salons, off-site excursions, and church services. Most of the support services are those that can be provided by a personal care worker. Some services may require a licensed specialist such as a physical therapist or a registered nurse who dispenses medication.

There may be light assistance with daily living activities, or occasional assistance with these during periods of minor illness. A few have gone a step beyond and offer infirmaries, which enable a resident to temporarily get a higher level of assistance such as following release from the hospital. A few offer aid with weekly baths and have a central customized bathing room containing special bathtubs with lifts and custom-designed showers for this purpose. The fixed monthly rate may offer a once-per-week service, with more frequent aid available at a slight additional cost. These services are normally associated with nursing homes, but when they are delivered in a retirement residence with supports, they can be valuable and delay the need for admission to a nursing home.

## Accommodation Style

Living arrangements fall into two categories: Independent Living and Supportive or Assisted Living.

*Independent Living*

Independent Living arrangements are for individuals or couples that are able to maintain an independent lifestyle but wish to do so in a secure and comfortable setting. Options generally include rooms or suites containing a kitchenette, optional meal plan programs, and recreational activities. They may offer the advantage of facilitating a later transition to Supportive or Assisted Living as the need arises without having to relocate to another facility.

*Supportive or Assisted Living*

These residences generally consist of semi-private or private home-like bedrooms that vary in size and include bath facilities. A few may also offer kitchenettes and balconies. Some offer fully furnished rooms, while others require residents to provide their own furnishings. There are organized activities such as bingo, daily exercise sessions, pet visitations, and excursions to malls and parks. Meals are provided in a common dining room, and medication is dispensed by a nurse according to the resident's medical requirements. Most facilities have a visiting doctor so residents can receive routine check-ups within the facility.

As the level of care required increases, the elder may be able to remain for a period of time in the facility with increased assistance from community services for activities of daily living such as bathing and grooming or by contracting with private services for on-site assistance. However, when the level of care required increases beyond this basic level, the resident will most likely need to move to a long-term care facility.

## Fees

In most provinces, the government does not subsidize the cost of running retirement residential facilities. The cost of supports, which would normally be provided in a program of home care, is generally government-funded. However, there may be some subsidization offered based upon income for the cost of accommodation. While most services are included in the fee, there are some that are offered at an additional cost such as laundry cleaning. Fees range from $900 to $6,000 per month. At the lower end of the scale, residents may be required to share a room and use communal bathroom facilities. At the high end of the scale, the resident may have a suite that includes a balcony, kitchenette and 4-piece private bath. The average cost is in the range of $1,600 to $2,500 per month for a private basic bedroom of average size that includes a 3- or 4-piece bath. Some government subsidized housing initiatives may offer supportive living with the cost of rent being geared to income and assets. The monthly fee may be as little as $600 per month, creating accessible, affordable housing for seniors to continue living in the community.

Rent increases are regulated under the same rent control guidelines that apply to any other rental accommodations.

## Admission

Some facilities may have waiting lists due to their popularity, while others may offer immediate vacancy with lists to "move up" to preferred rooms as openings arise. As the vast majority of rooms are private, the waiting lists tend to be the longest for shared accommodations as this level may be the most affordable for many seniors.

Retirement residences may offer the option to try the facility on a temporary basis such as one or two weeks prior to making the decision to move in.

## Checklist

The following checklist is a guide to selecting and comparing facilities. A tour of several facilities is recommended prior to making a decision as services and accommodations can vary from one place to another.

### Location and Structure

❏ Units are selected by resident, not assigned by the facility

❏ Unit matches the preferences and requirements (e.g., kitchenette, private bath, etc.)

❏ Residents can bring their own furniture if they wish

❏ Room is large enough to feel comfortable in for several hours at a time

❏ Room offers a pleasant view and/or balcony nearby

❏ Bedroom is in close proximity to the dining room and activity centre (Even though the resident may be able to walk a distance today, they may be unable to as health deteriorates)

❏ Room has an outlet for cable TV

❏ Room has an individually controlled thermostat for heat and air conditioning

❏ Room is equipped with an emergency call button

❏ Room is accessible by individuals using walkers and wheel chairs

❏ The grounds provide adequate parking for guests and visitors without a substantial parking fee

❏ The building has a controlled entrance so residents cannot wander without notice

❏ The room has a privacy lock

❏ There are sign-out sheets for residents so staff know when a resident is out

❏ The hallways are equipped with video cameras to monitor the safety of the residents

## Amenities and Services

❏ All required personal services are included in the basic rate

❏ Increased level of care is available at an additional charge without the need to move (e.g., incontinence, assistance with feeding, dressing, shaving, etc.)

❏ Assistance with medication is available from a skilled nurse

❏ Residents are included in the planning of activities and events

❏ There are excursions to local malls and parks

❏ There is transportation available to access local community events

❏ There is a religious service weekly that is the same denomination as the resident

❏ There are organized activities that are appropriate recreation for cognitively-impaired residents

❏ The staff ensure involvement of all residents in exercise programs to maintain their physical fitness in accordance with their capabilities

## Staff and Atmosphere

❏ The ratio of staff to residents is reasonable

❏ Staff appear to be friendly and helpful

❏ Staff are available as required and visible in the building

❏ Staff are willing to assist residents to ensure they are at the dining room in time for meals

❏ Staff are available and willing to help residents with mild dementia to find their way around the building

❏ The resident's prevalent language is spoken by many staff and residents

❏ Residents look happy and cared for

### Meals

❐ Meals are included in the basic rate

❐ Meals are served at a sitting time that is suitable to the resident

❐ Residents are free to sit with whom they choose

❐ Special meals are available if required by the resident such as kosher, vegetarian, etc.

❐ There are larger portions available for bigger appetites

❐ The menu offers a degree of variety of selection

❐ Controls are in place to ensure dietary requirements (e.g., diabetic) are met or medications are correctly dispensed

### Residential Contract

❐ The notice period required if the resident wishes to move out is not more than 30 days

❐ If the facility can no longer handle the medical requirements of the resident, they will provide the family with a minimum of 90-days notice

❐ There are no restrictions that appear unusual, broad, or vague

❐ The monthly fee is specific concerning what is included in the rate and costs associated with options

❐ There are no restrictions on vacations

❐ There is a cap on rental increases and appropriate advance notice

❐ There are subsidy provisions in place to assist a resident who has become financially unable to pay so they can remain there

## LONG-TERM CARE FACILITIES

### What Is It?

Residences that provide long-term care for people who need 24-hour nursing care are known as Care Centres, Long-Term Care Centres, Nursing Homes, and Homes for the Aged. They may be either for-profit or not-for profit. Those that receive a government subsidy are licensed and inspected by the province and a central single intake point assigns their beds so that those with the greatest need receive access first. Private providers are also emerging that do not receive government funding and which can be accessed directly on the basis of ability to pay. The cost for non-funded private providers is more than double the cost for those that receive a government subsidy.

### Regulations

All provinces have legislation that governs nursing homes; however, how far the legislation stretches varies. Standards are designed with the goal of ensuring a safe, secure lifestyle and quality of life and apply to all nursing homes in the province. Some provinces have minimum care standards whereby each resident must receive at least the daily minimum care hours per day. For example, Alberta requires a minimum of 3.6 hours of care per day, which includes both skilled and personal care. On the other hand, Ontario eliminated the mandatory minimum in place a number of years ago and new pending legislation is intended to reinstitute a mandatory minimum. Other areas monitored by legislation include the following:

- The physical environment such as fire regulations, maintenance, and comfort

- Hospitality services such as meals, housekeeping, and laundry

- Safety standards such as emergency preparedness, abuse prevention, and safety of environment

- Personal services such as social and spiritual opportunities, transportation, and personal choice

- Residential services such as the application and admission process

- Human resources such as employment standards, and workplace safety

- Management and administration standards such as corporate governance, insurance, and information management

Many statutes, codes and other legislation and regulations ensure suitable standards are met by nursing homes in these and other areas.

### Profile of Residents

An elder may require admission to a long-term care facility after either home care or retirement residential facilities can no longer provide the degree of assistance needed. The average age of residents upon admission to nursing homes is age 82. The average stay is in the range of 2 to 3 years. To be considered for admission, the person must be in need of 24-hour nursing supervision, medically stable, not expected to expire shortly, and not have a communicable disease.

### Services Offered

Long-term care facilities are equipped to provide nursing care on a 24-hour basis. This is accomplished with a team consisting of registered practical nurses and health care aides. There are physicians that visit on a weekly basis so that every resident is seen each week. Physiotherapists ensure that even residents who are bed-ridden receive exercise appropriate to their condition to maintain range of motion. There are mobile services for x-rays, dentistry, and foot care.

A variety of non-medical services are usually available such as hair-dressing, laundry, church services, and recreational activities.

A long-term care centre does not provide medical services for acute conditions that require hospitalization. Nor do most facilities provide care for conditions that require intravenous treatment.

The fee charged normally includes the following:

1. Room and board

2. 24-hour professional supervision

3. Routine care such as assistance with activities of daily living by skilled health care specialists

4. Regular and emergency treatment by either the resident's own doctor or the house doctor

5. Administering medication and treatments

6. Social and recreational programs which vary from facility to facility

7. Care for special dietary requirements

8. Laundry service for personal clothing

While all nursing homes provide assistance with baths and incontinence management, the frequency and method may vary from one home to another, and a caregiver should ask for details in advance when selecting a facility for their loved one.

## Accommodation Style

Facilities vary in size, ranging from some having as few as 50 beds to facilities that have 250 beds. They are licensed and inspected by the Ministry of Health. Tours are available for caregivers by appointment to view the facilities prior to making a decision.

There are generally three levels of accommodation: ward (i.e., four beds per room), semi-private, and private. The latter two are referred to as *preferred accommodation*, while the ward level is referred to as *basic accommodation*. Waiting lists are the longest for basic care as this is the only level that many people can afford, and for which government subsidies are available. Some provinces only offer ward-style rooms in older buildings with the new direction being to provide only semi-private and private accommodation. In

Nova Scotia, private rooms are assigned based on medical need, not based on ability to pay, with the rate charged being the same regardless of accommodation style.

Unlike rooms in retirement residences that are more home-like, long-term care facilities are designed to cater to residents with health conditions and rooms are consequently more similar to those found in a hospital.

## Fees

The cost of care consists of health charges plus room-and-board (accommodation) charges. In all provinces except Newfoundland, New Brunswick and Prince Edward Island, the government fully covers the health costs and the fee charged represents the accommodation fee. If the person cannot afford to pay at least the basic rate, a further subsidy is available based on income testing. The goal is to leave the person with a small comfort allowance in the range of $200 per month for incidentals. Newfoundland, New Brunswick, and Prince Edward Island still use an asset test in addition to income test to determine the rate charged. The cost can range from $1,200 for basic accommodation in provinces that cover the cost of health services to $4,500 per month. Rates are based on a per-day rate and are set by the Ministry of Health. In private nursing homes that do not receive government subsidy, fees can range up to $8,000 per month.

The lowest fees are found in Manitoba, and the highest fees are in the Atlantic provinces excluding Nova Scotia.

## Notifying Acceptance of Facilities

Upon receiving a call that an opening has arisen, the caregiver has 24 hours to decide whether they are going to accept the vacancy offered. Upon acceptance, the caregiver has an additional 24 hours in which to move the elder into the facilities. Special arrangements may be available to postpone the admission for up to a maximum of three days by payment of a fee. If an intended care recipient has been designated as a high priority and refuses the first available room offered, their name drops from the priority list and they are no longer designated as a high priority. If they accept the room even though it is not in a facility of their choice, they can remain wait-listed for another facility and later transfer when a room becomes available.

Moving a parent to a long-term care facility can be an emotionally traumatic experience for both the elder and the caregiver. Not only is it stressful to deal with the issue of facing the reality that the parent's health has deteriorated to the stage that continuous care is required, but the short time frame given for deciding whether to accept the facility vacancy is yet an additional source of stress. Caregivers should begin the process of touring various facilities well in advance of when the need arises. They will be under less stress and pressure from short time frames.

The caregiver should make the first visit to the long-term care home without an appointment as this will give a better indication of what the facility is like on a typical day. The caregiver should speak with the residents and ask their overall impressions. If possible, the caregiver should speak with relatives of residents for their feedback and opinions. Before making a final decision, the caregiver should visit several facilities to have a basis of comparison.

Once the caregiver has made a decision and the elder has been moved to the facility, the caregiver should take some time to document the elder's current condition in areas such as:

- Food and beverage intake levels

- Agility and range of motion in tasks such as dressing and grooming

- Mobility

- Vision and hearing

- Interests, hobbies, activities, favourite pastimes

- Disposition

- Special requirements

It is also a good idea to take a snap shot and place the current photo in the elder's room for visual comparison in their physical state of health. This may be valuable for monitoring the elder's condition over the first few months as staff will not have yet had a chance to know the full extent of the elder's capabilities, thus making it difficult for them to recognize early signs of deterioration.

## Checklist

### Health, Safety and Diet

❏ There is special consideration given to safety as demonstrated by the presence of hand rails in all halls and absence of carpets. There are clearly marked exits and halls are obstacle-free.

❏ Elevators and entrances are controlled in some manner to ensure elders with dementia cannot wander.

❏ There is a fixed weekly schedule for residents who need assistance with bathing. (i.e., Ask the number of baths given per week.)

❒ Residents suffering from incontinence are checked every one to two hours for a change of diapers. (i.e., Ask how often, as this varies based on personnel staffing levels. Also inquire whether diapers are cloth or disposable).

❒ The dining room is located on the same floor as the resident's room.

❒ There is a licensed dietitian on the premises who is responsible for supervision of daily meals.

❒ Family can request larger portions for an elder who has a large appetite.

❒ Staff members assist residents who have difficulty feeding themselves.

❒ Protocols are satisfactory for dispensing medication. The facility assumes responsibility for obtaining prescription refills. There is a pharmacy on hand.

❒ There is a doctor on the premises daily and one on call 24 hours.

❒ The ratio of staff to residents is satisfactory.

❒ There are physical therapy and rehabilitative services available.

❒ There is a smoking policy in place.

**Location, Structure and Premises**

❒ The location is convenient for family and friends to visit on a regular basis. There is a hospital nearby in case of an emergency.

❒ The facility displays a current operating license and does not have a history of serious violations.

❒ Hallways are wide enough for two wheelchairs to pass with ease.

❒ The main entrance provides wheelchair accessibility.

❒ There is air conditioning during the summer months with individual controls in each room.

❒ The furniture is provided and appears sturdy, beds have safety rails. Residents are allowed to bring a favourite side chair and to hang pictures on the wall.

❒ The resident can have a TV and/or radio if they wish in their room.

❒ The room contains its own bathroom.

❒ The room is equipped with an emergency call button near the bed and the toilet.

## Atmosphere

❒ The caregiver would personally feel comfortable routinely spending time at this facility.

❒ Staff and many residents speak the same language as the resident and share a similar cultural background.

❒ Staff are friendly to residents and visitors and there is a sense of warmth and caring.

❒ Residents look happy and well cared for.

❒ Residents are able to freely walk around the premises.

❒ The facility is clean, well maintained and odor-free.

## Recreation and Amenities

❒ There is a full-time activity director.

❒ Planned activities are available and cater to various conditions such as dementia.

❒ The activity director takes time to meet personally with the family to find out the new resident's interests and preferences and takes steps to integrate the new resident into activities.

❒ There is an activity room on each floor to ensure residents can access it without the need to find their way to another floor.

❒ Family members are able to participate as volunteers if they wish.

❒ There are religious services available within the premises on a weekly basis.

❒ There is a hair salon within the facilities.

❒ Able residents are taken for outside excursions at least once a week.

❒ The grounds contain adequate and pleasant outdoor space for summer picnics, barbeques, and other outdoor activities.

## Contract and Administration

❒ Visitors do not have to make an appointment before seeing their relative. Visitation hours are open throughout the entire day and evening.

❒ There are satisfactory billing options and it is clear what extra charges will apply.

❒ Laundry service is included in the contract without an additional charge.

❏ Regulations regarding annual vacation absences are not overly restrictive. The resident is allowed to leave for overnight weekend visits to family on an unlimited basis. There are satisfactory rules regarding alcoholic beverages.

❏ There is a satisfactory policy for holding a bed if the resident has to be hospitalized briefly.

❏ There are procedures and backups in place in the event of a power failure.

❏ A list of references is available.

The culture within the facility will impact the new resident's ease with which they are able to integrate into their new home. Therefore, when possible, the caregiver should look for facilities where language and culture are most similar to the elder's background. An elder whose first language is not English may experience difficulty in communicating with staff and other residents as their language skills begin to deteriorate with the slowing of cognitive processes.

### Respite in Long-Term Care Centres

Many long-term care centres reserve a limited number of beds for respite use. A caregiver who is considering various facilities as a future residence for their loved one might utilize the facility under consideration for respite purposes as a means of becoming more familiar with the people and services. These can be accessed by calling the local community service centre responsible for allocating beds in long-term care centres.

*Chapter 11*

# Long-Term Care Insurance: Policy Structures and Definitions of Care

## THE NEED

Canadians have one of the highest levels of social benefits in the world when health care spending is measured as a percent of GDP. Regardless of one's earnings, a provincial health card is all that is necessary to receive treatment. This is consistent with the principles of the *Canada Health Act* that everyone should have access to medically necessary health care, regardless of their ability to pay. There are five basic principles which are:

1. **Public Administration** — the system is publicly administered on a not-for-profit basis. Services can be delivered through contracts with the private sector, however, these are under the administration of the public sector.

2. **Comprehensiveness** — the plan provides that all medically necessary physician and hospital services are covered.

3. **Universality** — all Canadians must have access to these services.

4. **Portability** — all Canadians must be covered for services received in another province.

5. **Accessibility** — services must be available without user fees, extra billing, or other barriers to reasonable access.

Many people think that all aspects of health care fall within these guidelines. This widely held, but false idea, is the great Canadian social benefits myth. In fact, the *Canada Health Act* only applies to doctors' services and hospital services. Each province supplements these services with health care delivery funded by the province and the community. This includes services such as home care, continuing care, prescription drugs for seniors or special equipment. Provincial governments across Canada are now examining what is essential, what changes should be made to the services currently delivered, and what Canadians should be individually responsible for.

There is a clear movement towards emphasis on wellness, eliminating duplication in the system, less reliance upon hospitals and increased reliance upon services in the communities. There is also a movement towards focusing on affordability. This shift is already evident by reductions in the number of acute care hospital beds, shorter hospital stays, and increases in home care services provided in the community instead of the hospital.

Many Canadians feel that access to health services has declined, as evidenced by long waiting times, difficulties in getting appointments with specialists, and difficulties in getting hospital beds. As the highest users of health care services are the elderly, they are the people most impacted by changes since they have the greatest need. Government health care changes have led to concerns beyond access, and include fears regarding quality and safety.

Looking ahead, seniors have valid concerns regarding whether they will have to pay for services that they cannot afford and whether they will be able to get home care and long-term care when they need it. These changes not only affect today's seniors, but the growing population of tomorrow's seniors. As new technologies and new drugs are developed it changes the way illnesses are treated with the result being all segments of the population, not just the elderly, will spend less time in the hospital and more assistance will be required from home and community services. Seniors will have to compete with the general population for access to the community services that support their ability to remain at home.

Canadians have high expectations for their health care but provincial governments are starting to draw a line between what is essential for the government to fund, and what responsibilities belong to Canadians themselves. The aging process brings with it an ultimate reliance upon family and community or institutions for care in the final years. The government's growing emphasis on delineating between "need" and "want" means that people who would like to have choice in their elder years regarding where they live and who takes care of them must ensure that they have the financial ability to do so independent of government programs.

Long-term care insurance has emerged in the Canadian market to meet this need. It provides an alternative source of dollars to cover today's gaps in social benefits and those that may be there in the future. There are different approaches to long-term care insurance and consequently consumers have a variety from which to choose. The cost varies with each approach because the insurer is assuming a different risk. There are differences related to the type of services covered, the triggers for payment and various supplementary benefits that are either built into the contract or are available as an option at an additional cost. The long-term care insurance market is in its infancy and products will continue to evolve.

While it is sometimes thought of as an offshoot to disability insurance, long-term insurance is really a separate product category. The individual must satisfy the requirements of a specific definition in order for benefits to begin — this is quite unlike life insurance, where the triggering event (i.e., death) is easy to prove. For this reason, the consumer should examine policy provisions and work closely with their financial planner when considering which long-term care contract best meets their individual goals.

## POLICY STRUCTURES

There are three main structures for long-term care insurance (LTC) policies. These are:

1. Reimbursement-based models

2. Indemnity-based models

3. Income-based models

LTC policies can also be a combination of these, such as a policy which provides home care benefits on a reimbursement basis and facility care benefits on an indemnity basis.

### Reimbursement-Based Model

Under a reimbursement-based model, the insured must remit expense receipts for covered services that are then reimbursed up to the daily maximum entitled for that service. If the amount incurred falls below the daily benefit maximum, the contract usually guarantees that the unused portion will be carried forward by lengthening the number of days that benefits can be collected overall. As there is a contractual carry-forward provision, and since cheques for benefits are disbursed on a monthly basis anyway, the insurer may "ignore" the daily limits and administer the claim based on the monthly equivalent of the daily maximum. This procedure addresses the issue of multiple services received on the same day (and therefore exceeding that day's maximum) when no service is received later the same week. This could be due to caregivers' schedules and their availability to perform required services all falling on the same day. The practice of disregarding the daily cap would be an administrative practice and not a contractual guarantee. As such, procedures could change at a later date to a more literal interpretation of the contract.

As the insurer is only paying benefits for expenses actually incurred, this method of insurance usually costs less. As claims costs are kept down, this could help to avoid rate increases for a longer period of time.

## Indemnity-Based Model

Under an indemnity-based model, the insured provides evidence that a covered care has been received, and the insurer pays the stipulated daily benefit amount. Receipts are only required to verify that a covered care service has been received. If service costs exceed the daily maximum, there is no additional benefit payable. However, if they fall short of the daily maximum, the flat daily amount is still paid regardless. As a result, there is no "lengthening" at the back end as in the case of reimbursement benefits.

This model leaves potential for extra dollars to be available for use on services not covered, such as the purchase of medication or equipment. It tends to cost a little more as a result.

Under both the reimbursement and indemnity models, there are stipulations concerning *where* long-term care can be provided, *who* is able to provide the care to the insured individual (i.e., a relative, a paraprofessional), and *what* care services will be eligible for payment.

## Income-Based Model

An income-based model functions similar to a disability income policy. The insured purchases a particular benefit amount and this is paid regardless of the actual level of expenses incurred. There is no distinction made regarding *where* the care is provided — it can be at home or in a facility. There is no distinction regarding *who* provides the care — it can be a professional or a family member. It also does not distinguish regarding *what* service has been provided or the insured's care level. The dollars can be used to cover health care, cooking, cleaning, equipment, medication, facility room rates or any other expenditure the insured wishes to make.

As the income-based model provides the greatest flexibility in types of care, it is usually somewhat more expensive. The contract is notably simpler because there is no need for extensive definitions regarding types of care, eligible facilities and eligible caregivers.

All three models, (reimbursement, indemnity and income), contain other triggers that must be satisfied before a benefit will be paid.

## Hybrids and Other Variations

Hybrid policies are also appearing in the market as new forms of coverage bringing greater choice to consumers. These include conversion plans and pooled or shared benefits plans.

### Conversion Model

Conversion policies start out as another category of insurance such as disability income, critical illness, or term life insurance, and then eventually convert to long-term care facility coverage. This conversion may occur gradually over a compressed period of time such as five years, or instantaneous at a given age such as age 65. Nevertheless, the LTC coverage eventually provided is in accordance with the basic policy models and definitions of care described in this section. The advisor must look further to determine whether coverage is comprehensive including both home care and facility care benefits, or only the latter. Normally, a rider must be added to round out protection to include home care coverage and this should be done at the time of purchase, not at the time of conversion when the insured might potentially be no longer eligible due to their health status.

Conversion policies offer a creative way to address a current need that will diminish over time, and to simultaneously provide for a future need that will increase as the insured ages.

### Pooled Benefits Model

Another variation is the "pooled benefit", which is a hybrid of the income-based and indemnity-based models. As with other income-based plans, the policy does not stipulate *who* can provide care, consequently an informal caregiver may be tending to the recipient's needs. Like the indemnity-based model, benefit payment is impacted based on *where* care is received (home versus facility). Benefits double once the insured transitions from home care to facility care.

The insurance is purchased as a lump-sum amount (e.g., $500,000) from which a predetermined monthly amount is drawn (e.g., 2%), until such time as the pool is exhausted. The pool may be established for a single individual or a couple can draw from a common pool. For this reason, it is also referred to as a "Shared Benefits" plan.

A care recipient generally receives home care until such time as their needs have increased to a point where it is no longer cost effective to provide the level of support needed. At this time a move to a residential facility takes place. The pooled benefits model automatically increases the benefits when this move occurs. The overall pool remains the same and thus is depleted faster.

# DEFINITIONS OF COVERED CARE

The term "care" can become very confusing when reviewing an LTC policy contract. It is helpful to remember that the term "care'" is used in an LTC policy in four different contexts. These are:

1. Terms that describe care as a *location* such as "home care", "facility care", etc.

2. Terms that describe care as a *condition severity* or *level of care* such as "personal care", "intermediate care", "extended care", "chronic care", etc.

3. Terms that describe care as a *service* such as "home care support", "home health care", etc.

4. Terms that describe care as a *provider* such as "health care agency", "home care support agency".

To aid understanding, it helps to place the term in its context first - whether it is describing a location, a condition, a service, or a provider of service.

## Where Long-Term Care Can Be Provided

LTC policies can cover care in a variety of settings such as:

- **Home and Community** — this includes care services received in the home or at an adult day support centre. This is usually known as *Home Care Benefits*.

- **Residential Facility** — this includes care services received in an institution such as a nursing home also known as a long-term care centre. This is usually known as *Facility Benefits*.

Some contracts cover both Home Care Benefits and Facility Care Benefits on an integrated basis. This is referred to as an *Integrated Benefit contract*. Alternatively, some companies issue one benefit as the base contract to which the other benefit can be added as a rider. This enables the insurer to combine policy models and offer the Home Care segment as a reimbursement plan with Facility Care being covered on an indemnity basis, or to offer both Home Care and Facility Care as indemnity benefits yet have the flexibility to choose different plan designs for each portion of coverage.

It is important to determine the care setting for which coverage is desired, and to review the policy for any related restrictions or payment conditions.

## Home Care Benefits

The term "home care", as used in "Home Care Policy" is used in the context of "location" and "service". It encompasses both support services as well as health services received at one's primary residence.

### Home Support Services

This is a service description. It refers to assistance provided in a person's home to assist them with activities of daily living. It does not include treatment of an illness, disease or injury. The services must be provided by a home care agency and not by family members. Activities include administration of medication, assistance with exercise, personal assistance with feeding, dressing, transferring, toileting, and home management such as cleaning, cooking, and laundry. The service itself need not be performed by a paraprofessional, but would generally require that it be performed at the request of a physician. While most insurers do not allow the insured to choose their own service providers, some will consider services outside a home care agency with prior authorization.

### Home Health Care

This refers to health care provided in a person's home by a professional or paraprofessional other than a family member. The insurer may require that the care be arranged through a Home Health Care Agency at the request of a physician. Covered services are those that are medically related such as physical, speech, respiratory, and occupational therapy as provided by a registered nurse, nurse's assistant, or equivalent.

### Adult Day Support Centre

This refers to a centre where social and health services are provided during the day in a community setting to a group of adults that are primarily elderly or disabled. The policy may cover the delivery of services in such a setting as part of the Home Care Benefits. Although insurance policies may use the term "Adult Day Care", many government support services use the term "Senior Day Program" or "Day Centre". Programs offered in these settings usually consist of supervision, activities, meals, personal care, counseling and minor health care such as administering medication. The service is one that is attended daily or on specific days only.

## Facility Benefits

### Long-Term Care Facility

This refers to an institution that is licensed as a convalescent nursing facility. Policies may also include in this definition a retirement home or lodge if there is continuous nursing service and provided the insured's residence at the facility is medically necessary. A few policies may also include convalescent units in a hospital, however terms of the policy should be checked carefully as this is not normally covered by most contracts.

Specifically excluded are facilities for the treatment of alcoholism, drug addiction, tuberculosis, mental and nervous disorders, and facilities that are primarily for training and education.

There may be geographic restrictions in the policy. For instance, a definition might state that the facility has to be within Canada or North America. Other policies may state that facilities outside Canada are covered only if approved by the company.

## Levels of Care

Not all policies distinguish between levels of care. Some policies may use this as a means of identifying what benefit level is payable, or in what care setting (location) it will be covered. It also has a relationship to who may provide the type of care as this can have cost implications associated with it. For example, a company may not wish to cover a lower level care being provided by a higher paid caregiver as this might create unnecessary expense when the care could be administered at a lower cost. Or it may be used to determine if the care could be provided in a lower cost setting such as home versus facility.

The more common terms that are used appear below.

### Skilled Care

Skilled care refers to treatment for medical conditions requiring a licensed medical professional. Some examples of services that fall in this care level include physical therapy, speech therapy, respiratory therapy, and occupational therapy.

### Personal Care

Personal care is also referred to as **custodial care** and deals with care that may be provided by individuals other than licensed professionals and paraprofessionals, such as assistance with activities of daily living including bathing, dressing, transferring, toileting, and feeding. It may also include assistance with instrumental activities of daily living such as meal preparation, grocery shopping, and other home management tasks. A Personal Care Worker or Personal Support Worker usually provides these services.

### Intermediate Care

Intermediate care is continuous nursing care that is preventative or rehabilitative in nature. Intermediate care falls between personal care and extended care. It is care that is provided in periods of stable condition and includes for instance, administering injections to an individual at the request of a physician.

It is important not only to determine whether the LTC policy covers all types of care — personal, skilled, intermediate and extended care, but also to look at whether the insurer uses these care levels to determine where such care must be delivered.

## Extended Care

Extended care deals with a chronic condition or limitation that serves to maintain a standard of living. It is care that requires the attendance of a registered nurse and is at the order of a physician.

## Chronic Care

Some insurers use this term instead of "Extended Care" and define it as the irreversible presence of disease that would require care in a long-term care facility.

# Who Can Provide Home Care

Caregivers to an elder can include a wide range of people, but not all are necessarily recognized as providing covered care under the definition of the LTC policy. Policies that make this distinction will contain a definition for this purpose. For instance, a nurse through a home care agency that delivers assistance to the elder will qualify while typically the same assistance provided by a family member will not. Many LTC policies do not pay for care that is delivered by a family member regardless of the care level or the training that the family member may have. A few may contain a special provision to recognize a family member. However, this is not an issue with LTC policies that are income-based models because they do not distinguish regarding who provides the care or what the care service is.

Following are some of the more common terms that appear in LTC policies that relate to the topic of providers of care.

## Home Health Care Agency

This refers to an organization that provides health care services in the home by qualified professionals such as a registered nurse or a licensed social worker. Most LTC policies require home health care services to be provided through a home health care agency in order to be eligible for payment.

## Home Support Services Agency

This refers to an organization that provides home support services by or under the supervision of qualified professionals, such as a registered nurse or licensed social worker. Services may be in the category of home management including light housekeeping, meal preparation, and laundry. Most LTC policies require home support services to be provided through such an agency to qualify for payment. The individual cannot use an independent cleaning service or housekeeper for this purpose.

## Other Care Services

### Hospice and Palliative Care

This refers to services provided through a certified program by a hospice agency for the control of pain and symptoms related to a terminal illness. Usually, this benefit applies if the elder is not expected to live longer than six months. The program may include medical and health services to the elder and counseling support to the family members.

Some policies limit the benefit to a period such as six months. This is further subject to the overall maximum benefits elected under the policy.

### Respite Care

This refers to care provided during a period of time that the primary caregiver is unable to care for the individual. It is usually included in an LTC policy as part of home care benefits. Its intent is to give the family member temporary relief from the responsibility of the caregiver role. While some long-term care facilities set aside a number of beds for respite care use, not all long-term care insurance policies pay benefits for respite care when delivered in this type of setting. Therefore, the policy wording should be checked to determine whether relief is for day service only, or if it will cover 24-hour periods to allow the family to use a long-term care centre while they take a family holiday.

# Chapter 12

# Provisions That Define Eligibility

## STANDARD MEASURES THAT DEFINE ELIGIBILITY

Every Long-Term Care (LTC) policy specifies the changes in functional dependence that qualify the insured to receive benefits. There are two categories, which are:

- ADL-based definitions that describe functional limitations

- Cognitive impairment definitions

**207**

Policies also have other criteria that must be met, such as the need to be under the care and supervision of a physician.

## ADL-Based Definitions

An ADL-based definition is one that relates to the insured's ability to perform two or more activities of daily living. The focus is on functional limitation. As functional limitation can be determined by tests, it is an objective measure.

### Activities That are Measured

There are commonly five or six activities of daily living (i.e., ADLs) that are evaluated. These are:

- Bathing — the ability to wash oneself in a tub, shower, or by sponge bath

- Eating — the ability to feed oneself

- Dressing — the ability to put on and take off clothes or fasten and unfasten them

- Toileting — the ability to get to and from the toilet

- Transferring — the ability to move in and out of a chair, wheelchair, or bed with or without the aid of a cane or other supporting device

- Continence — the ability to maintain bladder control

There have been many studies conducted that reveal there is a strong relationship between deterioration in these functional areas and the use of acute and chronic care services. The scale was originally developed by an American physician, Dr. Sidney Katz.

LTC policies indicate that there must be a loss of two or more of these activities. A few companies use a five-category scale, but most use a 6-category scale. The variable is whether incontinence is an eligible condition or not.

### Measuring The Functional Loss

There are three stages of functional loss a person passes through. Initially, they may need assistive devices and will continue to cope well independently with these. An example of a device is a cane. Other devices include special adaptive cutlery, tools for reaching and grabbing, and tools that aid dressing. The second stage is the need for *standby assistance*. Standby assistance is when another person must stay within arm's reach so they can physically help if necessary, in order to prevent the person from injury. An example of this is when someone must be on hand while the person steps in and out of a tub to ensure they manage safely. The third level of assistance is *one-on-one assistance*. This is when the person requires hands-on physical assistance from another person to perform the task. An example of this is if someone must physically dress the insured, provide incontinence management, or physically aid the person to move from the bed to a chair or with personal hygiene associated with toileting.

Companies differ in terms of how they measure whether a functional loss satisfies their definition of functional dependence, consequently triggering payment of benefits. A few examples of different measures include the following:

- Needs standby or partial assistance from another individual

- Needs one-on-one assistance, i.e., is completely dependent upon another individual

- Cannot perform the task unaided or aided with the assistance of another individual or the use of a device

The most liberal definition is one that says the functional limitation is considered a loss of activity if the person requires standby or partial assistance from another individual. Sometimes policies do not consider an individual who could be fed with a tube as having satisfied the criteria for payment of benefits. This would be considered a very restrictive interpretation of "cannot perform the task unaided or aided with the assistance of another individual or the use of a device". By comparison, under the first two example definitions, if the only way a person could receive nourishment was through a feeding tube, this would be considered a functional dependence triggering payments. As can be seen, definitions control how soon the insured can receive benefits and the cost of the LTC policy will reflect this.

The loss of activities tends to occur in the reverse order that they were learned and this is believed to be due to the mental complexity associated with performing the task. Consequently, the first activity to go is usually the ability to bathe oneself, followed by dressing, then transferring, then toileting, and finally feeding oneself. A stricter definition for "feeding" would therefore, be of lesser concern than a more restrictive definition for bathing, as it is most likely that two or more ADLs would be lost before the ability to feed oneself is lost.

## Cognitive Impairment

This is another type of measure that appears in LTC policies generally in combination with an ADL definition. A cognitive ability refers to one's learning, memorizing, and processing abilities. Cognitive decline in seniors is a common occurrence, including problems with memory and speed of processing information. This is not what is meant by a cognitive impairment. Degenerative brain diseases such as Alzheimer's disease and Parkinson's disease cause brain cells to die resulting in cognitive decline. Other conditions that also result in an unusual decline in cognitive processes include severe brain injury such as stroke or trauma. Cognitive impairment in seniors is associated with increased mortality.

Cognitive impairment can be evaluated using standardized tests to ascertain reduction in short and long-term memory and general orientation. Cognitive impairment can be evident when an individual can still perform certain tasks, but requires verbal cueing in order to do so. An example of this is when a person can dress themselves, but must be told related steps such as "first put your arm in here", or "put your socks on before your shoes".

Some LTC policies recognize the need for verbal cueing as a cognitive impairment and therefore pay benefits based solely upon this loss. This is a valuable feature, given the high incidence of dementia in elders. Other policies contain stricter definitions.

LTC policies that contain an ADL-based definition generally stipulate that the insured satisfies the requirements if they have the inability to perform two or more activities of daily living or have a cognitive impairment. Cognitive impairment may be defined in the policy as the inability to think, perceive, reason or remember or requires verbal cueing, assistance or supervision from another person. For example, wandering is a common problem for people with Alzheimer's disease, and supervision by another person may be required to ensure their safety. A more narrowly defined definition may stipulate it as difficulties associated with memory, attention or loss of intellectual capacity that requires 24-hour supervision to help or protect the individual from personal injury to themselves or others and has lasted for a continuous specified period such as 90 days. The period of time required may not be stated in the policy, but may be a claims adjudication practice. This is not related to the elimination period in the policy. Regardless, to be covered, the condition must be due to an organic cause such as Parkinson's disease, Alzheimer's disease or Senile Dementia, or severe brain injury such as stroke or trauma. It cannot be the result of alcoholism or a non-prescription drug disorder or addiction.

## INSTRUMENTAL ACTIVITIES OF DAILY LIVING (IADLS)

An additional screen that may be used to assess a person's abilities deals with the less complex tasks of daily living. These less complex tasks are referred to as instrumental activities of daily living (IADLs). Examples of these activities are cooking, grocery shopping, laundry, bill paying, taking medicine, telephoning, and housekeeping. This measure is not used as the primary test because, although an individual who suffers the loss of ADLs generally has an inability to perform several IADLs, the reverse is not always true. IADLs cannot be reliably used as a predictor of whether someone will eventually suffer the loss of ADLs.

During the underwriting process the underwriter may probe further for a current loss of ADLs if there are some signs during the customer telephone interview of loss of IADLs. This is because many ADL-impaired individuals also have a loss of several IADLs. A policy should not be declined, however, if there is a loss of an IADL with no indication of loss of any ADLs or some other condition. There is a cultural issue associated with IADLs and measurement of loss tends to be more subjective than objective. For instance, in many cultures, males do not cook or purchase the groceries. Therefore, one's inability to prepare meals in the elder's later years, may not be based upon a medical change.

Loss of IADLs may be useful in terms of assessing the care and assistance required for an individual when developing a program of care such as the need for using an adult day support centre while caregivers are at work. Companies may not use it however, as a determinant of the need for facility care versus home care because it may not be substantiated as a medically-related need for facility residence. It is beneficial when reviewing LTC policies to ask about the company's practice in this area.

# THE ELIMINATION PERIOD

Every LTC policy contains an elimination period. This is the number of days of functional dependence that must pass before the insurer is responsible for paying benefits. It is similar to a deductible found in other types of insurance, in that expenses incurred by the insured during this period are not covered by the policy. The elimination period is selected by the insured from a range of option such as 0-days, 30 days, 60 days, and 90 days. The longer the elimination period, the less the policy will cost. This offers the individual one method for tailoring benefits to fall more closely within their allocated budget. It enables the individual to plan for the interim use of other disposable dollars if they wish, and to reserve the insurance for protecting against catastrophic financial losses.

Not all options are available with every company. Some companies restrict the 0-day option to facility care only. When selecting an elimination period, the individual should take into account that benefits are paid in arrears and not in advance. Therefore, under a 30-day elimination period, benefits would commence on the 60th day because no payment is due for the first month which represents the period not covered.

Policies differ as to how they count days towards satisfying the elimination period, and the point from which they start the measurement.

## Care Days and Calendar Days

There are two ways that LTC policies might measure satisfaction of the elimination period. They are:

(a) versions that measure care days; or

(b) versions that measure calendar days.

The care days method counts only the number of days that care is actually received and is the method often, but not always, used for home care benefits. For instance, if a physiotherapist came to the residence three times per week in the first month, this would equal a total of 12 days towards the elimination period. The calendar day method would count the entire week, and the elimination period would be satisfied sooner. This must be taken into consideration when selecting an elimination period and when comparing different policies' provisions and rates.

## Measurement Date

How does one determine the date functional dependence occurred? This is important because this date is the point from which the elimination period will begin to be counted. LTC policies may measure days from any of the following occurrences:

- The date of physician certification

- The date that covered care services are first received

- The date a care assessment has been conducted

- The documented date of a major event (such as a severe stroke) that documents dependence

- The date that a plan of care is approved

The policy contract will stipulate which method or methods are used.

## Period of Care

LTC policies generally state that the elimination period must be satisfied by a continuous period of care. This means that the individual has been continuously receiving home care benefits if this is covered under the policy, or has been continuously confined in a covered facility throughout the elimination period.

Recurrent periods of functional dependence may still be considered as one period if they are separated by less than 180 days. This means that the individual will not have to satisfy another elimination period following a short interruption once benefits have commenced. LTC policies do not generally allow the individual however, to accumulate separate periods of care to satisfy the elimination period.

Many LTC policies only require the individual to satisfy the elimination period for facility care once. The policy may allow for a combination of home care and facility care days to be combined together for satisfying the elimination period. For instance, this resolves a situation where an individual who has a 90-day elimination period receives home care for 60 days followed immediately by admission to a long-term care facility. Once the individual has been in the facility for 30 days, the total 90-day elimination period will be satisfied. A policy that requires separate elimination periods for home care and facility care would mean that no benefits would be payable for the 60 days of home care as the 90-day requirement had not been satisfied. An additional 90 days would need to pass following admission to the long-term care facility before benefits would begin.

## Plan of Care

Some companies offer the services of a care coordinator or care advisor on an optional basis as a value-added benefit. The role of the care coordinator is to work with the insured and his or her caregivers to develop a plan of care. The use of this service is voluntary at claim time. Some older LTC policies used the services of a care coordinator as part of the initial assessment in determining the insured's eligibility for benefits during a claim. The recommended plan of care that emerged from the initial assessment was subject to approval by both the insurer and the insured. However, refusal to accept the plan of care, could result in the insured not being eligible for benefits under these older contracts. This method helped to ensure the person was using the most cost effective means for obtaining services.

Policies today offer the services of a care coordinator at the insured's option and they perform an important service of helping both insured and their informal caregivers to navigate the complex health care system and to obtain valuable care assistance available in the community and through government programs. Some policies include this benefit as an annual right at the company's expense for as long as benefits are being paid. Another variation is the right to have a free first assessment, with further care plans being at the insured's own expense. The insured can either choose to implement the plan through the care coordinator, or on their own. If they choose to work through the care coordinator, any expenses associated with the implementation would be at the individual's own expense (the LTC policy is their source of funds to use towards this).

## DAILY BENEFIT AMOUNT

The daily benefit amount determines how much is payable for various types of covered care. It represents the maximum covered per day of care received. Daily amounts are usually purchased in increments of $10. Benefit amounts range from $10 to $350 per day. Under an integrated plan, the amount elected is usually the same for both home and facility care. When home care is purchased as a rider to a base plan of long-term facility care, separate amounts may be purchased for each.

Some policies calculate benefits on a weekly or a monthly basis instead of a daily basis. These policies have the advantage of resolving the issue of multiple services being received on the same day for home care and exceeding the daily maximum. Plans calculated in this manner are usually income-model policies and do not measure what care services were received or how the money was spent.

Reimbursement-based home care plans will pay for actual expenses incurred up to the daily maximum limit. If the full amount is not required, the extra is carried forward to lengthen the number of days or months for which benefits can be collected. Indemnity plans pay the fixed daily amount upon evidence that a covered care service has been received. If expenses fall below, the daily benefit amount remains the same, however if expenses exceed the daily benefit amount, then the maximum limit applies.

## MAXIMUM BENEFITS

The maximum benefit refers to the overall maximum time period that the LTC policy will cover. It is sometimes referred to as a **benefit period** or the **maximum benefit limit**.

There are a variety of these periods from which the individual can choose, such as one year, two years, five years, 10 years and lifetime. The benefit period may be calculated in days instead of years for home care benefits, such as 730 days.

### Overall Maximum Benefit Limit

Some policies use a multiple of the daily rate to determine the overall maximum benefit limit, such as 2,000 times the daily rate. Using $100 as the basic daily rate, then the overall maximum would be equal to 2,000 × $100 = $200,000. This method of calculation recognizes that when care days (instead of calendar days) are used to calculate benefits, then the number of years is less relevant than is the overall dollar amount covered by the plan. It is sometimes used in an integrated policy of home and facility care because both share the pool of available benefits. That is, in the above example, the individual can receive up to $200,000 of home care, facility care, or a combination thereof.

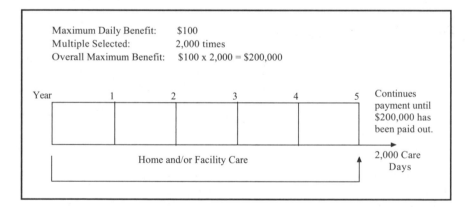

### Maximum Benefit Period

The benefit period method places more specific limits on each type of care. For example, an individual might purchase 730 days of home care benefits plus 1,825 care days (i.e., five years) of facility care benefits. This method is sometimes found in LTC policies that use the rider approach for adding home care benefits to a base contract of facility care benefits. In this instance, the individual could claim up to 730 days of home care. Some plans will then subtract the amount collected from the available benefit period for facility care, which in this example, would leave a remainder of three years as the maximum for facility care. In other words, the benefit periods in some plans run simultaneous as illustrated in the diagram below, not consecutive. Note that not all plans which treat home care benefits as a rider work in this fashion, and the advisor should be clear on this point when presenting the plan to the client.

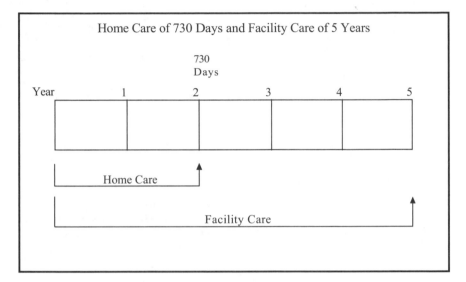

The elimination period is not counted in this calculation. Furthermore, as the actual benefits are per day, only the cumulative total of days that home care was actually received are deducted from the duration for facility care. Consequently, the elapsed calendar time may be longer than five years.

## Pooled Benefit Plans

Under a pooled benefit plan, the *amount of insurance* is selected at the time of purchase as a lump sum similar to how one might purchase life insurance or critical illness insurance.

The *monthly benefit amount* paid out during a claim is a preselected percentage such as 1%, which reduces the size of the remaining pool dollar for dollar. The percentage selected determines how quickly the pool is exhausted. The care setting also impacts how quickly the pool is depleted since the benefit increases for facility care and therefore reduces the remaining pool sooner. The pool is a finite amount that is not replenished.

# EXCLUSIONS AND LIMITATIONS

## Standard Exclusions

Every insurance contract indicates, in addition to the risks that are covered, a number of risks that are not covered. By excluding certain conditions, the insurer is able to make the coverage more affordable. Most exclusions are standard from one company to another and unlikely to be a cause for concern. These include:

(a) intentionally self-inflicted injuries or attempted suicide;

(b) occurrences while in the military;

(c) alcoholism;

(d) drug addiction from chemicals not prescribed by a physician;

(e) commission of a criminal offense; and

(f) mental and nervous conditions that do not have an organic cause.

## Pre-Existing Conditions

Some contracts contain a limitation on payment of benefits for conditions that existed prior to applying for coverage. For instance, they may require the individual to have had no treatment for a continuous period of time such as the immediate six months prior to receiving a period of care for the condition. Although prior and existing conditions are generally dealt with during the underwriting process, this provision helps to protect the company against anything that was missed or that may only surface after issue of the policy. It should not replace the process of thorough underwriting up front.

It is critical that each policy be reviewed to determine what exclusions and limitations will apply at the time of a claim, and to understand how a pre-existing condition will be treated.

# Chapter 13

# Other Provisions, Features and Options

# STANDARD PROVISIONS

## Guaranteed Renewable

### Policy Series

Most Long-Term Care (LTC) policies fall within the "guaranteed renewable series". This means that the policy cannot be cancelled if the insured pays the premium on time or within the defined grace period. However, the insurance company reserves the right to make future premium changes for all insureds within a particular class. The rate change is most likely to occur if the company identifies a negative trend over a period of time, as opposed to a single year of poor experience within the block. Adjustments cannot be applied to a sole insured, but must be applied to all members of the same class. The term "class" can refer to a particular age group, geographic group, or all insureds covered by a particular policy series. It may even be defined as insureds covered by policies issued in a specific year or having a particular elimination period. The group must be large enough for the experience to be statistically credible.

When an insured purchases a policy with a "level premium", they should be aware that the level premium features does not mean the company completely forfeits the right to adjust premiums, as this provision is subject to the allowable adjustments under the "guaranteed renewable" provision.

LTC insurance is still relatively new in the Canadian market, and as such, companies do not have lengthy historical experience of insured lives upon which to base their rates. While every effort is made to strike conservative pricing assumptions, the fact remains that the guaranteed renewable provision acts as a safeguard to the insurer to allow them to adjust rates if there is a need based upon the company's actual claims experience.

### Limited Guarantees

Some companies provide a limited guaranteed period during which rates cannot change. For example, the policy may stipulate that during the first five years, the company guarantees that the rate will not be changed. Some older policies contain a provision that should a rate increase become necessary, it will not exceed a percentage maximum overall such as 20% or 25% above the original base premium. Unfortunately, new policies today no longer provide this valuable guarantee, however some do promise that rates will not be increased after a period of time such as 20 years or age 75. These features provide the insured with some protection against escalating prices that could result in the insured no longer being able to afford the coverage at the time they may be most likely to need the protection. Given the limited experience data available for claims under this type of insurance, each represents a valuable feature for the insured.

## Waiver of Premium

The waiver of premium benefit is normally a standard provision in an LTC policy contract not requiring an additional cost. It provides that premiums will be waived after a period of 90 days. Contracts may differ regarding whether they stipulate that the insured must be continuously confined during this period, or whether they simply require that the individual has received covered treatment for a continuous period of 90 days. This difference in wording impacts whether premiums will be waived for periods during which the insured receives home care benefits. Many people have illnesses that are gradually debilitating, and are initially assisted within their own home for as long as possible. Such periods would not be covered under the waiver of premium provision if the contract stipulates confinement as a requirement. This may be due to the fact that some home care provisions count "care days" and not "calendar days" which may be intermittent.

Some contracts provide that the premium will be waived "as it falls due". This would mean that if the policy is paid annually and the premium falls due during a period of confinement, then the full annual premium will be waived. Some contracts may provide that if the premium is not currently being paid monthly (for instance, annual or semi-annual premium payments), the frequency will be changed to monthly and waived during periods that the insured continues to be eligible for benefits. This relieves the company of the requirement to pay the full annual premium unless the insured remains eligible for the entire 12 months.

As with other forms of insurance, any premiums paid during the initial 90 days are reimbursed upon qualifying for the Waiver of Premium benefit. It is critical that the individual understands that premiums must continue to be paid during the first 90 days even though they could be receiving benefits. Also, it is imperative that the individual confirm with the insurer that the conditions for waiver have been fully satisfied before they cease paying premiums to avoid any limitations that may be related to counting only care days versus calendar days, or only counting facility confinement days versus benefits-paid days. To do otherwise would risk a policy lapse for non-payment of premium right at the time the individual has suffered health changes that would entitle them to benefits.

## Indexing of Benefits During a Claim

Some policies contain a provision whereby an insured that is on claim for more than 12 months receives an increase in monthly benefits. The monthly indemnity is increased each January by an amount equal to the Consumer Price Index subject to a stated maximum such as 3 or 4%. This helps to guard against erosion of the benefits caused by inflation while receiving benefits over an extended period of time. This provision is distinct from an Inflation Protection Rider that can be added for pre-claim indexing.

This is a valuable provision, but is not found in all LTC policies and thus is an essential point for the advisor to discuss with the client.

Some companies may offer this feature as a "bundled benefit" within the optional Inflation Protection Benefit Rider, coupling together both pre-claim and on-claim indexing of coverage.

The advisor should review this provision to determine important issues such as:

- What happens to increased coverage if the claim is for a temporary period only — does the insured have the right to buy up' the increased amount, and if so, at what rate?

## Coordination of Benefits

LTC insurance is for the purpose of providing a source of dollars to cover expenses that may not otherwise be available. Given the current level of social benefits that exist in Canada, some policies require the submission of evidence that benefits have been applied for first under any government program. Thereafter, they will consider payment. In this instance, it is important to ascertain whether it is only the application for such benefits that must have occurred, and not the approval or receipt of benefits. Coordination with government benefits is a method of eliminating duplication of payment, similar to the concept of reimbursement versus indemnity. For this reason, this provision is often found in reimbursement-based models.

Government benefits may not be the only form of benefit coordination. Some contracts avoid the risk of over-insurance by including an offset provision against other sources of insurance including both private and public sources. Over-insurance occurs when an individual has a total amount of insurance that exceeds the insurance company's maximum issue limits. This is a concern to insurers because of the fear that it may lead to an increased tendency to claim for benefits. The premium charged for the insurance has been based on an expected rate of claims. When claims exceed this expected rate, the company suffers a loss. This eventually leads to a price increase for new insureds and can also result in a rate increase for existing insureds under the guaranteed renewable provision. This also helps to protect the insurer from changes the government may make in the future to social benefits.

It is important to review this provision when considering the purchase of multiple policies to fully understand the impact on the existing policy.

## Non-Payment of Premium

As people age, there is a greater risk that a premium may not be paid when it is due. The risk is even greater for an individual who has developed a form of dementia or other illness that affects memory such as Alzheimer's disease. This could unfortunately occur just prior to becoming entitled to benefits or while waiting to satisfy the waiver of premium provision.

Therefore, it is critical to examine the features and provisions within the contract that help to guard against coverage going out of force.

### Grace Period and Extensions

All LTC policies provide a 30-day **grace period** following the due date of the premium during which the coverage remains in effect. Some policies contain more generous provisions beyond 30 days. One company offers at its discretion, to extend the grace period for up to six months upon submission of satisfactory evidence that a cognitive impairment or a mental-nervous disorder has contributed to the unintentional oversight of paying the premium. This is a very valuable benefit.

### Special Offer

Some policies contain a special offer following the grace period that provides the individual with a guarantee that they can put the policy back in force without having to re-qualify medically if they pay the premium within a stipulated period of time such as two weeks. The insurance is not considered to be in force during this time as it is during the grace period. A claim would not be paid that occurs during this two-week special offer period.

### Reinstatement

All LTC policies also include a provision for reinstatement of a policy that has lapsed following the end of the grace period. This refers to the individual's ability to restore the policy as it was originally and to bring its values up to date. The reinstatement provision requires the individual to prove that they still qualify for the insurance medically and to pay the back premiums. Because there is a possibility that the individual has not disclosed some pertinent information, the contestable period begins again with respect to information given on the application for reinstatement. The right to reinstate expires after the policy has been out of force for a period, such as 3 months.

### Third-Party Notification

Some companies deal with the concern that an individual may forget to pay a premium, by allowing the election of an alternate contact to be made on the application form itself. A person may appoint, for instance, an adult son or daughter to help ensure that coverage does not lapse unintentionally. If a premium is not paid by its due date, a duplicate notice will be sent to the stated contact. The problem with relying on this is that alternate contact names and numbers become stale with the passage of time. Often, people do not think to contact the insurer to advise that the alternate contact has moved or changed telephone numbers. Some companies try to address this by sending a notice to all of its LTC policyholders requesting updated information.

While it is not a perfect solution to ensuring premiums remain paid up to date, it is a valuable option that should be utilized.

# NON-FORFEITURE PROVISIONS

LTC policies may be purchased by someone in their 40s or 50s. Unless the policy has options for limited payment, premiums may be paid for 30 to 40 years before the need arises to claim for benefits. Insurers know that although LTC insurance should be purchased for the long-term, some people who buy it will cancel the insurance or forget to pay premiums. This lapse assumption is a critical part of how insurers develop prices for premiums. Some companies may take the approach that the premiums paid from policies that lapsed belong to the insurance company and rates are set with this assumption in mind. Some companies take the approach that the premiums paid by a particular individual should belong in part to that person if they later cancel or terminate the coverage.

Non-forfeiture provisions, often associated with life insurance that contains cash surrender values, are used by some companies in LTC insurance to return a portion of the premiums that have been paid by the insured, if they later cancel or lapse their LTC policy. The methods used by companies are:

- Reduced paid-up insurance

- Extended term insurance

## Reduced Paid-Up Insurance

The **reduced paid-up insurance** method provides that the insured will be entitled to a reduced benefit that requires no further premiums to keep the policy in force. It is based on a philosophy that having some insurance is better than having no insurance. The amount of the reduced paid-up insurance varies based upon the original age at purchase and the number of years the policy has been in force at the time of cancellation or lapse. For example, an individual who purchased an LTC policy at age 40 may be eligible after 10 years of paying premiums, to have a reduced paid-up policy equal to 50% of the amount they purchased. An individual who is age 70 at the time of purchase, may have a fully paid-up policy at age 85. The paid-up insurance is often for facility care only and does not apply to the home care portion of the policy. The insured should read this provision carefully as they may be forfeiting home care benefits.

Opponents of this method feel the downside to this form of non-forfeiture provision is seen when termination of the policy occurs very early, such as in the policy's first ten years when the amount of paid-up insurance purchased may be too small to be of significance.

When a company initiates a rate change under the guaranteed renewable provision, it cannot adjust policies that have been placed on reduced paid-up status.

The reduced paid-up values are guaranteed and are stated in the policy at the time of purchase.

## Extended Term Insurance

The term insurance method ensures that the amount of coverage originally purchased is preserved for as long as possible. For example, the coverage may remain unchanged and in force for a period of 80 months. The period of time would vary based upon the age of the individual at the time of purchasing the policy and how long the LTC policy has been in force.

The philosophy behind this method is that it is better to have an adequate amount of coverage, and when it is in the form of temporary insurance, the cost is less than what it is for reduced paid-up. Consequently, it better protects the individual who ceases to pay premiums in the early years, such as five or 10 years from the date of purchase, because the amount of paid-up benefits that could be bought at this time would be too small to be of significance to the individual.

As with reduced paid-up insurance, when a company initiates a rate change under the guaranteed renewable provision, it cannot adjust policies that have been placed on extended term status.

The extended term values are guaranteed and are stated in the policy at the time of purchase.

## Value to the Insured

Non-forfeiture options offer the individual one more way of dealing with the issue of non-payment of premiums. This may occur because someone forgets to pay a premium and the first three lines of lapse defense fail (i.e., grace period, third party notice, special offers). Additionally, the individual may have become uninsurable and not qualify under the reinstatement provision to place the coverage back in force. Coverage is often purchased by seniors who must pay premiums from their fixed income for many years before the need for long-term care will arise. Their ability to continue to pay premiums may change. An increase in premiums by the insurer may make the insurance no longer affordable. Financial circumstances, particularly for women, may change if pension benefits end with the death of the spouse. Some individuals may decide that their priorities have shifted and simply decide not to continue the insurance. Policy provisions and contracts themselves may change in the future, and the individual may wish to obtain more current coverage.

Non-forfeiture options are an area for comparison when evaluating different companies' policies and plans as they form an important part of the benefit provisions purchased. Not only must the individual ensure that the policy contains an option, but table values can vary from one company to another. The type of option that is contained in the policy will impact the premium charged for the insurance and this must be kept in mind when comparing rates.

## SPECIAL FEATURES

In addition to the standard provisions contained in LTC policies, companies add special features to distinguish their policies from competitors. While these features may be bundled into the basic policy, there is a cost associated with them. Therefore, the individual must consider whether the feature is one that they would purchase if available as a separate option, and what the likelihood will be of using the benefit. Many special features fulfill a valuable service but if affordability becomes a later issue, these built-in features cannot be stripped from the policy to lessen the cost.

### Bed Reservation Benefit

When living in a long-term care facility, an individual who becomes ill may require transfer temporarily to a hospital. During this period of time, the facility will continue to charge the usual daily rate. The Bed Reservation Benefit is a provision that pays the fee required to hold the room for the period of hospitalization. However, every facility has a maximum time frame for which they will hold a bed. Therefore, the agreement with the facility itself, should be reviewed to determine how long a resident can be absent during which the room will remain assigned to them. The Bed Reservation Benefit does not alter the facility's contract provision in any way, it merely ensures that the insurance benefit does not cease during the period of time that the individual is not in the facility.

The LTC policy will also indicate a maximum time per year for which this benefit will be paid. This is generally in the range of 15 to 30 days.

### Emergency Response Benefit

The Emergency Response Benefit is a rider contained in some LTC policies whereby the insurer will pay for the monthly cost of an emergency response system if it is medically required. To be eligible for payment the individual must be receiving benefits under a home care benefit. It does not pay once the individual is confined to a facility.

The Emergency Response Benefit provides peace of mind to caregivers and the elder that should the elder take ill when alone in the home, a medical emergency response team can quickly be notified.

### Upgrade Assurance Provision

The Upgrade Assurance Provision is a form of guarantee to the insured that if the company introduces changes to provisions within its contracts offered to new applicants, these same changes will be automatically available to the insured. The insured must indicate their decision to purchase the upgrade within a defined period of time such as one or two months following its availability. The upgrade will not be granted if the individual is currently collecting benefits. The time limitation helps to protect the company from anti-selection that could otherwise occur. Anti-selection refers to a person's tendency to wait to see if the benefit will be needed and then to elect the change at that time.

By electing benefits only when their health is failing, the cost of claims is higher than what would normally be expected to occur. This ultimately results in increased premiums for everyone.

The insurance company will reserve the right to increase the premium and may even require that the new rate for the entire policy be at the current age of the insured. Therefore, it is important to check the rate impact before electing any such updates. A change that occurs after the policy has been in force for 10 years could have a very significant increase in premiums when adjusted to a current age basis.

The Upgrade Assurance Provision is particularly beneficial to someone who may no longer be able to qualify medically for new coverage and who is willing to pay more for improved features. LTC insurance is still in its infancy in Canada and continuous product improvements can be expected to occur as this type of insurance evolves.

## Medical Equipment Assistance Benefit

The Medical Equipment Assistance Benefit provides reimbursement for the rental of medical equipment necessary in the treatment of an individual while they are receiving home care. The policy will state the maximum benefit payable and this is usually in the range of $4,000 to $6,000. The benefit does not cover equipment that would ordinarily be found in one's home, or that could be used by family members for some purpose. For instance, it would not pay in a situation where an individual rents a piece of fitness equipment for use in physiotherapy as it could be used by family members for recreation.

Some companies may stipulate that the equipment is required as outlined in a plan of care. While the benefit is intended to cover rental costs, it may be possible for the individual to purchase the equipment under this benefit if the cost to do so would be less than the cost of renting.

This provision may be in the form of an optional benefit and require an additional premium. As provincial insurance programs offer some financial assistance in this area, the individual should ask about any integration of government programs with this benefit.

## Discounts for Joint Policies and Shared Benefit Policies

Some companies offer discounts when both spouses purchase coverage simultaneously. Qualifying for the discount may require both spouses to have identical plans. In most cases, spouses will likely need similar coverage. However, if one spouse requires lesser protection, then the savings associated with such a plan should be compared to the cost savings associated with the discount. Joint policies offer the advantage of each spouse having independent coverage, but the risk is that the proceeds may be exhausted under one long before the second spouse has a need for long-term care.

Pooled benefit plans (also known as Shared Benefit Policies) offer the option for sharing benefits with a spouse under the same contract. Should the couple later separate, the policy can be divided with each spouse receiving half of the remaining pool. As the monthly benefit is calculated as a percentage of the pool, it is doubled so that the benefit amount during a claim will be the same. For example, a joint policy of $400,000 with a monthly benefit of 1%, becomes two single policies of $200,000 with a monthly benefit of 2%. Consequently, when drawing the benefit, the fund will be depleted in half the time (maximum 50 payments instead of 100). In order to qualify for dividing the contract, some conditions must be satisfied. For example, neither spouse must be collecting benefits at the time of separation, nor have collected a benefit in the prior 180 days, nor be awaiting satisfaction of the elimination period in order to start collecting a benefit.

## OPTIONAL RIDERS

Optional riders are benefits made available at an additional price. Some options broaden the base coverage such as the addition of a Home Care Rider to a basic Facility Care policy. When a rider approach is used to broaden basic protection, the individual must be sure to understand which provisions of the policy apply to both the basic policy and the rider and whether there are separate terms of eligibility for each portion of coverage.

Other options serve to enhance the protection. These options are not essential to having a quality basic program of LTC insurance, but enable a person to tailor coverage to their preferences and concerns. As LTC insurance is still in its infancy in the Canadian market, there is not a wide range of options available. The three most popular options at this time are:

- Return of Premium at Death
- Inflation Protection Rider
- Future Purchase Option

### Return of Premium at Death

The Return of Premium at Death Rider operates as a death benefit by returning a portion of premiums paid if the insured dies while the plan is in force. The benefit is graded upward the longer that premiums have been paid. For example, it may return 10% (or as much as 50% with some companies) of premiums once 10 years of premiums have been paid, to 100% if premiums have been paid for 20 or more years at the time of death. It addresses the concern that someone may pay premiums for many years until their death, without having a need for the insurance. It is a method of dealing with the cash build-up in a policy and returning it to the individual whose premiums generated it. In this respect, it performs a similar function to non-forfeiture provisions but differs in that the triggering event is the death of the insured and not the non-payment of premiums.

Disability insurance is another form of insurance that makes available a Return of Premium Rider, known as "ROP". While the LTC policy version is sometimes referred to as "ROP", the two riders are not the same. The version associated with disability insurance is designed to return some or all the premiums upon fixed intervals such as 10 or 20 years when the insured's claims have been below a threshold amount. The triggering event is not restricted to the insured's death, as it is with the LTC policy version.

There are a couple of variations in the Return of Premium Rider for LTC policies. One version of the benefit provides that some portion of the premiums may still be returned at death of the insured despite a benefit having been paid. In this instance, the company would first deduct an amount equal to any benefits paid to the date of death. The insured does not need to be on claim at the time of death for the benefit to be payable. The policy must have been in force for a minimum time, such as 10 years.

Another version of this benefit provides for return of premiums at death for policies that have been in force for a short period such as five years. As the build-up in the policy is faster, the related premium is greater. There may be a further stipulation that no claims can have occurred for facility care, or otherwise there is no return of premiums at death. Home care claims will not affect entitlement in this instance.

When the rider is purchased, the LTC policy will contain an amendment that shows a schedule for return of premium based upon the number of years the policy has been in force.

The additional premium for this rider varies based on the version, but can range anywhere from 25% to as high as 60% more. This charge must be evaluated against the use of the premium for another purpose, such as increasing basic coverage to a higher level or the purchase of life insurance. It nevertheless helps to address the concern of paying for a benefit and not requiring the use of it.

## Inflation Protection Benefit

As the population continues to age, an increased number of people are becoming concerned with the cost of medical care during their elder years. This has led many individuals to purchase LTC insurance during their pre-retirement years when the cost is less. However, the erosive effects of inflation can diminish its purchase power over an extended period of time. The inclusion of an inflation protection rider helps to guard against this.

For an additional premium, the individual can have their daily and maximum benefit limits increase at a fixed annual rate such as 2% or 3%. Generally, there is no corresponding increase in the annual renewal premium related to the new increased coverage, however as products are continually changing, the advisor should check the terms of coverage so that any related changes in cost are explained to the client at the time of purchase. The indexing can continue for an extended time, such as 15 or 20 years. The rider may specify an overall maximum to which benefits will increase, after which no further increases will occur.

This form of pre-claim indexing helps to ensure that regardless of changes in an individual's health, coverage will automatically increase each year. Some versions of this benefit continue increases even during a claim for benefits.

If the insured cannot afford to continue the cost of the rider, they may terminate the rider, but this may mean they will lose the increased benefits as the policy amount may revert back to the original amount of coverage issued.

As the cost of health care is projected to increase substantially when the bulk of baby boomers reach the age of retirement, this may well be one of the most valuable optional benefits available.

## Future Purchase Option

The Future Purchase Option provides another method for increasing coverage after issue. Under this benefit, the policy owner has the right to purchase additional coverage at specified option dates in the future without providing evidence of continued good health. For instance, the periodic options may occur in three-year intervals up until a specified age such as age 80. The amount the policy owner can buy is limited to a "per option" amount such as 2 or 3%, or it may be calculated based on the consumer price index up to a stipulated maximum. There will also be an overall maximum beyond which coverage cannot exceed based on the sum of original base coverage together with any increased amounts. For instance, an example of an overall maximum may be $10,000 total coverage. This maximum may even take into consideration any long-term care insurance purchased through another provider.

Unlike the Inflation Protection Benefit which usually requires no further increases in premiums, under the Future Purchase Option, increased coverage is usually offered with a corresponding increase in premiums, with the cost of the new coverage being determined based on the insured's attained age at the time of purchase.

The increase does not occur automatically as it does under an Inflation Protection Benefit rider. Instead, the policy owner must apply for coverage when the option comes due and within a specified window of time after which the right to exercise the option is lost until the next option date is due.

Some versions of this rider provide that if two consecutive option dates occur without the policy owner exercising their right to increase coverage, no further options will be available and the rider terminates.

# Chapter 14

# Evaluating Long-Term Care Policies

## CONSIDERATIONS IN SELECTING A POLICY

No policy is perfect. Furthermore, what suits one individual may not satisfy another person's needs. The "best LTC policy" is the one that contains the right balance between benefits and price based upon the individual's hierarchy of concerns. Young seniors tend to place greater emphasis on the loss of assets such as retirement income and savings. As seniors continue to age, less concern is placed on asset erosion and concern with the "softer" issues increase — issues such as quality of life, freedom of choice, dignity, and independence. Therefore, it is important to keep all of these concerns in mind when planning long-term care insurance.

The following are some areas to consider when evaluating an LTC policy.

- Flexibility in types of care

- Ease of qualifying for benefits

- The cost today

- Precautions against forgetting to pay a premium
- Guarantees related to future premium increases

## FLEXIBILITY IN TYPES OF CARE

It is helpful to think of care requirements as a continuum. As people age, their disabling conditions change from mild to severe, requiring appropriate changes in their level of care. Given the choice, most people want to remain in their home as long as they can. In fact, statistics indicate that most seniors with disabling conditions continue to live in the community as compared to those that live in institutions. It is estimated that by 2011, there will be more than 1.5 million disabled Canadian seniors living in the community as compared to the 312,000 who will live in institutions. Even though the number of seniors living in long-term care facilities will increase 60% between 1986 to 2011, the fact remains that by far the majority of elders with disabling conditions will be treated in the community before they enter a facility.[1]

Home care is made possible when there is assistance available from professional and paraprofessional home services to support the assistance being provided by the family member who has taken on the role of caregiver. The installation of special housing adaptations such as handrails or entrance ramps may also be required. While the government provides some financial assistance with home care and home health care, there are limits to the number of hours they will cover. Eventually, it becomes cost prohibitive for the individual to remain at home and the decision must be made to move to a facility with full time nursing care.

This makes it very important that any LTC policy considered contains a combination of both home care benefits and facility care benefits. Home care should be defined in the contract to include home health care, home support services, and adult day support centres or other community support service. Facility care should be defined as including retirement residences that have 24-hour nursing staff for light assistance, nursing homes (public, private and charitable), and chronic care facilities. The policy should also indicate that other facilities and community support services will be considered by mutual agreement, because the health care field will continue to evolve, the names and nature of facilities and services is likely to change quite dramatically over the next 20 or 30 years. For example, the number of people with Alzheimer's disease is expected to increase sharply. The government and the health community are looking at different ways to care for people with Alzheimer's disease. An LTC policy may become outdated if the wording is too restrictive to only the nature of services that exist today.

Flexibility in types of care is closely linked to the model of LTC policy selected. For instance, a policy that is based on the income model will offer the greatest flexibility in personal choice of care because there is no

---

[1] Government of Canada Web Site, FACT FILE, www.hc-sc.gc.ca/seniors-aines/seniors/pubs/disabled.htm.

distinction made regarding where the care is provided — it can be at home, in a day facility, or in a residential facility. Neither is there a distinction made regarding who provides the care — it can be a professional, an unskilled paid worker, or a family member. Furthermore, there is no distinction regarding what the service is that is being provided, The dollars can be used to cover the cost of housekeeping, cooking, or health care. As the flexibility is highest under this type of contract, the premium is generally the greatest. To determine if the person is eligible for benefits, an assessment is conducted to confirm the loss of two or more covered activities of daily living or the loss of cognitive impairment. The grey area associated with this type of contract is when does a condition satisfy the definition of a "loss", so that the elimination period will begin to be counted, as the triggers are not care-provider or facilities related. Despite this, it may take less time to satisfy the elimination period because calendar days are counted instead of care days.

An income-based model also eliminates the need to first pay for services out of one's own pocket and wait for later payment from the insurance company. An individual who is willing to trade off some flexibility in return for premium savings, may want to consider either the indemnity or reimbursement models, with the greatest savings being associated with the latter.

Under a reimbursement model, the individual must be prepared to assume additional paperwork in the form of expense tracking and remittance of receipts, similar to an insurance plan that covers prescription drugs. Also, there is usually a coordination clause with government benefits and other insurance policies, requiring the individual to first apply through these sources. This is because a reimbursement model is intended to cover only what is not being covered by the government. The fact that only actual expenses incurred for home care treatment above those not covered elsewhere are reimbursed, acts as a means of keeping premiums more affordable and could lessen the risk of a price increase down the road. As the insurer has the right to review every expense before determining payment, there is the possibility that if lower-cost care is available for the service provided, the insurer might want to limit payment to the equivalent amount only. Some reimbursement policies are actually a combination of two models with home care benefits paid on a reimbursement basis and facility care benefits paid on an indemnity basis. In this instance, the daily rate benefit amount purchased is the flat amount paid.

Under an indemnity model, the individual might be required to work through an assigned case worker who develops a plan of care. This may be helpful to the family member who has assumed the caregiver role, as they can assist with information and access to government programs. However, as they work on behalf of the insurer, if lower-cost services are available, the insurer might be reluctant to approve a plan of care. The elder has the right to refuse a treatment plan, if not satisfactory to them, as most contracts provide that both the insurer and the elder must agree to the plan of care. This method offers the advantage that the individual will know what costs for services are going to be covered in advance of receiving treatments, as opposed to the reimbursement method that evaluates the payment after being incurred.

Another area for consideration is whether the contract provides that care days or calendar days will be used to satisfy the elimination period. When care days are counted, only the actual days that services are received are used towards the elimination period. If a program of home care consists of visits from the community nurse every other day, then it will take twice as long to satisfy the elimination period as one that counts calendar days from the first day that a covered care service is received.

Scheduling of services could be an issue in this respect. For example, if two different services are required, and both can only come on the same day of the week, there may be some days during which no service is being received and hence not count as a "care day" towards satisfying the elimination period. There is also the issue of whether the service and the provider are both considered as covered under the plan.

## EASE OF QUALIFYING FOR BENEFITS

While currently, almost every insurance company in Canada uses activities of daily living (ADL) as a measure of eligibility in their LTC policies, there are some differences in the application of this definition. A few companies may measure only five activities, while most companies measures six activities. The standard five activities include:

- Bathing
- Dressing
- Transferring
- Toileting
- Feeding

The additional activity that may be included is incontinence. There can also be a difference regarding how "loss" is measured and the point at which the ADL is considered an eligible "loss". A hierarchy exists with regards to how frequently the order of loss occurs, with the general order in accordance with the listing above. The exception tends to be incontinence, as this ADL can occur at any point. It usually is a loss that occurs in conjunction with another ADL loss.

A policy with less restrictive definitions for "toileting" and "feeding" may not be as valuable as one that contains less restrictive definitions for "bathing" and "dressing". As ADLs are a primary trigger to benefit eligibility, any comparison of policies must include evaluation of how the company measures the loss of an ADL.

All LTC policies currently available with ADL-based definitions also include cognitive impairment as an alternative to requiring the loss of an

ADL. The deterioration in mental ability must be due to an organic cause as in the case of Alzheimer's disease and Parkinson's disease. There may be differences as to how a company measures a cognitive loss. Some companies may be satisfied that an individual who requires verbal cueing to complete an activity such as dressing, has satisfied the definition of cognitive impairment. Other companies may require that the individual needs 24-hour supervision as they otherwise may be a harm to themselves or others. Despite the elimination period selected, there is usually a prerequisite time frame that the individual must have suffered from the condition. Some companies do not state this time frame in their policies but have an administrative practice applied by their claims department such as 90 days. While it may be helpful to know what the company's practice is, a small difference between companies regarding an administrative practice today should not be the basis of a purchase decision as non-contractual procedures will change over a 20 or 30 year period.

## THE COST TODAY

While most companies require premiums to be paid as long as coverage remains in force, several companies have taken innovative steps to lessen the burden of premium costs in later years.

There is a trend towards plans offering a limited payment period after which the policy is considered fully paid-up. Depending upon the age at purchase, premiums may be fully paid up between 10 to 25 years. Consider an individual who is 45 years old and pays premiums for 20 years. When they retire at age 65, they may have a fully paid-up long-term care insurance plan. This also helps to protect against the risk of later increases in premiums because once the policy is paid up, no change can be made to the premium. The plan may even provide that if death occurs and the benefits have not been required, the premiums are returned.

Another innovative method of paying the cost of long-term care insurance while earning power is still at its highest, is through one company's use of a deposit account feature. This method allows for *ad hoc* contributions to an insurance account that functions like a bank account, including the fact that interest is paid on funds, which can be withdrawn at any time. As the funds are not locked-in, any interest earned is reportable for income tax. This method has the advantage of enabling the individual to make withdrawals in case of a financial emergency without jeopardizing the insurance.

## PRECAUTIONS AGAINST FORGETTING TO PAY PREMIUMS

Memory and recall fade as a natural part of the aging process, and an individual may forget to pay a premium on time. There are some features that lessen the risk that the insurance policy will lapse as a result of "forgetfulness". Other safeguards only cover situations where there is evidence that a cognitive impairment may have caused the oversight.

**Premium Frequency** — Most companies find that policies paid on a pre-authorized chequing basis have the lowest rate of lapse. It is a good idea for long-term care insurance to be paid on an automatic bank withdrawal basis.

**Third Party Notice** — Many companies allow the individual to name a third party that will be contacted in the event of non-payment of premium. This is usually done at the time of purchasing coverage in the application form itself. While optional, it is advisable to provide this information and to maintain it by submitting annual updates to the company if telephone numbers or addresses of the third party change.

**Extended Grace Period** — The policy may provide for a limited extension to the grace period at the company's discretion if the individual has a cognitive impairment and it can be shown that the non-payment of premium was related to it. This provision is a good feature, but the individual must understand that a connection must be shown between the condition and the non-payment of the premium. It is solely at the company's discretion as to whether the extension will be granted. Therefore, this should not be considered the strongest safeguard against non-payment of premium.

**Non-forfeiture Options** — Some companies make provisions for a return of the cash build-up in the policy to the person insured, in the event they stop paying premiums. This may be either in the form of providing

(a) continued insurance for the same amount for as long a period as the cash build-up will cover. This is a form of Long-Term Care "term insurance".

(b) continued insurance for a reduced amount but for the full duration of the policy.

The individual is not given a choice between these options. Each form has advantages and disadvantages. The term insurance method ensures that the amount of coverage is preserved for as long as possible, while the reduced benefit version ensures that no matter when the claim occurs, some amount will be payable. The down side to the term insurance method is that it could expire before a claim occurs, however it is a more favourable method for non-payment that occurs early in the life of the policy. The disadvantage to the reduced benefit version is that if the non-payment of premiums occurs very early in the contract life, the amount may be too minimal to be of any value. Its strength is in situations when the non-payment occurs after many years of paying premiums. Either method, however, is preferable to a policy that offers no return but keeps the cash build-up in the company instead.

When comparing premiums, the schedule of non-forfeiture values must also be compared because this has a direct impact on price. The richer the option, then the higher price will be barring other factors that might offset this difference in another provision in the contract.

# GUARANTEES RELATED TO FUTURE PREMIUM INCREASES

Long-term care insurance has been available in Canada for a relatively short period. The volume of business in force is also relatively small as compared with other product lines. This means there has not been sufficient time or volume to study the impact of claims as compared with pricing assumptions. It has been said that the greatest variable is in the area of medical technology improvements that can keep sick people alive longer. There have been studies regarding this, and what they have found is that there is a longer "healthy period", too. In other words, "healthy life expectancy" is extending, not just the total life expectancy.

While companies will not guarantee that rates will never change, they will provide a guarantee that rates will not change in the first five years. Some older contracts went further than this and guaranteed that if a rate was increased, it could not increase again for at least 5 more years. A newer form of guarantee is that premiums will not change once the policy has been in force and premiums paid for at least 20 years. Another form of guarantee is age-based with the promise of rates not changing after reaching age 75, subject to a stated minimum premium-paying period being satisfied.

Under older plans, some companies issued policies that provided a guarantee concerning the maximum amount by which the rate can increase overall from the original rate. This provides a degree of comfort that at the inception, the individual has a commitment concerning the most they will have to pay for their coverage. Prior to making any changes to old coverage, the advisor should examine features related to premium guarantees that might be lost if coverage is replaced in favour of new plans.

Associated with this, is the flexibility offered in making future changes to the policy. Some insurers guarantee that the individual will have the right to purchase improvements without medical evidence, by paying the cost associated with buying the policy today. Of equal importance, is whether the contract allows for reduction in benefits if the insured can no longer afford the plan. A bundled contract offers less flexibility than one that has separate riders that can be tweaked or eliminated entirely to reduce the cost. Some companies may not be able to administratively handle reductions in policy amounts. This is an area that should be considered when reviewing a policy contract.

# LONG-TERM CARE INSURANCE CHECKLIST

The following checklist will assist the planner in the review and design of long-term care insurance. The individual must also consider their relative importance to them personally and should use **weighting** as a tool in the evaluation process.

1. What care alternatives are covered?

   ❏ Home care

   ❏ Home health care

   ❏ Respite care — does it also cover respite care in a long-term care facility?

   ❏ Home hospice/palliative care — is there a maximum time?

   ❏ Adult day support centres

   ❏ Retirement residences

   ❏ Long-term care facility

   ❏ Chronic hospital unit

2. Can family members provide care?

3. Will the benefit pay if the individual is in a facility outside of Canada?

4. Are the services of a care coordinator:

   ❏ Mandatory

   ❏ Optional

   ❏ Not available

5. Are home care benefits:

   ❏ Reimbursement-based

   ❏ Indemnity-based

   ❏ Fixed income-based

6. Are facility care benefits:

   ❏ Reimbursement-based

   ❏ Indemnity-based

   ❏ Fixed income-based

7. What is the formula for calculating the benefit amount?

8. What is the maximum period for which benefits will be paid?

9. What ADLs are used to trigger benefits? How are they described?

10. What other conditions will trigger benefits?

    ❏ Accident or sickness rendering an individual to require facility care

    ❏ Cognitive impairment — including Alzheimer's disease, Parkinson's disease, etc.

    ❏ Doctor's certification

❐ Medical necessity caused by chronic illness

11. Is a condition rendering temporary loss of ADLs also covered?

12. Does the policy require:

❐ An assessment of activities of daily living?

❐ An assessment of cognitive impairment?

❐ Physician certification of need?

❐ A prior hospital stay?

❐ Other?

13. Can premiums be paid monthly on a pre-authorized chequing basis?

14. How frequently can premiums be increased by the company?

15. Is there a limit beyond which premiums cannot be increased?

16. How long do premiums have to be paid?

❐ Lifetime

❐ Limited pay period _____ years or to age _____

17. Are premiums waived after 90 days for:

❐ Facility care only

❐ Home care and/or facility care

18. What is the elimination period for each type of covered care?

19. Does another elimination period have to be satisfied in transferring from home care to facility care?

20. Can non-consecutive days of disability be used to satisfy the elimination period?

21. Are "care days" or "calendar days" counted towards the elimination ·period?

22. Do recurring incidences have to be due to the same·cause in order for the claimant to resume receiving benefits without satisfying another elimination period?

23. What defense levels are there to protect the policy from lapse in the event of oversight of premium payment?

❐ Third party notification

❐ Non-forfeiture provision (reduced paid-up, extended term coverage)

❐ Extended grace period

❐ Other _____

24. What optional benefits/enhanced features are or can be included in the policy?

   ❐ Return of premium at death — number of years after which premiums can be returned? Does a claim forfeit the right to a return?

   ❐ Cost of living increase before a claim

   ❐ Cost of living increase during a claim

   ❐ Medical equipment reimbursement

   ❐ Bed reservation benefit

   ❐ Guaranteed right to purchase new provisional upgrades

   ❐ Other(s): _____

25. Does the policy include a pre-existing condition limitation?

   ❐ No

   ❐ Yes: For what period of time after policy purchase are conditions not covered?

26. What exclusions are contained in the policy? (e.g., attempted suicide, alcohol, etc.)

27. What offsets are contained in the policy? (e.g., government, other policies, etc.)

28. Is there a discount offered when both spouses purchase policies simultaneously?

29. Can spouses share the same benefit pool?

*Chapter 15*

# Plan Design Considerations

## INTRODUCTION

An individual who is considering the purchase of a Long-Term Care (LTC) policy should work closely with a financial planner or insurance agent who has experience and training in long-term care insurance. The first step in the process is to select the policy structure (i.e., income-based, indemnity-based, reimbursement-based model, or one of the new hybrid plans) as this is the foundation of the contract. Thereafter, the plan can be tailored to fit the individual's priorities and constraints. This stage is also known as "programming" and occurs after the financial planner has completed a detailed information-gathering meeting with the individual.

## GATHER RELEVANT INFORMATION

The process of gathering pertinent details is commonly referred to as the *fact-finding stage*. The financial planner will use this information to obtain a quote for the individual.

### Personal Data

- Birth date and gender

- Confirmation regarding landed immigrant status if not Canadian

- Usual daily activities including hobbies — frequency and number of hours per day/week

- Whether there is a Power of Attorney for personal care

- Plans regarding relocation from the current home

- Plans regarding relocation in retirement to another province

- Family members and current support network

Although most companies do not charge rates based upon gender, the planner will consider other issues that are often gender-related and could impact decisions such as coverage amounts, elimination periods, and covered care options. Examples of issues that will be considered include termination of pension income upon death of a spouse, the increased incidence of disability amongst women, and their likelihood to be both in a caregiver and care recipient role during their elder years.

### Health Data

- Current general health status and significant medical conditions

- Whether the individual currently receives assistance from another person or device such as the use of a cane or walker, or assistance with activities such as dressing, bathing, eating, and whether they have difficulties with bladder control

- Whether the individual has had any major illnesses in the past two years such as cancer, dementia, diabetes, stroke, or paralysis

- Whether the individual has been hospitalized in the past two years

- Whether the individual is currently on medication

The purpose of the preliminary health data is to enable the financial planner to complete any preliminary inquiries with various insurance companies that might better define the best type of coverage and plan design given any current health implications.

## Financial Data

- Whether the individual is currently retired or expected date of retirement

- The individual's current level of income — whether it is fixed, increasing, or decreasing

- Percentage of the above earnings that comes from government pension sources

- Other expected sources of income

- Amount annually that the individual is comfortable to set aside for the purpose of LTC insurance

- How long the individual would be able to pay for care in the absence of insurance

An individual should not "stretch" to purchase the most expensive form of LTC insurance and risk the potential of having to later reduce or terminate the coverage due to lack of affordability. Rates can change in the future, and an increase could result in the cost becoming prohibitive. LTC insurance should be purchased for the long term. Premiums should cost what the individual can manage without a change in their current life style. Knowing how long a person can manage without insurance, helps to ascertain an appropriate elimination period for the coverage that balances cost containment and risk exposure.

## Existing Sources of Benefits

- Any current sources from which home care and long-term facility care may be paid

- Any existing personal and group insurance plans

The financial planner will determine the total amount of coverage available through current sources including government programs. The individual should bear in mind that government sources are likely to change over the next 20 or 30 years, and may not be the same when required. A person's health may deteriorate in the meantime so there is a risk in deferring the planning process until such time as government cutbacks occur. A plan that is independent of government sources is one that the individual controls and can be assured that it will fulfill their personal objectives for continuing care.

# DETERMINE THE AMOUNT OF COVERAGE

The move towards community-based care, and people's desire to remain in their home as long as possible, means that an adequate amount of home care coverage is critical in every plan. There are differences in government subsidization from province to province, particularly related to residential facility care. These differences must also be considered.

A trade-off that involves the amount of coverage is generally not advisable. It is better to have the right amount of coverage under a reimbursement-based policy for instance, than to select the most expensive policy model and have insufficient insurance.

The two major considerations, then, in determining the amount of coverage to purchase are:

1. What are the costs associated with personal care, health care, and facility care? How much of this is covered by the government?

2. How much of the cost can the individual afford, or choose to personally cover?

## The Cost of Care

The cost of care varies based upon the nature of the service performed and who provides the service. Following are some examples of costs. It should be noted however, that in Newfoundland, New Brunswick, and Prince Edward Island, where there is both income and asset testing, the cost can be considerably higher for individuals whose income and assets preclude them from qualifying for government subsidization of medical costs:

### Community Services

| | |
|---|---|
| Professional Services (nursing, physiotherapy, etc.) | $25 to $35 per hour |
| Paraprofessional Services (health care aids, etc.) | $10 to $20 per hour |
| Community Volunteer Services (Meals-on-Wheels) | no charge or small charge (depending upon province) |
| Adult Day Support Centres | $16–$20 per day or $300–$400 per month (5-day week) |

### Residential Facilities

| | |
|---|---|
| Respite Care | (short stay) $30 to $40 per day |
| Nursing Home Basic (Ward) | $45–$55 per day or $1,500–$1,700 per month |
| Nursing Home Semi-Private | $60–$70 per day or $1,800–$2,100 per month |
| Nursing Home Private | $70–$80 per day or $2,100–$2,400 per month |
| Retirement Homes | $1,600–$6,000 per month |

As indicated, these costs vary somewhat from province to province. All are subject to annual increases usually tied to the Consumer Price Index. The rates illustrated above represent the room charge after any government subsidization to the facility for care services and social programs. Depending upon the resident's ability to pay, subsidies for the room charge may be available through the Ministry of Health.

### Government Subsidization

Long-term care is partially covered by the provincial government. Another portion of the cost is covered by the local municipality. The balance is paid for by the resident.

No one is denied access to a long-term care facility. However, the variables are how long the individual must wait, the choice of facilities, and in the level of accommodation. Those who can pay have greater access. This is because there are longer waiting lists for basic accommodation than there are for semi-private or private rooms. People who require government financial assistance to pay their portion related to room charge only have access to public facilities at the basic accommodation level. Additionally, the basic level is most popular because many people, even though they do not require government assistance, still lack affordability for paying semi-private or private fees.

### Home Care versus Facility Care

The cost of home care is initially less than the cost of facility care. However, as the condition continues to deteriorate, the cost of home care exceeds the cost of facility care.

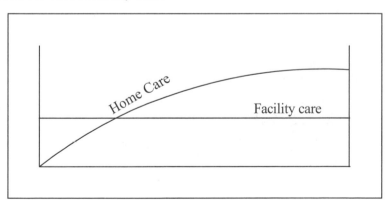

When calculating the amount of benefit, it may be desirable to include more than the current cost of basic facility care. This will provide the individual with greater flexibility regarding where care is received. It will help deal with the issue of inflation, and when coverage is not reimbursement-based, additional dollars will be available for medication, adaptive devices, minor home renovations, or even possibly relocation expenses to be closer to a family member that will be sharing caregiver responsibilities.

## Insurance Limits

Some LTC policies calculate benefits on a"per day" basis, some use a "per week" basis, and some use a "per month" basis. There is even a lump-sum version that pays benefits monthly as a percentage of a benefit pool. The range of available coverage is provided below:

|         | Per Day | Per Week | Per Month |
|---------|---------|----------|-----------|
| Minimum | $20     | $140     | $600      |
| Maximum | $300    | $2,000   | $10,000   |

An average benefit amount is one that is in the range of $100 to $150 per day or $3,000 to $4,500 per month.

## Taxation of Benefits

While it is generally assumed that benefits received from an LTC policy are tax-free, the Canada Revenue Agency (CRA) has yet to clarify their position. Some industry experts have suggested that the structure of an income-based model is such that it could be deemed to be an annuity and therefore taxable. A more recent opinion is that the income model would be treated as accident and illness insurance, and consequently be tax-free when paid for personally. It would be prudent to make certain clients understand that the taxation of LTC benefits is still something of a grey area and will remain so until the CRA and/or the Department of Finance issues an official ruling.

The premiums paid for coverage are generally not deductible. However, there may be circumstances for reimbursement-based contracts that could differ and therefore, an individual may wish to consult their accountant on this matter.

# SELECT THE ELIMINATION PERIOD

The elimination period refers to the number of days (either care days or calendar days, depending on the terminology used in the contract), that must go by before benefits under the policy will begin to be paid. There are a range of elimination periods from which the individual may select such as 0-day, 30-day, 60-day, and 90-day. As benefits are paid in arrears like pay cheques, the first benefit cheque on a 90-day elimination period will actually be received at 120 days or four months. This must be considered when making a selection. The shorter the elimination period, the higher will be the cost of the plan. There is a trade-off that must be made between cost and the initial self-insurance period.

The purchase of insurance is primarily to protect against catastrophic loss. While a 60-day wait may be financially inconvenient, having insufficient benefit for the long term would be much more devastating.

The best rule of thumb is to consider the amount of out-of-pocket expenses that can be covered personally prior to benefit payments. Using an average of $3,500 per month in expenses, the following total cost would be incurred:

| Elimination Period: | 30-day | 60-day | 90-day |
|---|---|---|---|
| Cumulative Total | | | |
| 1$^{st}$ Month | $3,500 | $3,500 | $3,500 |
| 2$^{nd}$ Month | $7,000 | $7,000 | $7,000 |
| 3$^{rd}$ Month | Ins. Starts | $10,500 | $10,500 |
| 4$^{th}$ Month | | Ins. Starts | $14,000 |
| 5$^{th}$ Month | | | Ins. Starts |

The above chart reflects the fact that no payment is made for the elimination period, and the first payment follows one month after the end of the elimination period (i.e., cheques are paid in arrears, not in advance).

When the policy counts care days to satisfy the elimination period, the individual may want to select a shorter elimination period than one that uses calendar days because it will take longer to satisfy it. The number of care days in a week (i.e., the days a care service is actually received) is often less than seven calendar days.

## SELECT THE BENEFIT PERIOD

The benefit period is the overall maximum that the LTC policy will cover. Some policies refer to this as the Overall Maximum Benefit Amount. It may be measured in days or years. For example, it may be 2,000 care days or it may be five years.

### Facility Care Benefits

The average stay in a nursing home is about two years. However, this is often preceded by care in a retirement home with supports. While everyone may wish to have a lifetime benefit, the minimum considered should be at least two years, or more ideally, five years.

### Home Care Benefits

Home care benefits include home support services, home health services, and services provided in an adult day support centre. With the movement towards community-based services, there will be an increase in the number of elders treated in day support centres, particularly those with Alzheimer's disease. Therefore, the minimum benefit period considered should be at least two years, or more ideally five years. Contracts that offer integrated coverage eliminate the guess work of selecting a separate benefit period for home care and facility care.

The individual should be careful, however, when selecting benefit periods for plans that have home care attached as a rider in policies where the benefit periods for facility care and home care run simultaneously and not consecutively. Any period for which home care is used is deducted from the benefit period for facility care in some policies. For instance, when there is a five-year benefit period for facility care plus a two-year benefit period for home care, if the individual uses the full two years of home care, this leaves a remainder of only three years for facility care. Furthermore, if the individual actually receives treatment in the home for three years, followed by facility care thereafter, they will have a gap in benefits for a 12-month period because the home care benefits would cease at the end of the two-year benefit period. Therefore, to resolve this issue, it is desirable under this type of plan, to purchase coterminous benefit periods of at least five years.

## THE DECISION REGARDING WHETHER TO INSURE

### Income Comparison

There is a significant risk that a married couple will encounter the need for one of them to have home and/or facility care while the other continues to live at home. If the cost of this additional care is $50 per day or $18,250 per year, at a 30% marginal tax rate, a couple will require $26,000 taxable income per year to pay for one person's care. If the couple has a combined retirement income of $45,000 this leaves $19,000 for the remaining spouse to cover personal living and home maintenance expenses.

### Asset Comparison

Using the same illustration from above and assuming the couple can earn 6% yearly on investments, it would require $450,000 invested in income-generating assets to generate $26,000 pre-tax dollars to cover the cost of one spouse's personal and health care needs. Or, if the couple was to encroach upon capital, and the combined home and facility care period lasted five years, the couple would require assets in the range of $100,000 without regard to tax implications. In reality, the average cost is more likely to be in the range of $115 per day.[1] Consideration must be given to the need for medication, assistance devices, and minor home adaptations that may be required. The true cost of home care also includes the informal network of caregivers such as family, a person's religious community, and friends. Eventually, both spouses may require care.

## THE MYTH ABOUT SOCIAL HEALTH CARE

Many Canadians continue to believe that the government will provide home care services when they need them. Often it is difficult to look ahead to the years when the need for facility care may be a necessary reality. There is the belief that this too will be provided by the government. Some of this confusion arises from the fact that the government currently subsidizes the medical portion of costs of long-term care. There are provincial differences regarding this subsidization, most notably in Newfoundland, Prince Edward Island, and New Brunswick where there are stringent "means" tests to determine eligibility for the medical subsidization that is automatic in other provinces regardless of earnings levels. Therefore, the costs to be borne by the individual are much greater in these provinces. The "means" testing includes both asset and income tests. Above a certain level, the individual could be required to bear the full cost of facility care. Even in provinces with medical subsidization, the residential portion of costs to the individual is still very large.

Further confusion arises from current testing to determine additional subsidization of the residential portion. Those without the means to pay, can apply for a government subsidy. There is no guarantee that 20 years from today, the government will continue to fund the cost at today's levels. In fact, it is highly improbable when one considers the shrinking tax base caused by an aging population coupled with the nation's increasing need for health care.

This means that a sound financial plan today must include an income source for health care costs in one's senior years.

---

[1] *LTC Insurance: Live Your Last Years with Dignity*, by Diana Bacon-Pearson.

# Chapter 16

# Underwriting and Claims

# HEAD OFFICE DATA COLLECTION

Every insurance company looks at the current physical and mental status of the individual who is applying for insurance to determine whether they have conditions or limitations that would preclude them from qualifying.

Tools that the underwriter uses to evaluate the risk include:

- The application

- The financial planner's cover note

- Customer interview — by phone or face-to-face

- Attending Physician Statement

- Paramedical

This process begins with the financial planner and the application form, and is known as **field underwriting**.

## The Application

The financial planner completes the application during a face-to-face interview. This is the primary tool used by the financial planner for field underwriting and the underwriter for risk evaluation. It contains almost all of the information the underwriter will need to make a decision. The financial planner's personal observations and inputs are also an important part of risk evaluation and each application contains a section for the planner's remarks. An application should never be completed by telephone or through the mail since a major component of the underwriting process concerns evaluating the person's current ability to manage independently in their environment. There may also be licensing and potential legal issues that are breached when a planner does not personally see the applicant and complete the form in person.

Many applicants for long-term care insurance are seniors. Whenever possible, the person who may eventually assume a caregiver role or act as advisor to the caregiver should also be present. Most often, this will be an adult son or daughter of the applicant. This may be the same person who has been granted Power of Attorney for Personal Care to act on their behalf.

Thorough and accurate completion of the application is critical. Incomplete or incorrect details can lead to delays in issuing the policy, and can result in the individual's insurance coverage being denied at the time of claim for misrepresentation. Proper completion is therefore, equal in importance to the process of planning and design of benefits.

The information collected in the application falls into three main categories. These are:

(a) personal information,

(b) coverage information, and

(c) health information.

Through a separate telephone interview process, initiated by the underwriter, lifestyle information is also collected.

## Personal Information

Personal information includes details such as name, address, birth date, gender, occupation, and whether the individual has a Power of Attorney for personal care. The insurance company wants to know there is someone who is able to act in the individual's behalf if they later suffer from a cognitive impairment. There will be the need for this person to make medical and personal care arrangements, such as decisions on residential facility living.

## Coverage Information

Coverage details include information on existing insurance and selection of the plan that is being applied for. The individual selects a plan design, benefit amount, elimination period and benefit period upon which rates are based. Any optional benefits requested are also included in this section. Some companies offer rate discounts when both spouses apply for coverage. This should be clearly indicated on the application. Eligibility for rate discounts may require that both spouses apply for identical plans. This requirement avoids a situation where an application is submitted for a nominal amount in order to get a reduced premium for the other spouse. This practice can lead to anti-selection issues and excess underwriting costs being assumed by the insurance company.

## Health Information

Health information gathered includes details concerning medical history, medications being taken, current living status, abilities and limitations of daily activities, and changes from the past year.

## Other Information

In-depth financial information is not required for long-term care insurance, as it is for disability insurance, because income is not being insured. However, the financial planner will want to ensure that the individual has the financial ability to maintain the coverage over many years. In addition, some companies' LTC policy maximums are based on the earnings of the person being insured.

The application forms a legal part of the contract, and is signed by both the individual applying for coverage and the financial planner.

## The Financial Planner's Role

The financial planner asks probing questions to solicit detailed information in all areas of the application for eventual submission to the insurance company's head office underwriter. Inclusion of a cover memo is the financial planner's opportunity to give the underwriter a more descriptive visual of the macro picture. While the application form gathers micro-level details, the underwriter's decision will be based upon a macro look at all factors and their inter-relationship. This is also what is known as "the complete person" philosophy.

Great emphasis is placed on the individual's current activity level, mental acumen, and general lifestyle.

The financial planner can facilitate the underwriting process by enclosing a memo that covers additional details such as the following:

- How physically active the individual is. Do they participate in activities such as daily walks, sports such as golf or tennis, gardening, etc? By listing any activities, the underwriter gains a better image of their mobility.

- How involved they are in community activities. Do they belong to a social centre, play cards, provide volunteer assistance, etc? This indicates a mentally healthy lifestyle adjustment.

- Whether they are currently acting in a caregiver role to someone else. If so, how frequent, what does this involve, and what is their relationship to the individual? There may be stresses in their life, and their ability to cope with them is important.

- The frequency with which they travel on vacations, method of travel, length of stay and destinations.

- The hobbies they undertake and the regularity with which they perform them.

- Examples of their mental ability to master new tasks. Have they recently learned to use a new electronic device such as a personal computer, a pocket diary, etc?

- Examples of activities performed routinely that involve planning, organizing, or abstract thinking.

- Physical limitations such as the use of a cane. How long have they used one, and is the use of it related to a recent accident or an illness?

Have they ever fallen without it? Is it a single or multi-pronged cane? Do they use it in the home as well as outside the home?

- Description of the person's support network. Do they live alone, and are their adult children in town? Do they have a spouse and, if so, what is their health condition? The support network is a major underwriting factor and impacts on a person's ability to remain in the home with the assistance of a caregiver.

- Description of their general disposition and outlook on life. Do they tend to express pessimistic statements, or do they exhibit an optimistic approach to issues and life in general?

- Description of any changes in the individual's activities or behaviours from the prior year. What were they able to do last year that they cannot do now?

Part of the financial planner's role is to prescreen, and this involves ensuring that people are not put through the process of applying for coverage to ultimately be turned down, when there was a clear indication up front that the person would not meet the submission criteria. An example of this would be an individual who currently has problems performing an activity of daily living such as dressing or ambulating. Other situations where the financial planner should not submit an application include the following:

- Inability currently to independently perform an activity of daily living (eating, dressing, walking, transferring, toileting, bowel incontinence); and

- Present signs of memory loss, confusion, disorientation, or unusual inhibition.

The financial planner also explains the overall process to the individual including the fact that they can expect to receive a telephone call from the insurance company's staff interviewer for the purpose of verifying or clarifying information contained in the application. The call is an important part of the underwriting process and one that is both routine and confidential.

## Customer Telephone Interview

The customer interview is often referred to as a Lifestyle Interview and is usually completed by telephone. It is a key source for the underwriter to evaluate mental acuity. This is accomplished by asking the applicant a series of questions such as the name of the current prime minister, the current date, the person's address, and so on. The interviewer will also ask questions to determine the individual's ability to perform instrumental activities of daily living such as grocery shopping, bill payment, and home management.

The applicant's ability to use and communicate effectively using the phone for the interview is one indicator itself that the interviewer uses to determine the applicant's cognitive abilities.

The interview is a cost-effective way to also verify, clarify and expand on information contained in the application including the individual's current ability to care for themselves, the use of devices, and their handling of medication. In some instances, it may eliminate the need for ordering an Attending Physician's Statement and this not only reduces the cost of underwriting, but also reduces the time required to reach a decision on the applicant' eligibility.

## Face-to-Face Interview

In some cases, the underwriter may arrange for a face-to-face interview with the applicant instead of a telephone interview. It may also be an automatic requirement based on age and amount of coverage applied for. This enables them to obtain a better idea of the person's capabilities by viewing them in their surroundings. The interview is conducted by a registered nurse through a paramedical company or by a case coordinator from a case management company. The objective is to gather first-hand information on the person's abilities to perform activities of daily living (ADLs) and instrumental activities of daily living (IADLs), such as home management and to observe their gait and general appearance. An abnormal gait may be visible such as a tendency to take small slow steps, swaying, shuffling or hesitation in walking. These may be an indicator of an underlying condition such as Parkinson's disease, a stroke, or another neurological disease. Non-neurological conditions can also cause a noticeable unusual gait such as arthritis, heart disease or breathing problems.

## Attending Physician Statement

Companies have established criteria for determining whether an Attending Physician Statement (APS) will be required. Certain medical conditions, medication, or histories will trigger the necessity of ordering a report from the applicant's personal physician. Companies may also order a statement automatically for applicants who are above a certain age. As compared to disability insurance applications, there are fewer Attending Physician Statements ordered.

The APS is a key tool used by the underwriter to determine severity of conditions. With additional information from the applicant's physician, the individual may be able to qualify for long-term care insurance despite a particular condition in their medical background.

## Paramedical

Certain amounts of insurance, certain ages, and certain conditions may necessitate that the applicant complete a paramedical with a registered nurse who will come to the home for this purpose. The test includes a medical questionnaire, blood pressure readings, and weight check. This is completed at the expense of the insurance company.

## RISK EVALUATION

The key objective of the underwriter for long-term care insurance is to determine the ability of the individual to remain self-sufficient.

### Underwriting Factors

Family history plays a significant role in the underwriting process. Some illnesses are passed on from one generation to another. Other areas that are of significance include cognitive testing, and the infrastructure and support network that the applicant has available to them.

Underwriting factors include the following:

- Age
- Gender
- Smoking Habits
- Medical history
- Build
- Physical condition
- Mental acuity
- Home environment
- Current abilities with ADLs
- Current abilities with IADLs

Although the company may not have non-smoker rates, the underwriter is still interested to know of the smoking habits of the applicant as other conditions may be impacted by this. For instance, a person who has asthma and who smokes is a greater risk.

### Medical History

Applicants must qualify medically for insurance. Although it relates to insuring a person's health, the underwriting of LTC insurance is quite different than a disability insurance policy. There are some conditions that are not insurable such as Alzheimer's disease, Parkinson's disease, AIDS, multiple sclerosis, muscular dystrophy, manic depression, paralysis, and leukemia. Despite this, there are many conditions that are still insurable with sufficient passage of time, or contingent upon their severity. The following are some examples of conditions that would be considered for long-term care insurance on some basis.

- Mild cases of arthritis

- Previous back disorders that are fully recovered
- Mild cases of cerebral palsy that do not require assistance from devices
- Bypass surgery fully corrected, beyond six to eight months
- Diet-controlled diabetes or with low levels of oral insulin
- Pacemaker with stable condition for more than four months

These examples illustrate that even an individual who has some medical history of surgery or health conditions, should still consider long-term care insurance. Most companies have prescreening questionnaires to help ascertain if a person is automatically ineligible for coverage based on certain health conditions.

During the underwriting process, the underwriter looks for indications of full recovery pertaining to a previous condition, a satisfactory passage of time, and other positive factors such as a strong family network, good cognitive skills, and a healthy lifestyle overall.

## THE DISTINCTIVE NATURE OF LTC INSURANCE

While LTC insurance is often associated with other types of "Living Benefits" such as critical illness insurance and disability income insurance, there are many factors that make this risk distinct from other forms of insurance. The underwriter takes this into consideration when evaluating an applicant's eligibility for coverage.

### Factors That Make the Risk Unique

#### • Cognitive Impairment Will Trigger Payment of Benefits

What is the applicant's current ability to think, perceive and remember? Are there signs that suggest deterioration may be likely in the future that is not simply age-related slowing? Alzheimer's disease is a progressive condition that appears gradually over many years, even as long as 10 years. Early symptoms will affect the eligibility for buying LTC insurance. For this reason, various tests are used that measure mental acuity. Some tests measure short-term memory, while others are used to measure other cognitive abilities.

Short-term memory exercises are designed to increase likelihood of a favourable outcome (higher scores) by individuals who do not have a dementia, and identify those who do have a dementia as indicated by lower scores. Dementia affects short-term memory, and this is what these tests are designed specifically to measure. An example of an exercise that may be used is the Five-Word Memory Test. After looking at five words, the person is asked to identify the target word that matches a certain category such as "house" = building; "tea" = beverage. Recall is then tested, by means of the examiner asking the person to recall the five words. Next, an unrelated distraction task is assigned and then a delayed recall test is performed. If the person cannot recall all five words, the examiner offers the cue category (e.g., "What was the building?"). Someone with dementia often forgets words even when given a cued recall. Lower scores will indicate a memory deficit. A person in an anxious state who does not have dementia might not be able to remember all the words during free recall, but will be able to recall when given the proper cue words.

Other tests that measure cognitive abilities include the Short Portable Mental Status Questionnaire (SPMSQ), which is an observer-related 10-item instrument that assesses orientation, memory and concentration.

### • Chronic Conditions often Lead to Eventual Physical Dependence

Is there evidence of any prolonged symptoms that are known to reoccur or deteriorate over time? The presence of chronic disease can be an indicator of increased likelihood for the need for long-term treatment. Arthritis is one such condition that may affect seniors and worsens with time. There are many forms such as rheumatoid arthritis, degenerative joint disease, and osteoarthritis. Some forms of arthritis may not be considered a problem, while others may necessitate a decline. An important consideration is whether the condition requires treatment or medication, and whether the medication is steroidal or non-steroidal. The length of stability period between episodes is another aspect of risk assessment. If there has been a recent weight bearing joint replacement, or low-dose steroid use, it will be necessary to postpone the application until the applicant has shown stability for six months or more. Since arthritis is a condition that usually worsens with time, the underwriter may limit the benefit period and lengthen the elimination period if a contract is offered, as there is a risk it could eventually affect the insured's ability to perform activities of daily living.

### • Older Adults often have Co-morbid Conditions

Does the applicant have more than one condition that together increase the risk of either on its own? Some conditions that occur independent of others may be of little concern, but when they occur in combination with another, there is an increase in morbidity. A co-morbid condition is a secondary condition that affects a primary condition. A person with stable medication-controlled diabetes that has shown stability for at least six months is likely to be a favourable risk. But the same condition in another person who also has a circulatory or kidney disease, is likely to be declined for coverage.

### • Age Often Affects Functional Capacity in Activities of Daily Living

Does the person show any signs of deficits in functional capacity in ADLs? If the applicant currently needs assistance with two or more ADLs they are not a candidate for LTC insurance. Also, inability to perform several instrumental activities may be an early indicator the person will eventually experience a functional loss of capacity in ADLs and they too, are not a candidate for LTC insurance. A person who currently uses a device such as a four-pronged cane, a wheelchair, a motorized cart, or a lift is not a candidate for LTC insurance. However, a person who uses a single-prong cane may be a candidate, depending on other factors.

### • One's Physiological Age May Be Greater Than Chronological Age

Does the person look older physically than they really are? Physiological age can be thought of as the visual effects of "wear and tear" on the body. Different factors may contribute to it such as having lived a sedentary lifestyle, poor nutritional habits, chronic illness, or surgery. Medication taken over an extended period of time or certain medical treatments such as chemotherapy and radiation also affect the body. Psychological factors such as anxiety and depression also cause excess stress on the body. Visual cues of "wear and tear" can be indicators of higher morbidity risk.

### • Frailty is a Serious Risk in Older Adults

Does the person look frail? Physicians consider frailty as a valid and important indicator of the future risk of institutionalization. While there is no actual clinical definition for the term, "frailty", it can be conceptually described as "a state of vulnerability".[1] Dr. Linda Fried, Director, Division of Geriatric Medicine and Gerontology at John Hopkins University School of Medicine developed a rules-based definition. It has proven to be reliable at identifying people who are at increased risk. Those with three or more symptoms are much more likely to have a serious disability from a relatively minor injury or sickness.

The symptoms include:

— A slow walking speed

— Unintentional weight loss

— Poor grip strength or muscle tone in limbs

— Feeling exhausted or poor self-reported endurance

— Low physical activity level

Adults who are frail are at greater risk for both acute and chronic illness. They also face greater risk associated with falls, have a higher rate of disability and higher mortality. Utilization rates for home care services, hospitalization, and nursing homes are greater amongst the frail than for those who are not frail.

For these reasons, someone who exhibits signs of frailty is an unlikely candidate for LTC insurance.

---

[1] Fried L, Tangen C, Walston J et al., *Frailty in older adults: evidence for a phenotype*, J. Gerontol Med Sci 2001; 56A: M146-M156.

### • Osteoporosis and Falls Place Older Adults at Higher Risk

Does the person have osteoporosis or a hunched forward stature? Seniors have an increased risk of falls and falling leads to a much greater risk of permanent institutionalization. As many as one in three seniors experience a fall annually, and close to half of all nursing home admissions can be traced back to a fall being the underlying cause. Falls often result in hip fractures. Fractures of the hip, wrist and back are often attributed to osteoporosis, which is a disease characterized by low bone density. While women are more often affected than men due to its hormonal relationship, some males are also at risk. Men may develop osteoporosis if they have certain illnesses, a low testosterone level, are smokers, take certain medications, or are sedentary.

Sarcopenia (age-related loss of skeletal muscle) is another condition that bears some similarity to osteoporosis. The combination of the two leads to significant frailty amongst older adults.

Osteoporotic fractures can be caused by even a slight amount of stress that normally would not create a break in someone who does not have osteoporosis.

Compression fractures caused by a collapsed vertebra can also be an indicator of osteoporosis, and may be identified visually by a hunched forward or bent stature. There may also be a loss of height associated with it. Severe cases can even result in significant pressure on internal organs and impact breathing.

A bone mineral density test measures the density or thickness of the bone, by determining the amount of mineral (calcium) in a specific area of the bone. The more mineral in the bone, the greater the measure is of bone density or bone mass. A DEXA scan (dual-energy x-ray absorptiometry), is a low-radiation machine used to measure bone mineral density (BMD). It measures density at the hip and spine and is considered predictive of the risk of fractures.

*T-scores* are used to identify osteoporosis in post-menopausal women. It measures the bone density of a post-menopausal woman as compared with an average young normal adult, and is therefore a relative measure. A T-score below the threshold score of -2.5 is generally considered osteoporosis, however other factors must be taken into consideration such as the history of compression fractures and use of steroid medications.

The underwriter needs to know specific T-scores, medication taken including type and dosage, the existence of any current limitations in activities, the use of any mobility aids, history of any fractures, and degree of loss of height. A person with low T-scores may still be a favourable risk for LTC insurance so long as other risk factors are also good.

● **Many Older Adults Take Multiple Medications and Have More Than One Doctor**

Does the person see more than one physician and routinely take more than one medication? Often, seniors are referred to more than one specialist with each one treating a different condition and prescribing an additional medication. The dosage may eventually become too strong because of changes in body weight or simply because over time the kidneys and liver might work less efficiently at eliminating the medication from the system and cause build-up. This can lead to side effects such as dizziness, weak spells, sudden drops in blood pressure, fatigue and even confusion which might be mistaken for early signs of dementia. All of these conditions place the senior at greater risk of injury.

Underwriters need to know a complete list of physicians that tend to the person, medications they take including over-the-counter medication and herbal remedies as these can also have an impact on the person's health.

● **Social Connection Has a Positive Impact on Independence in Older Adults**

Does the person stay active and socially connected? Provide the underwriter with a memo outlining examples that demonstrate the applicant is well-adjusted socially and has a strong support network. For more information on this, revisit the section earlier in this chapter on, "The Financial Planner's Role".

● **Weight Changes Place Older Adults at Greater Risk**

Has the person experienced a gain or loss in weight? Obesity can create complications such as excess wear and tear on joints, which can in turn lead to the need for hip or knee replacement surgery. There is also an increased risk of type 2 diabetes associated with obesity, as well as heart disease, obstructive sleep apnea, osteoarthritis and some forms of cancer. With obstructive sleep apnea, the person stops breathing for a minute or so during sleep due to a partial obstruction of the airway, which occurs during sleep. This can happen many times during a single night and in severe cases, can lead to heart disease and stroke. Continual sleep deprivation also places the person at greater risk of injury during the day.

Being under weight can also be dangerous, as this is associated with frailty in older adults. It can be an indicator of an underlying condition that is yet undiagnosed. It may be that the person is not preparing proper meals for themselves either because they don't feel like eating alone, or because they are having difficulty with the associated activities such as grocery shopping and/or meal preparation. Loss of weight leads to an increased risk of infection and this makes the person more susceptible to illness.

# METHODS OF DEALING WITH INCREASED RISK

When an applicant has a condition that is insurable, but increases their likelihood to claim, the underwriter uses one of the following methods to adjust the coverage for this increased risk that the insurance company faces.

- Increase the premium (known as a *rating*)

- Exclude the condition from coverage under the policy (known as an *exclusion*)

- Reduce the benefit amount from what was applied for (known as a *benefit reduction*)

- Alter the plan design to lessen the coverage by either lengthening the elimination period or reducing the benefit period (*amended plan design*)

Most companies do not like to use the exclusion method. It poses the risk that the individual will pay premiums for many years on an insurance policy and not be able to claim for a particular condition that could be the cause of their need for care. It is also ineffective in dealing with *secondary causes* and therefore, does not protect the insurance company adequately either.

Some applicants will be found to be uninsurable. The rate of declination for long-term care is less than the rate for some forms of insurance, such as disability insurance. This is due, in part, to the prescreening role performed by the financial planner and the fact that conditions that would preclude a person from having disability insurance are not necessarily uninsurable conditions for long-term care insurance.

# THE PROCESS OF UNDERWRITING

On average, the underwriting process takes about four to six weeks. One of the greatest delays in the process is in obtaining reports from attending physicians when one is required. An applicant may assist in obtaining a faster response by asking their physician to expect the report and to respond promptly upon its receipt.

## Requesting Information Disclosure

When the underwriter has made a decision, it will be communicated to the financial planner for advising the applicant. In the event of an amended offer or a declination notice, the underwriter will not release details of the rationale behind their decision to the financial planner when it involves confidential medical information as this would breach the signed confidentiality agreement. Generally, any details of this nature will only be released to the applicant's attending physician in the form of a letter and the applicant can arrange to meet with their physician to discuss the details. This procedure is designed to protect the applicant. The insurance company will require a letter by the applicant that authorizes them to release the information to the attending physician.

In the event that medical tests were conducted in regards to the insurance, and they were found to have abnormalities, most companies will notify the applicant's physician immediately so the health condition can be addressed.

### Ten-Day Look

Once the policy has been forwarded to the financial planner for delivery to the applicant, the individual has 10 days to consider whether they wish to accept the insurance or to return it for a refund of any deposit they have paid. They are protected during this time if they have completed the delivery requirements.

An individual who has been given a policy that necessitated an increase in premium or a change in the plan due to their medical history, should take advantage of the Ten-Day Look while they are considering their options. It is better to have some protection than to have no protection in instances where it was necessary for the underwriter to reduce coverage. If given the choice of having a policy with an extra premium rating or an exclusion for a condition, it is always better to pay the extra premium and have full coverage. A policy has been charged with an extra premium because the condition is one that means there is a greater likelihood of needing the insurance than the average person. That is exactly when the individual *should* have the protection.

While taking advantage of the Ten-Day Look, the individual can work together with their financial planner to determine if another company can be more competitive on their offer of insurance. In the meantime, by placing the coverage in force under the 10-day right, the individual is protected should something happen. If the search for alternate coverage takes longer than 10 days, the individual can pay for their coverage on a month-to-month basis and only terminate it after they have been successful in obtaining a policy on a preferred basis. The financial planner can facilitate a faster process in this regard, by the use of preliminary inquiries for conditions that they suspect may be an underwriting concern.

When comparing two companies' offers, rates that are substantially lower or an overly generous underwriting process could be indicators of potential problems during a claim. While most companies do a thorough job of underwriting up front, some companies may wait until the claim arises to investigate pre-existing conditions.

### Medical Information Bureau (MIB)

The Medical Information Bureau is a non-profit membership organization of insurers that exchanges information on applicants. The application form contains an authorization that the individual signs to allow the companies to share information with the bureau. A member company is required to code information they learn about the applicant into the MIB data base during the underwriting process. This information can only act as a "red flag" and cannot be used on its own to decline or amend a policy. The underwriter checks for flags and if found, develops information through other sources such as customer telephone interviews or attending physician statements. Any information that the underwriter has developed must be coded into the MIB for use by other member companies.

This is an essential part of the underwriting process, and is used by all insurance companies. An individual who disagrees with a decision, has the right to contact the MIB and to have remarks added to their file. Prior to doing so, they should try to first resolve the difference with the insurance company through the financial planner.

## WHEN THE INSURANCE BECOMES EFFECTIVE

Most companies provide that the insurance only goes into effect upon the delivery of the policy and payment in full of the outstanding premium. This is further subject to no changes having occurred in the person's health from the time the application was completed. There is no interim insurance protection during the underwriting period.

When a financial planner discovers that there has been a change during the underwriting process or prior to delivery of the policy, they are required to get in touch with the head office of the insurance company and to return the policy without delivery. In some situations, it may be still possible for the coverage to be placed in force, but only after the insurer has been notified and had the opportunity to review the health change for implications.

There may be forms for the applicant to sign upon receipt of the policy if there were details missing from the application form or if coverage has been altered from the plan applied for. These are referred to as amendments and form a legal part of the insurance contract. The policy should always be delivered in person by the financial planner and reviewed with the applicant.

## THE CLAIMS PROCESS

### Introduction

The process of applying for benefits differs with each company. When the LTC policy requires that the individual work through a care coordinator, the first step is to get in touch with the care management company. They will arrange to meet with the individual, complete an evaluation, and prepare a plan of care. The proposed plan of care must be approved by the individual and by the insurance company prior to its implementation. The individual will know at the onset of the claim what care services the company is willing to pay for.

Some LTC policies require the individual to first apply for government benefits. This is accomplished by contacting the local community services centre who will send out a case manager to interview and evaluate the individual and to develop a plan of care. Local community services will be considered as well as the need for the individual to have residential facility care.

Some LTC policies require that the individual contact the company's benefits department and the process is initiated without concern for whether government benefits have been applied for. They may make available the use of a care coordinator on an optional basis that can be used at the individual's discretion. Because the service is optional, there is no impact on whether benefits will be provided based upon the plan of care developed by the coordinator or whether these services are used at all.

In all three instances, the community services centre will eventually become involved as they control access to entering long-term care facilities and to accessing community support programs.

## Satisfying the Conditions for Payment

The individual will be evaluated to determine whether they have satisfied the conditions for payment. This will most likely include a series of tests such as cognitive testing, and/or physician certification related to the loss of ADLs. Some companies may require the use of one of their own appointed physicians for this purpose.

As indicated, some LTC policies may require the use of a company-appointed care coordinator as a condition for payment. Care coordinators perform services such as helping to determine the best place for care to be received (i.e., home versus facility care, etc.) and help to make sure the individual gets care appropriate to their condition. When family members live far away, they can also be a contact to provide feedback to the family concerning the medical condition and care the individual is receiving by giving them a regular care report. This helps to use the benefits most effectively under the policy. They will know how to access the local support services and may even be able to help facilitate faster access by their familiarity with the people and the system. Care coordinators can help to explain to the insurer why certain forms of care are required. They also work with the individual's physician in developing the best plan of care.

Because no one knows who will be around when the need arises, it is a good service to have available.

## Time Limitations for Claim Submission

Every LTC policy contains a time limitation for the submission of a claim. Insurers do not generally waive this limitation when the claimant is delinquent. Most policies provide that the claim for benefits must be reported within 30 days where possible, and evidence provided within 90 days. In no event can this be later than one year when there has been a just cause for delay. The individual should take these time frames seriously because an otherwise legitimate cause for claim can be denied.

The individual should not wait until the end of their elimination period to file their claim. Nor should they wait until after the community care coordinator has developed a plan of care. Companies that require the individual to first have applied for benefits through the government programs do not require for the plan to be developed and approved by community services, only that the process has been initiated.

The LTC policy will also stipulate the time frame within which the company must provide payment following satisfactory proof of claim. Some companies guarantee payment will be within 30 days, and others indicate the right to make payment within 60 days following receipt of evidence.

The individual must remember to pay their premiums throughout this process. Although policies contain a waiver of premium benefit after 90 days, the policy can lapse during the initial three months if premiums are in default. This would invalidate the claim for benefits. The measure with some policies is not calendar days, but is instead care days. So 90 days may require more than three calendar months to satisfy the waiver of premium provision. Premiums should continue to be paid until the insurance company has confirmed that conditions have been met for their waiver. Some policies do not waive premiums during periods of home care or count home care days towards its satisfaction. The individual must check carefully to determine if the waiver only applies for periods of facility care so that coverage does not lapse at such a critical time.

As the individual may be experiencing a memory loss or cognitive impairment, the caregiver must be fully aware of all of these limitations and conditions so that coverage does not lapse and claims are submitted within the required time frames.

Where possible, it is recommended that the individual establish a pre-payment account with the insurance company so that premiums are always being paid in advance and not infringing upon the grace period.

The financial planner should conduct an annual meeting with the individual and their intended caregiver to review these terms as everyone's memory fades with the passage of time.

## Interpretation of ADLs

Different companies place different interpretations regarding what constitutes a loss of an ADL. While the family physician may indicate that a person suffers from a loss of an ADL, this diagnosis does not always translate into a claim eligibility. The individual must fully satisfy the definition that the insurance company gives. In this respect, the benefits department will look for reports on symptoms, not diagnosis from the personal physician, and reach their own determination regarding eligibility. This emphasizes the advantage of having an LTC policy that contains multiple methods of qualifying for benefits and not one solely based on loss of ADLs.

Every insurance company will have established department guidelines concerning how long a loss must have occurred for it to satisfy the definition of a loss. Often, the period of time required is a consecutive 90-day period. This is necessary because a condition may come and go intermittently at the initial onset and therefore, not meet the policy's definition. This requirement is different than the elimination period, which is similar to a deductible in other forms of insurance.

When an individual is claiming under a cognitive impairment, companies will have established guidelines for this as well. While many such conditions are related to Alzheimer's disease, there are other forms of dementia that would qualify too. The benefits department may look for any or all of the following:

- The period of time assistance is required. Does the individual require 24-hour supervision or are they able to manage for periods of time on their own?

- Would the person be considered to be a danger to themselves or to others if they did not have supervision? For instance, someone may be on medication for a life-threatening condition and would die if they forgot to take their medication or if they took too much. This would be considered circumstances where they would be a danger to themselves without supervision.

- The use of independent tests are available to validate that dementia exists, and that the person does not merely suffer from forgetfulness. It must be determined that an organic cause exists. Everyone experiences diminished recall as a natural part of the aging process, but not everyone gets dementia.

Some policies only require that a physician certifies facility care is medically necessary, together with evidence that government programs have been applied for. This could entitle the individual to collect benefits earlier than waiting for evidence of ADL loss or cognitive impairment.

## Benefit Payment

Some companies offer a direct deposit for benefit cheques to be credited to the individual's bank account. This eliminates concerns with losing cheques or forgetting to cash them. It also avoids the issue of a person having mobility difficulty.

## Contestable Period Claims

When a claim occurs within the first two policy years, the insurance company will check for discrepancies between statements made in the original application and information provided at the time of claim. A material misrepresentation will most likely result in the immediate rescission of the policy and no benefit will be paid. When the policy has been in force for more than two years, the only basis upon which the insurance company can rescind the policy is when they can prove fraud. This is when the individual will most appreciate the thoroughness that was given during the underwriting process and the orientation to detail given by their financial planner.

Most companies conduct their investigation up front rather than waiting to search for details at the time of a claim. This thoroughness has sometimes been referred to as "red tape" or "a hassle", but in reality it represents an assurance that unexpected information is unlikely to result in an unpaid claim later. If revealing certain information results in the insurance being declined, it is better to have discovered this up front than to have paid premiums for several years and had the benefits rescinded for non-disclosure.

## Financial Planner's Responsibilities

The financial planner's role is to encourage the individual and their caregiver to comply with the terms of claim submission promptly, and can review these procedures with them. It is not wise for the planner to become directly involved in advising the individual on care or treatment options. It is not the role of the financial planner to complete the claims forms or to counsel the individual on whether the condition experienced by the individual will qualify under the policy definitions. There have been situations of incorrect advice being given by planners attempting to make interpretations and litigation is never a pleasant occurrence for anyone involved.

The insurance company does not generally deal through the financial planner during the claim, as information is confidential, and the insurer must be able to deal direct with the individual or their caregivers.

## Claims for Pre-Existing Conditions

All companies have conditions for which they will not pay benefits. These are usually standard exclusions such as service in the military, self-inflicted injuries, confinement for alcoholism or drug addiction, and mental and nervous conditions that do not have an organic cause.

Some policies also contain a pre-existing condition limitation. This is different than an exclusion. It refers to a condition for which you have received treatment or been experiencing symptoms of prior to applying for coverage. During a specified time, such as six months following the purchase of the policy, a claim would not be paid for a pre-existing condition. A claim which occurs within the defined time frame will also be evaluated to determine whether it is related to a pre-existing condition. This does not replace the need to disclose everything at the time of underwriting. Even though it could result in a policy that is issued on a rated basis or being declined altogether, there would otherwise be the risk of denial of a claim due to fraud when the omission was intentional.

## Assuris

Some Fraternal Benefit Societies offer programs of home care, facility care, or long-term care insurance. Although all life insurance companies that do business in Canada must by law join the Assuris consumer protection plan (formerly known as CompCorp), Fraternal Benefit Societies do not fall within this category, and therefore do not belong to Assuris. Consequently their clients are not protected in the event of insolvency. Clients who have purchased their long-term care insurance through a member company are protected. Information concerning limits, combination formulas, and illustrations of payouts are contained in their Web site at: http://www.assuris.ca.

# Chapter 17

# Frequently Asked Questions

## FINANCIAL PLANNING

### How much does it cost in Canada to reside in a nursing home?

The cost of residential nursing care is $1,500 to $2,400 per month in institutions that receive government subsidy in provinces other than New Brunswick, Prince Edward Island, and Newfoundland. Costs in the latter three provinces are double as means testing is still in place. Not only does the cost vary by province, by level of accommodation, but also between public and private facilities. Private facilities that do not receive government subsidization can cost up to $8,000 or more per month.

### How does Canada's health care system compare relative to other countries?

Canadians have one of the highest levels of social benefits in the world when comparing spending on health care measured as a percentage of GDP.

### What is the projected growth rate for seniors living in institutions?

The number of seniors with disabilities who live in institutions will grow by 60% from just under 200,000 in 1986 to more than 312,000 in 2011.

### What is meant by the term "long-term care"?

It refers to the assistance given to people who have a chronic condition or limitation that restricts or prevents them from living independently. It differs from traditional care because it serves to maintain a standard of independent living while not necessarily expecting to correct or improve the condition.

### What is long-term care insurance?

It is insurance purchased for the purpose of providing a source of dollars to pay for long-term care provided at home, in the community, or in a residential facility.

### Who buys long-term care insurance?

It is most often purchased by people between the ages of 55 and 75. However, it makes sense to buy it as early as age 45. Some plans provide limited payment options that would enable benefits to be fully paid up by age 65. An individual could consequently pay for their coverage during their earning years and not on a fixed retirement income. The key determinants concerning candidacy are whether the person is in good physical and cognitive health, has some level of disposable income to put towards it, and has a clear reason as to why they are buying the coverage.

## THE ROLE OF THE CAREGIVER

### Who is most likely to be a caregiver?

Women are more likely to become caregivers, but men can also find themselves caring for a sick spouse. Adult children often find themselves eventually in a role as caregiver to an ailing parent.

### What is Alzheimer's disease and how is it different from the normal aging process?

Alzheimer's disease is the leading cause of dementia and represents 64% of all forms of dementia. It destroys nerve cells in the brain and is not a normal part of aging. While memory and recall fade with age, Alzheimer's disease patients suffer from a progressive, degenerative and irreversible dementia.

### How will the aging of Canada's population be affected by Alzheimer's disease?

The number of people with Alzheimer's disease is expected to grow from 316,500 Canadians to over 3/4 million people by 2031.

### What are the challenges associated with long distance caregiving?

There are issues related to: frequent travel to check on the status of parents; financial, physical and emotional strain; and feelings of guilt, anger, frustration and anxiety.

### What is the career impact on a person who becomes a caregiver?

There are changes in one's social activities, holiday patterns, availability for work-related events, sleeping patterns, expenses incurred, and personal changes in one's health.

### What are some early warning signals that an elderly parent may need help?

Early signals that should be investigated include changes in weight, lateness in paying utilities and other bills, clothes that are not kept clean, and odors in the home.

### How many Canadians will be over the age of 80 in 2021?

One-quarter of the Canadian population will be over the age of 80 in 2021. In 1931, only 6% of Canadians were over age 65. This means that most Canadians will be in a caregiver role at some point during their lives.

### How much of Canada's population lives in a long-term care facility today?

Approximately 6% to 8% of elderly Canadians live in institutions today. There is a strong informal support system in Canada.

## CONTINUING CARE

### What is meant by "continuing care" and the "continuing care system"?

Canada's health programs for seniors is under provincial jurisdiction and is generically referred to as the "continuing care system'". The objective of the system is to assist individuals to live independently and, when they can no longer do so in their own home, to assist them in obtaining facility-based care. The term reflects that care is a continuum with many components delivered over an extended period of time. Care is multifaceted and combines aspects of both health services and social services.

### How are services accessed?

Most provinces have a single entry point system that controls access to services enabling prioritization on a "most needed" basis. Individuals do not have to go to multiple agencies to get services and they can work with a single coordinator to access programs.

### How is prioritization on a "most needed" basis achieved?

An assessment is conducted and a plan of care is developed for services most appropriate to the condition.

### What is meant by "income and asset testing"?

An individual's income and assets are measured against a threshold figure in certain provinces to determine what they will pay for facility care. Those below the threshold receive some government subsidization, and those above pay the full cost of medical and room and board charges. Testing is done in Newfoundland, New Brunswick and Prince Edward Island. Those who do not qualify for subsidy may expect to pay from $3,000 to $4,000 per month.

### Aren't subsidies available in all provinces?

Other provinces cover the cost of medical services and only charge the room and board portion of facility care to the individual. Those who cannot pay for this, can apply for a room and board subsidy. Those who do not receive a room and board subsidy can expect to pay from $1,500 to $2,400 depending upon the facility and the level of accommodation.

### Are retirement homes that are classified as supportive living (assisted living) facilities also accessed through this manner?

Only in a couple of provinces. Generally, in most provinces you must apply directly to the facility. They do not receive government subsidy in most provinces.

## COMMUNITY AND HOME CARE SERVICES

### What is the purpose of home care?

It may serve to accomplish one of three objectives: maintain a person's ability to live independently and prevent further health deterioration; act as a substitute for long-term care in an institutional setting; or be a short term alternative for delivering acute care.

### What types of services can be provided as part of home care?

There are two categories of services, these being health care services and personal support services (personal care or custodial services). Health care services are provided by licensed skilled professionals and unlicensed trained personnel.

### What is meant by "respite care"?

This refers to care provided by another person or agency for the purpose of giving the primary caregiver a break from their responsibilities. It may be an informal arrangement with a neighbour, or a formal arrangement through a day facility or a long-term facility. It is an important and vital part of care giving.

### What services are offered by adult day support centres?

They are centres for elders with physical or mental limitations to spend the day in a supervised group setting away from home. The individual must be able to perform activities of daily living. Centres enable elders to remain in the community longer outside of institutions.

### What are the average costs of adult day support centres?

The cost varies but is usually in the range of $300 to $400 per month. While much less than the cost of facility care, services are generally for a five-day week. In the majority of provinces, they are accessed directly and do not form part of the government single entry system. Some centres specialize in handling elders with dementia such as Alzheimer's disease.

### What is a social centre?

A social centre functions as a social and recreation club for seniors to go to daily or occasionally. For a nominal annual fee, members have a place where they may enjoy activities such as playing cards. They cater to healthy seniors and not ailing seniors that require medical assistance.

## RESIDENTIAL FACILITIES

### What regulations are in place for retirement residences with supports?

In most provinces, retirement residences are not part of the continuing care system and not subject to the same regulations as nursing homes. They are subject to the *Landlord and Tenant Act*, municipal zoning, fire and public health regulations.

### What assistance do they provide to their residents?

There are two types of facilities, independent living facilities and supportive or assisted living facilities. Independent living facilities are for those who wish to live in a comfortable setting free from responsibilities of home maintenance. They may have a kitchenette and optional meal plan. Supportive or assisted living facilities are for residents who require light assistance with personal care such as medication dispensing and meals.

### How much does a retirement residence with supports cost?

While the rates vary, fees can range from $900 to $6,000 per month, with the average cost being about $1,600 to $2,500. The cost is impacted by the level of accommodation, facilities such as private baths, balconies, and room size. In some government-subsidized housing with supports, where rent is geared to income, the cost can be as little as $600 per month.

### How long does it take to get into a retirement residence with supportive living?

Many can be accessed immediately. Those that are more popular may have a waiting list. They are not subject to the queuing that occurs with nursing homes that can take from six months to two years.

### What are the levels of accommodation offered in long-term care facilities?

There are usually three levels of accommodations which are basic (ward), plus two preferred levels: semi-private and private. Not all facilities offer private rooms. Queuing is the longest for basic (ward) level, as this is the only level that provides government subsidy for room and board based on earnings.

### What care services are available in long-term care facilities?

They provide 24-hour nursing care including personal and health care. They have visiting physicians, physiotherapists, mobile services for x-rays, dentistry, and foot care. However, they do not provide services for acute conditions that require hospitalization.

### How does one notify acceptance of a long-term care facility?

Upon receiving a call that an opening has arisen, the caregiver is given 24 hours to decide. Thereafter, they are given an additional 24 hours in which to move the elder into the facility. Special arrangements can be made to extend this to a maximum of three days by payment of a fee.

## POLICY STRUCTURES AND DEFINING "CARE"

### What types of policy structures are available for long-term care insurance?

There are three types of policy structures a person can choose from: indemnity-based plans; reimbursement-based plans; and income-based plans. Indemnity-based plans require the individual to provide evidence that a covered care service has been received, and then pay the stipulated daily benefit amount regardless of the actual expense incurred. Reimbursement-based plans pay for covered expenses in the actual amount incurred upon submission of a receipt up to the daily maximum. An income-based plan pays a fixed weekly or monthly benefit regardless of the expenses incurred or the nature of the service received or the relation of the person who has provided the care service. Newer hybrid versions are emerging in the industry, which are variations of these, such as conversion models and pooled-benefit models. Conversion models start out as another form of insurance such as critical illness, disability income or life insurance and eventually convert to facility care coverage. Pooled-benefit plans start with a lump sum amount from which the individual withdraws a predetermined monthly amount and can be shared with a spouse.

### What does the term "care" mean in an LTC policy?

The term "care" can be used in four different contexts. There are terms that describe care as a location, a condition severity or level of care, a service, or a provider. It aids understanding by first determining in which context the term "care" is being used.

### What is meant by "levels of care"?

Skilled care refers to treatment for medical conditions requiring a medical professional. Personal care refers to custodial assistance such as help with activities of daily living. Intermediate care is continuous nursing care that is preventative or rehabilitative in nature. Extended care deals with a chronic condition that serves to maintain a standard of living. Chronic care is the irreversible presence of disease that would require care in a nursing home facility.

### Who can provide care at home?

Some LTC policies specify that care is not covered that is provided by a relative. These policies require an outside organization such as a home health care agency. Policies that are income-based models and pooled-benefit plans do not specify and consequently care may be provided by a family member.

### What is home hospice and palliative care?

This refers to services provided through a certified program by a hospice agency for the control of pain and symptoms related to a terminal illness. It is covered by most LTC policies if the individual is not expected to live longer than six months. It includes medical and health services as well as counseling to family members.

## PROVISIONS THAT DEFINE ELIGIBILITY

### How do companies determine that a health change has occurred that qualifies for benefits?

Companies use different measures such as the loss of activities of daily living (ADLs) and cognitive impairment definitions. The LTC policy will clearly state the definitions used by the issuing company. ADLs include bathing, eating, dressing, toileting, transferring, and continence.

### Are ADL-based definitions the same from one company to another?

No. Some companies measure five only, while others measure six (continence). They also vary in their interpretation of what constitutes a loss. The measure of functional loss can be the need for standby assistance, the complete dependence upon another individual, the inability to perform the task unaided or aided with the assistance of a person or device. Price varies according to how liberal the definition is.

### Is cognitive impairment defined the same by all companies?

No. Just as ADL definitions can vary, so does the interpretation of a cognitive impairment. Some companies may accept the need for verbal cueing in performing tasks such as dressing as a cognitive impairment. Other definitions include the need for 24-hour supervision, in the absence of which the person may be of harm to themselves or others. In all cases, the cause must be organic as in the case of Alzheimer's disease and Parkinson's disease, and not related to normal aging.

### What is an Instrumental Activity of Daily Living (IADL)?

This refers to a person's ability to perform less complex tasks of daily living such as cooking, grocery shopping, laundry, bill paying, taking medication, using a telephone and housekeeping. It is not usually a primary measure of loss because even though an individual who suffers the loss of an ADL may be unable to also do IADLs the reverse is not true.

### Do policies differ in how they count days to satisfy the elimination period?

Yes. Some policies might count care days and some might count calendar days. Those that use the care day method only count days in which a covered care service was received. This method if used, is generally applied only to the home care benefits. It will take longer to satisfy the elimination period by counting only care days than it does by counting calendar days as the latter includes all days on a calendar basis.

## PREMIUM-RELATED PROVISIONS

### Does the term "level premium" ensure that my rate will never change?

No. It means that there are no scheduled rate increases and benefits have been priced with the intent that they will stay level for the full duration of the contract. Most LTC policies are issued as a "guaranteed renewable" series. This means that the policy cannot be cancelled by the insurance company, but the insurer does reserve the right to make future premium changes for all insureds within a particular class if there is adverse experience within that group. Some older policies contain a guarantee stating the maximum overall increase above the original base premium. Another practice used in older policies was to guarantee the intervals at which rates could be adjusted such as five years from the previous adjustment. Today, companies offer payment options whereby policies can be fully paid up in 20 years or by age 65, after which premiums cannot be adjusted, or they may state an age such as age 75, after which no further premiums can be adjusted. Normally a minimum of 20 years of premium payments is required.

### Does the waiver of premium benefit apply to the whole contract?

No. Some companies only apply the waiver of premium feature during periods of facility confinement. In a few cases, the waiver of premium feature may require an additional premium if the company offers it as an optional benefit instead of a built-in provision.

### What methods are used to account for the risk that a person with dementia may forget to pay premiums?

Companies differ in the safeguards they offer. The range includes extending the grace period where there is evidence of dementia being the cause, special reinstatement offers immediately following the grace period, third party notification to a designated party, non-forfeiture provisions and pre-paid premium account options.

### Can the insured select the non-forfeiture option of their choice?

No. Companies determine this in their design structure and price accordingly for it. There are different philosophies followed. Some companies offer a reduced paid-up option because they believe some insurance should be in place for having paid premiums for so long. Some companies offer a form of LTC "term" insurance because they believe the same amount of coverage should be in place although for a shorter period of time. One method favours situations where premiums have been paid for a lesser time, and the other favours situations where premiums have been paid for so many years that coverage could be almost fully paid-up.

### What is a pre-paid premium account option?

Some insurance companies make available an account that functions like a bank account for future premiums. The money deposited earns interest and is used to automatically pay premiums. If required, funds can be withdrawn at any time.

# EVALUATING LONG-TERM CARE (LTC) POLICIES

### What should one consider when evaluating different LTC policies?

There are five areas one should understand. The first relates to the flexibility the contract offers in types of care. The second is the ease of qualifying for benefits. The third is the cost of insurance today. The fourth is the safeguards included in the event that a premium payment is forgotten. And the fifth is the guarantees that are related to protecting the individual against future premium increases.

### What type of LTC policy offers the greatest flexibility?

An income-based model offers the greatest flexibility. There is no distinction regarding where care is provided, who provides the care, or what the service is that is being provided. However, this does not mean that it is automatically the best policy for everyone. There are other considerations that one must evaluate, such as price, ease of qualifying for benefits, future guarantees against premium increases, and safeguards related to premium payment oversight.

### Which version provides the best protection overall?

There is no perfect policy. The best one is the policy that satisfies the individual's personal needs by balancing benefits and price according to their priorities. Individuals should keep in mind that their priorities will change as they age. They will transition from an asset focus in their young senior years, to a concern with the softer issues of quality of life, freedom of choice, dignity, and independence.

### Is it advisable to purchase facility care only and use the government programs for home care?

Although there will be a substantial increase in the number of elders living in facilities as Canada's population continues to age, the majority of seniors will be cared for in the community through home care assistance. This will place a tremendous strain on the government to fund this increased need from a shrinking tax base. People who like to control their own circumstances, are well advised to have home care benefits in their policy.

### How important are guarantees related to future premium increases?

Long-term care insurance has been available in Canada for less than 20 years. The number of contracts in force are still relatively small as compared with other forms of insurance. More time is needed to study the impact of claims as compared with pricing assumptions. No one can say how adequate the pricing models will be 30 to 40 years from now.

## PLAN CONSIDERATIONS

### What are some of the considerations when selecting an elimination period?

The individual must consider how long they can afford or choose to fund an initial period of care themselves. They must also determine whether the elimination period is satisfied by care days or calendar days because a shorter elimination period might be required when the care days method is used. They must remember that benefits are like pay cheques, they are paid in arrears so the first one will not be received until a month following the end of the elimination period.

### How long should the benefit period be?

The individual must consider the affordability of longer periods. Too short of a benefit period will place the individual in jeopardy of running out of benefits. Too long of a benefit period may make the cost prohibitive down the road for maintaining the insurance. The average stay in a nursing home is two years but this is often preceded by a period of time in an assisted living facility and/or home care. Most people will be adequately covered with a five-year benefit plan.

### How is preliminary health information used by the financial planner during the plan design stage?

The planner uses this information to submit preliminary inquiries to various insurance companies who offer opinions on their probable underwriting action for different health conditions. It helps the planner to tailor benefits to better meet the individual's needs. It offers some insight as to whether there may be a potential premium rating that must be accounted for in the plan design stage regarding overall cost and affordability. It minimizes the chance of someone going through the application process and being declined for insurance.

### How much should a person spend on average for premiums on LTC insurance?

Premiums should be a cost that the individual can manage without a change in their current lifestyle. An individual should not "stretch" to purchase the most expensive form of LTC insurance and risk the potential of having it later reduced or terminated due to lack of affordability. A buffer must be left in case the insurance company increases premiums down the road under the guaranteed renewable provision.

### Can an individual purchase as much LTC insurance as they would like?

No. Insurance companies set maximums that they allow. These maximums will also take into consideration plans that are in force with other companies. Over-insurance is an industry concern since, in other product lines, it has led to an increased tendency to claim for benefits.

## UNDERWRITING AND CLAIMS

### How does the underwriter gather information to base their decision?

The underwriter gets information from the application, the financial planner's cover note, a customer interview that is conducted either by telephone or by a visiting professional, a statement from the person's attending physician, and from a paramedical as required. The primary source is the application form itself, and a thorough and accurately completed form will minimize the need to turn to other sources for additional data.

### What is the purpose of conducting an additional interview when the financial planner has already done so?

An essential part of the underwriting process is to verify information through third-party sources. The telephone interview enables the underwriter to collect independent information on lifestyle issues.

### What is the primary objective of the underwriter when reviewing an application for long-term care insurance?

The primary objective of the underwriter is to determine the ability of the individual to remain self-sufficient. To do this, they look at a number of factors in the risk evaluation process including age, gender, medical history, build, physical condition, mental acuity, current abilities with ADLs and IADLs. Another significant area to the underwriter is the infrastructure and support network that the applicant has available to them.

### Is the underwriting of an LTC policy as rigorous as disability insurance?

The process is thorough, but different. There are conditions that would prevent someone from purchasing disability insurance that do not disqualify the person from buying long-term care insurance. Fewer Attending Physician Statements are required. The average underwriting time is usually less. The rate of decline is closer to that of life insurance.

### What is the most important thing to remember when claiming for benefits?

There are maximum time frames within which the notice of claim and claim forms must be submitted. In the absence of a compelling reason for missing the deadline, the claim can be denied. The person most likely to be in a caregiver role should be well-versed in the coverage that the elder has purchased and understand this important provision of the contract.

# Topical Index

**283**